MEI STRUCTURED MATHEMATI

THIRD EDITION

Additional Further Pure Mathematics

Terry Heard
David Martin
Bob Francis

Series Editor: Roger Porkess

Acknowledgements

The Publishers would like to thank the following for permission to reproduce copyright material:

Helicon Publishing RM plc from *The World Weather Guide*, Pearce & Smith, 1993 (page 48); British Library Reproduction (L35/46 opp 59876015) from *A History of Mathematics*, Carl Boyer, 1968 (Wiley International Edition) (page 126).

Every effort has been made to trace all copyright holders, but if any have been inadvertently overlooked the Publishers will be pleased to make the necessary arrangements at the first opportunity.

OCR accept no responsibility whatsoever for the accuracy or method of working in the answers given.

Illustrations were drawn by Tony Wilkins.

Orders: please contact Bookpoint Ltd, 130 Milton Park, Abingdon, Oxon OX14 4SB. Telephone: (44) 01235 827720. Fax: (44) 01235 400454. Lines are open 9 am to 6 pm, Monday to Saturday, with a 24-hour message-answering service. Visit our website at *www.hoddereducation.co.uk*.

First Edition published in 1998
Second Edition published in 2002
Third Edition published in 2005 by
Hodder Education, an Hachette UK company,
338 Euston Road
London NW1 3BH

Impression number 10 9 8 7 6 5
Year 2010 2009

Typeset in 10.5 on 14 Minion by Phoenix Photosetting, Lordswood, Chatham, Kent.
Printed and bound in Great Britain by Martins The Printers, Berwick-upon-Tweed.

A catalogue record for this title is available from the British Library

ISBN-13: 978 0340 889 961

MEI Structured Mathematics

Mathematics is not only a beautiful and exciting subject in its own right but also one that underpins many other branches of learning. It is consequently fundamental to the success of a modern economy.

MEI Structured Mathematics is designed to increase substantially the number of people taking the subject post-GCSE, by making it accessible, interesting and relevant to a wide range of students.

It is a credit accumulation scheme based on 45 hour units which may be taken individually or aggregated to give Advanced Subsidiary (AS) and Advanced GCE (A Level) qualifications in Mathematics and Further Mathematics. The units may also be used to obtain credit towards other types of qualification.

The course is examined by OCR (previously the Oxford and Cambridge Schools Examination Board) with examinations held in January and June each year.

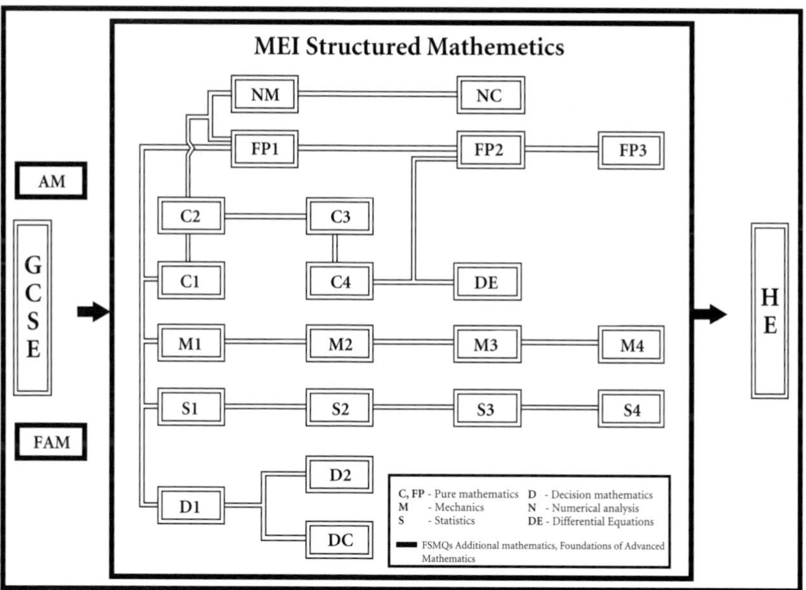

This is one of the series of books written to support the course. Its position within the whole scheme can be seen in the diagram above.

Mathematics in Education and Industry (MEI) is an independent curriculum development body which aims to promote links between education and industry in mathematics. MEI produce relevant examination specifications at GCSE, AS and A Level (including Further Mathematics) and for Free Standing Mathematics Qualifications (FSMQs); these are examined by OCR.

In partnership with Hodder Murray, MEI are responsible for three major series of textbooks: Formula One Maths for Key Stage 3, Hodder Mathematics for GCSE and the MEI Structured Mathematics series, including this book, for AS and A Level.

As well as textbooks, MEI take a leading role in the development of on-line resources to support mathematics. The books in this series are complemented by a major MEI website providing full solutions to the exercises, extra questions including on-line multiple choice tests, interactive demonstrations of the mathematics, schemes of work, and much more.

In recent years MEI have worked hard to promote Further Mathematics and, in conjunction with the DfES, they are now establishing the national network of Further Mathematics Centres.

MEI are committed to supporting the professional development of teachers. In addition to a programme of Continual Professional Development, MEI, in partnership with several universities, co-ordinate the Teaching Advanced Mathematics programme, a course designed to give teachers the skills and confidence to teach A Level mathematics successfully.

Much of the work of MEI is supported by the Gatsby Charitable Foundation.

MEI is a registered charity and a charitable company.

MEI's website and email addresses are www.mei.org.uk *and* office@mei.org.uk.

Introduction

This book completes the series covering the pure mathematics units for Further Mathematics in MEI Structured Mathematics. This is its third edition and is designed for use with the specification which was introduced in 2004; the two earlier editions were entitled *Pure Mathematics 6*.

This book explores five main topics. Chapters 2 and 3, on multivariable calculus and differential geometry, are little changed from those in the previous editions, while Chapter 4 on groups is effectively a subset of the earlier chapter on abstract algebra. In the new specification the organisation of vectors and matrices has been altered and the work on vectors is brought together in the new Chapter 1. The reorganisation of the material in the first four chapters has been carried out by Terry Heard.

Matrices are developed throughout the three Further Mathematics books, culminating in their application to Markov chains in this book; the convention used is consistent with that in the earlier books so that probabilities are presented as column vectors, rather than as rows as is commonly the case in statistics. This chapter assumes that you have a calculator able to handle matrices.

Since you need to prepare just three of these topics for the assessment of the course, the five chapters are almost completely independent and may be tackled in any order. You are expected to have covered the material in all the earlier books, including the hyperbolic sine and cosine functions from *A2 Further Pure Mathematics* (*FP2*). You should also be aware that, in Chapter 2, you are expected to use the vector product to find a vector perpendicular to two vectors and this is covered in Chapter 1. Of course, we hope that you will read the whole book.

The text is designed to be accessible to students who have to work on their own for much of the time. The frequent activities are a means of getting you involved in your learning (replacing to some extent the interaction you might have had with a teacher) and should not be skipped; answers or hints to all activities and exercises are provided. In addition, the material is supported by on-line resources as part of the Further Mathematics Network, *www.fmnetwork.info*.

The topics here overlap considerably with some university work, so we hope that this book may help to smooth the transition into higher education. For this reason (and for mathematical reasons too) we have, in places, gone beyond what is strictly needed for examination purposes (as detailed in the current specification), either in the extent of coverage or in the level of rigour used. We hope that the material presented here may be of use to students on some other Further Mathematics courses and also at university. If you have been enthused by the mathematics in this course and would like to know more about careers involving mathematics, try looking on the website *www.mathscareers.org.uk*.

We would like to thank the many people who have helped with the work in this book, contributing valuable ideas at various stages, including Nick Lord, Gerry Leversha, Randal Cousins and Peter Mitchell, and also our own families, especially Heather Martin, for their support when energy was flagging.

Terry Heard, David Martin, Bob Francis

Key to symbols in this book

This symbol means that you may want to discuss a point with your teacher. If you are working on your own there are answers in the back of the book. It is important, however, that you have a go at answering the questions before looking up the answers if you are to understand the mathematics fully.

This is a warning sign. It is used where a common mistake, misunderstanding or tricky point is being described.

This is the ICT icon. It indicates where you should use a graphic calculator or a computer.

This symbol and a dotted line down the right-hand side of the page indicates material which is beyond the criteria for the unit but which is included for completeness.

☆☆ Harder questions are indicated with stars. Many of these go beyond the usual examination standard.

Contents

1 Vector geometry

I pulled out, on the spot, a pocket book, which still exists, and made an entry, on which, at the very moment, I felt it might be worth my while to expend the labour of at least ten (or it might be fifteen) years to come. But then it is fair to say that this was because I felt a problem to have been at that moment solved, an intellectual want relieved, which had haunted me for at least fifteen years before.

William R. Hamilton, writing on 16 October 1858 about his invention of quaternions on 16 October 1843

Multiplying vectors: the scalar product

In *A2 Pure Mathematics*, Chapter 11 you met the scalar product $\mathbf{a}.\mathbf{b}$ of two vectors, $\mathbf{a}$ and $\mathbf{b}$:

$$\mathbf{a}.\mathbf{b} = |\mathbf{a}||\mathbf{b}|\cos\theta$$

where θ is the angle between $\mathbf{a}$ and $\mathbf{b}$, the result being a scalar (figure 1.1).

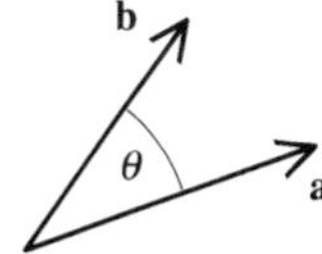

Figure 1.1

In two dimensions: $\mathbf{a} = \begin{pmatrix} a_1 \\ a_2 \end{pmatrix}$ $\mathbf{b} = \begin{pmatrix} b_1 \\ b_2 \end{pmatrix}$ $\Rightarrow$ $\mathbf{a}.\mathbf{b} = a_1b_1 + a_2b_2$.

In three dimensions: $\mathbf{a} = \begin{pmatrix} a_1 \\ a_2 \\ a_3 \end{pmatrix}$ $\mathbf{b} = \begin{pmatrix} b_1 \\ b_2 \\ b_3 \end{pmatrix}$ $\Rightarrow$ $\mathbf{a}.\mathbf{b} = a_1b_1 + a_2b_2 + a_3b_3$.

Using the scalar product is an efficient way of finding the angle between two vectors. It is particularly convenient if you want to test whether two vectors are perpendicular, as then the scalar product is zero.

The scalar product also enables you to write down the equation of a plane: the equation of a plane is $\mathbf{n}.(\mathbf{r} - \mathbf{a}) = 0$, where $\mathbf{a}$ is the position vector of the point A on the plane, $\mathbf{r}$ is the position vector of a general point on the plane, and $\mathbf{n}$ is a 'normal', a vector perpendicular to the plane (see figure 1.2). This equation can be rearranged as $\mathbf{n}.\mathbf{r} = \mathbf{n}.\mathbf{a}$, a scalar constant.

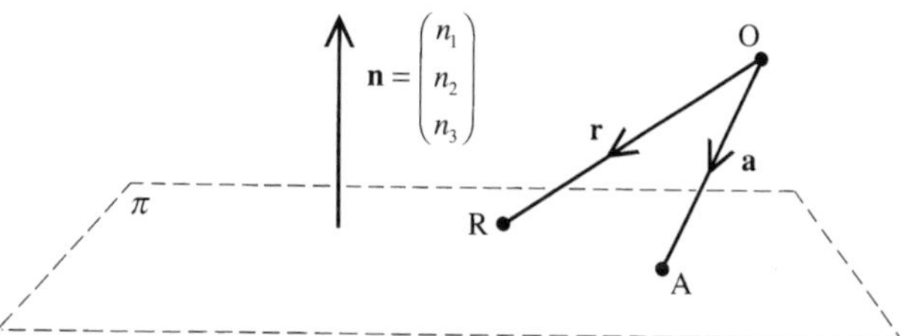

Figure 1.2

If $\mathbf{n} = \begin{pmatrix} n_1 \\ n_2 \\ n_3 \end{pmatrix}$ and $\mathbf{r} = \begin{pmatrix} x \\ y \\ z \end{pmatrix}$ the equation can be further rearranged as

$n_1x + n_2y + n_3z + d = 0$, where d is a constant. (This is known as the cartesian form.)

Suppose, for example, an architect is designing a new roof with several triangular sections (figure 1.3). She decides she needs to find the cartesian equation of the plane containing the triangle with vertex A(3, 2, 10) and sloping edges given by the vectors $\begin{pmatrix} 8 \\ 1 \\ -4 \end{pmatrix}$ and $\begin{pmatrix} 7 \\ 4 \\ -4 \end{pmatrix}$. If she could easily find a normal $\mathbf{n}$ for the plane, finding the equation of the plane would only involve evaluating $\mathbf{n}\,.\,\mathbf{a}$. The normal $\mathbf{n}$ is perpendicular to both $\begin{pmatrix} 8 \\ 1 \\ -4 \end{pmatrix}$ and $\begin{pmatrix} 7 \\ 4 \\ -4 \end{pmatrix}$ so the problem reduces to one of finding a vector perpendicular to two given vectors. One such vector is the vector product, which is now introduced.

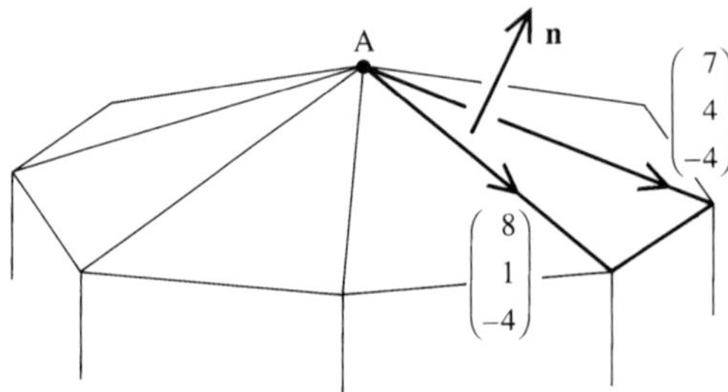

Figure 1.3

Multiplying vectors: the vector product

The *vector product* of $\mathbf{a}$ and $\mathbf{b}$ is a vector perpendicular to both $\mathbf{a}$ and $\mathbf{b}$; its magnitude is $|\mathbf{a}||\mathbf{b}|\sin\theta$, where θ is the angle between $\mathbf{a}$ and $\mathbf{b}$. The vector product of $\mathbf{a}$ and $\mathbf{b}$ is written as $\mathbf{a} \times \mathbf{b}$. Thus

$$\mathbf{a} \times \mathbf{b} = |\mathbf{a}||\mathbf{b}|\sin\theta\,\hat{\mathbf{n}}$$

where θ is the angle between $\mathbf{a}$ and $\mathbf{b}$, and $\hat{\mathbf{n}}$ is a unit vector which is perpendicular to both $\mathbf{a}$ and $\mathbf{b}$.

There are two unit vectors perpendicular to both $\mathbf{a}$ and $\mathbf{b}$, but they point in opposite directions; we sometimes say they have opposite *senses*. The vector $\hat{\mathbf{n}}$ is chosen such that $\mathbf{a}$, $\mathbf{b}$ and $\hat{\mathbf{n}}$ (in that order) form a right-handed set of vectors: if $\mathbf{a}$ and $\mathbf{b}$ are both horizontal, and if an anticlockwise rotation (between 0° and 180°) is needed to turn $\mathbf{a}$ to point in the same direction as $\mathbf{b}$, then $\mathbf{a} \times \mathbf{b}$ is the upwards vertical, as illustrated in figure 1.4. If you point the thumb of your right hand in the direction of $\mathbf{a}$, and your index finger in the direction of $\mathbf{b}$, then your second finger, coming 'up' from your palm, points in the direction of $\mathbf{a} \times \mathbf{b}$.

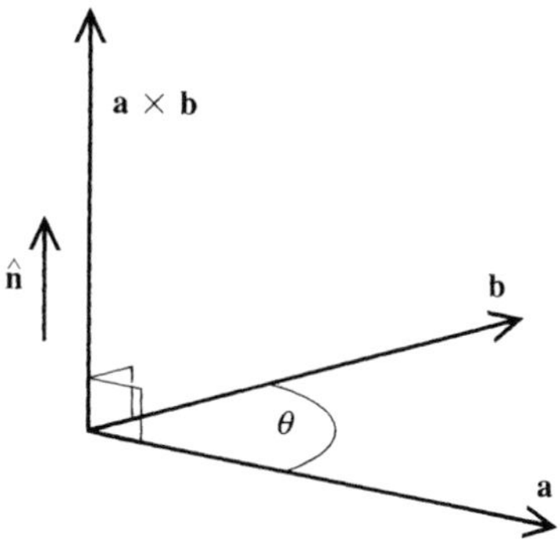

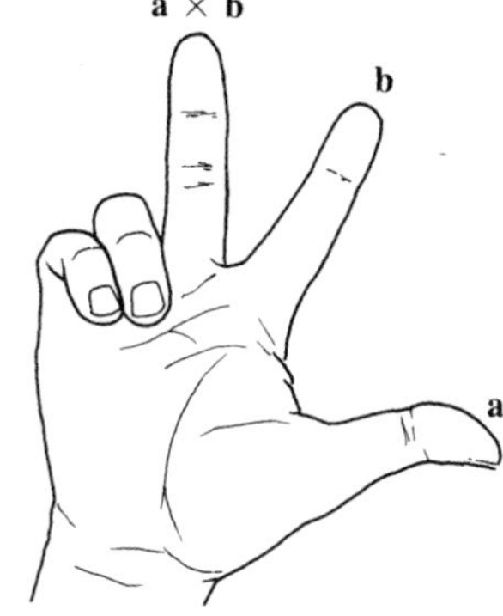

Figure 1.4

The following are important properties of vector products.

1 *The vector product is anti-commutative*

The vector products $\mathbf{a}\times\mathbf{b}$ and $\mathbf{b}\times\mathbf{a}$ have the same magnitude but are in opposite directions, so that $\mathbf{a}\times\mathbf{b}=-\mathbf{b}\times\mathbf{a}$. This is known as the *anti-commutative property*.

2 *The vector product of parallel vectors is zero*

This is because the angle θ between two parallel vectors is 0° or 180°, so that $\sin\theta=0$. Thus $\mathbf{a}\times\mathbf{a}=\mathbf{0}$ and in particular $\mathbf{i}\times\mathbf{i}=\mathbf{0}$.

Notice that $\mathbf{a}\times\mathbf{b}$ is also $\mathbf{0}$ if $\mathbf{a}$ or $\mathbf{b}$ is $\mathbf{0}$.

3 *Multiplication by scalars*

If m is a scalar, the vector $m\mathbf{a}$ has magnitude $|m|\,|\mathbf{a}|$; $m\mathbf{a}$ and $\mathbf{a}$ have the same direction if m is positive, but opposite directions if m is negative. Similar comments apply to $n\mathbf{b}$ and $\mathbf{b}$. Whatever the signs of m and n,

$$(m\mathbf{a})\times(n\mathbf{b})=mn(\mathbf{a}\times\mathbf{b}).$$

4 *The distributive property of vector product over vector addition*

The property that $p(q+r)=pq+pr$, whatever the values of the numbers p, q and r, is known as the distributive property of multiplication over addition. It enables you to change a product into a sum of two simpler products – in doing so the multiplication is 'distributed' over the two terms of the original sum. Similarly, the process of forming a vector product is distributive over vector addition:

$$\mathbf{a}\times(\mathbf{b}+\mathbf{c})=\mathbf{a}\times\mathbf{b}+\mathbf{a}\times\mathbf{c}$$

This is clearly true for the trivial case of $\mathbf{a}=\mathbf{0}$, as then both sides simplify to $\mathbf{0}$, but we postpone the general proof to page 33.

The alternative form of the distributive property also holds, for

$$
\begin{aligned}
&\mathbf{a} \times (\mathbf{b} + \mathbf{c}) = \mathbf{a} \times \mathbf{b} + \mathbf{a} \times \mathbf{c} \\
\Rightarrow \quad &-\mathbf{a} \times (\mathbf{b} + \mathbf{c}) = -\mathbf{a} \times \mathbf{b} - \mathbf{a} \times \mathbf{c} \\
\Rightarrow \quad &(\mathbf{b} + \mathbf{c}) \times \mathbf{a} = \mathbf{b} \times \mathbf{a} + \mathbf{c} \times \mathbf{a}
\end{aligned}
$$

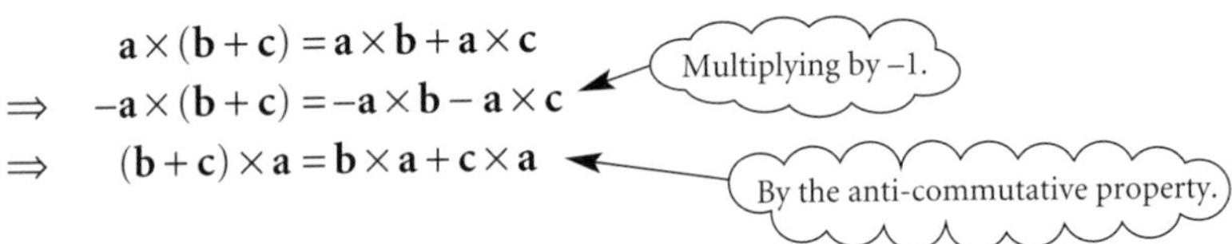

5 *The vector product in component form*

We shall shortly prove that if we express vectors **a** and **b** in terms of their components, so that $\mathbf{a} = a_1\mathbf{i} + a_2\mathbf{j} + a_3\mathbf{k}$ and $\mathbf{b} = b_1\mathbf{i} + b_2\mathbf{j} + b_3\mathbf{k}$, then

$$\mathbf{a} \times \mathbf{b} = \begin{pmatrix} a_1 \\ a_2 \\ a_3 \end{pmatrix} \times \begin{pmatrix} b_1 \\ b_2 \\ b_3 \end{pmatrix} = \begin{pmatrix} a_2b_3 - a_3b_2 \\ a_3b_1 - a_1b_3 \\ a_1b_2 - a_2b_1 \end{pmatrix}.$$

ACTIVITY 1.1

In this activity you may find it helpful to take the near edge of a rectangular table as the x axis, the left edge of the table as the y axis, and to hold a ruler pointing vertically upwards to represent the positive z axis, as in figure 1.5.

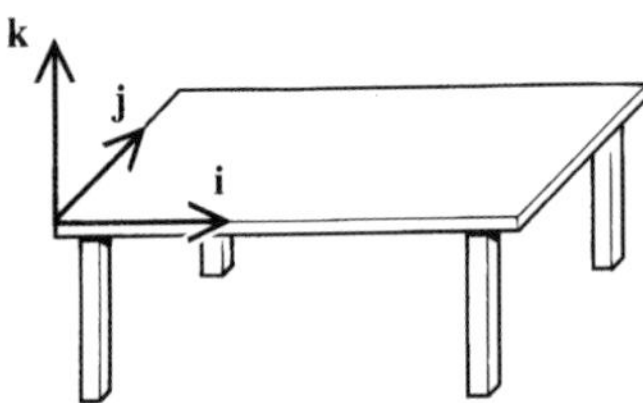

Figure 1.5

Use pens to represent:

- **i**, the unit vector pointing to the right along the x axis;
- **j**, the unit vector pointing away from you along the y axis;
- **k**, the unit vector pointing up along the z axis.

The vector product of **a** and **b** is defined as $\mathbf{a} \times \mathbf{b} = |\mathbf{a}||\mathbf{b}| \sin \theta\, \hat{\mathbf{n}}$, where θ is the angle between **a** and **b**, and $\hat{\mathbf{n}}$ is a unit vector which is perpendicular to both **a** and **b**, such that **a**, **b** and $\hat{\mathbf{n}}$ (in that order) form a right-handed set of vectors.

Using the definition, check the truth of each of the following nine results:

$$
\begin{array}{lll}
\mathbf{i} \times \mathbf{i} = \mathbf{0} & \mathbf{i} \times \mathbf{j} = \mathbf{k} & \mathbf{i} \times \mathbf{k} = -\mathbf{j} \\
\mathbf{j} \times \mathbf{i} = -\mathbf{k} & \mathbf{j} \times \mathbf{j} = \mathbf{0} & \mathbf{j} \times \mathbf{k} = \mathbf{i} \\
\mathbf{k} \times \mathbf{i} = \mathbf{j} & \mathbf{k} \times \mathbf{j} = -\mathbf{i} & \mathbf{k} \times \mathbf{k} = \mathbf{0}.
\end{array}
$$

(This is the first place in your work with vectors where it has been important that the positive x, y, z axes form a right-handed set.)

If $\mathbf{a} = a_1\mathbf{i} + a_2\mathbf{j} + a_3\mathbf{k}$ and $\mathbf{b} = b_1\mathbf{i} + b_2\mathbf{j} + b_3\mathbf{k}$, then

$$\begin{aligned}\mathbf{a}\times\mathbf{b} &= (a_1\mathbf{i} + a_2\mathbf{j} + a_3\mathbf{k}) \times (b_1\mathbf{i} + b_2\mathbf{j} + b_3\mathbf{k}) \\ &= a_1b_1\mathbf{i}\times\mathbf{i} + a_1b_2\mathbf{i}\times\mathbf{j} + a_1b_3\mathbf{i}\times\mathbf{k} \\ &\quad + a_2b_1\mathbf{j}\times\mathbf{i} + a_2b_2\mathbf{j}\times\mathbf{j} + a_2b_3\mathbf{j}\times\mathbf{k} \\ &\quad + a_3b_1\mathbf{k}\times\mathbf{i} + a_3b_2\mathbf{k}\times\mathbf{j} + a_3b_3\mathbf{k}\times\mathbf{k} \\ &= \mathbf{0} + a_1b_2\mathbf{k} - a_1b_3\mathbf{j} - a_2b_1\mathbf{k} + \mathbf{0} + a_2b_3\mathbf{i} + a_3b_1\mathbf{j} - a_3b_2\mathbf{i} + \mathbf{0} \\ &= (a_2b_3 - a_3b_2)\mathbf{i} + (a_3b_1 - a_1b_3)\mathbf{j} + (a_1b_2 - a_2b_1)\mathbf{k}\end{aligned}$$

Using properties **3** and **4** several times.

Since $\mathbf{i}\times\mathbf{i} = \mathbf{0}$, $\mathbf{i}\times\mathbf{j} = \mathbf{k}$, $\mathbf{i}\times\mathbf{k} = -\mathbf{j}$, etc.

Thus $\mathbf{a}\times\mathbf{b} = \begin{pmatrix} a_1 \\ a_2 \\ a_3 \end{pmatrix} \times \begin{pmatrix} b_1 \\ b_2 \\ b_3 \end{pmatrix} = \begin{pmatrix} a_2b_3 - a_3b_2 \\ a_3b_1 - a_1b_3 \\ a_1b_2 - a_2b_1 \end{pmatrix}.$

The first component of $\mathbf{a}\times\mathbf{b}$ is the value of the 2×2 determinant $\begin{vmatrix} a_2 & b_2 \\ a_3 & b_3 \end{vmatrix}$ (see *AS Further Pure Mathematics* (*FP1*) page 31) obtained by covering up the top row of $\begin{pmatrix} a_1 \\ a_2 \\ a_3 \end{pmatrix} \times \begin{pmatrix} b_1 \\ b_2 \\ b_3 \end{pmatrix}$; the second component is the negative of the 2×2 determinant obtained by covering up the middle row (note the sign); and the third component is the 2×2 determinant obtained by covering up the bottom row. You can therefore write

$$\mathbf{a}\times\mathbf{b} = \begin{pmatrix} a_1 \\ a_2 \\ a_3 \end{pmatrix} \times \begin{pmatrix} b_1 \\ b_2 \\ b_3 \end{pmatrix} = \begin{vmatrix} a_2 & b_2 \\ a_3 & b_3 \end{vmatrix}\mathbf{i} - \begin{vmatrix} a_1 & b_1 \\ a_3 & b_3 \end{vmatrix}\mathbf{j} + \begin{vmatrix} a_1 & b_1 \\ a_2 & b_2 \end{vmatrix}\mathbf{k}.$$

Note this sign.

EXAMPLE 1.1

Calculate $\mathbf{a}\times\mathbf{b}$ when $\mathbf{a} = 3\mathbf{i} + 2\mathbf{j} + 5\mathbf{k}$ and $\mathbf{b} = \mathbf{i} - 4\mathbf{j} + 2\mathbf{k}$.

SOLUTION 1

$$\mathbf{a}\times\mathbf{b} = \begin{pmatrix} 3 \\ 2 \\ 5 \end{pmatrix} \times \begin{pmatrix} 1 \\ -4 \\ 2 \end{pmatrix} = \begin{pmatrix} 2\times 2 - 5\times(-4) \\ 5\times 1 - 3\times 2 \\ 3\times(-4) - 2\times 1 \end{pmatrix} = \begin{pmatrix} 24 \\ -1 \\ -14 \end{pmatrix}.$$

SOLUTION 2

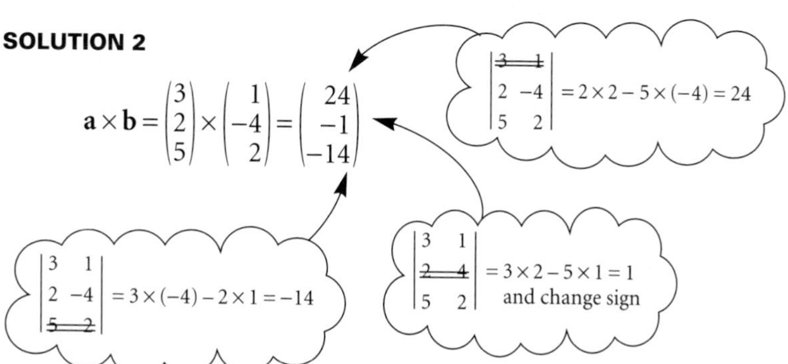

a × b = (3, 2, 5) × (1, −4, 2) = (24, −1, −14)
3 1 / 2 −4 / 5 2 = 2 × 2 − 5 × (−4) = 24
3 1 / 2 −4 / 5 2 = 3 × 2 − 5 × 1 = 1
and change sign
3 1 / 2 −4 / 5 2 = 3 × (−4) − 2 × 1 = −14

EXAMPLE 1.2

Find $\mathbf{n} = \begin{pmatrix} 8 \\ 1 \\ -4 \end{pmatrix} \times \begin{pmatrix} 7 \\ 4 \\ -4 \end{pmatrix}$ and hence find the equation of the plane which contains the point A(3, 2, 10) and the vectors $\begin{pmatrix} 8 \\ 1 \\ -4 \end{pmatrix}$ and $\begin{pmatrix} 7 \\ 4 \\ -4 \end{pmatrix}$.

(This is the architect's problem posed on page 2.)

SOLUTION

$$\mathbf{n} = \begin{pmatrix} 8 \\ 1 \\ -4 \end{pmatrix} \times \begin{pmatrix} 7 \\ 4 \\ -4 \end{pmatrix} = \begin{pmatrix} 1\times(-4)-(-4)\times 4 \\ -(8\times(-4)-(-4)\times 7) \\ 8\times 4 - 1\times 7 \end{pmatrix} = \begin{pmatrix} 12 \\ 4 \\ 25 \end{pmatrix}$$

The cartesian equation of the plane is $12x + 4y + 25z = \text{constant}$. As (3, 2, 10) is on the plane, the constant is $12\times 3 + 4\times 2 + 25\times 10 = 294$.

The equation of the plane is $12x + 4y + 25z = 294$.

ACTIVITY 1.2

Some calculators can handle vectors. If yours does, or if you have access to a computer algebra system that handles vectors, find out how to use it to calculate the vector product of two vectors.

Note

It is wise to check that your result is perpendicular to both **a** and **b**. This can be done by checking (perhaps mentally) that the scalar product of your result with both **a** and **b** is indeed zero.

? Is it possible to find the vector product of two two-dimensional vectors?

EXAMPLE 1.3

Find the cartesian equation of the plane which contains the points A(3, 4, 2), B(2, 0, 5), C(6, 7, 8).

SOLUTION

You need to find a vector which is perpendicular to AB and BC (and CA).

$$\overrightarrow{AB} = \begin{pmatrix} 2 \\ 0 \\ 5 \end{pmatrix} - \begin{pmatrix} 3 \\ 4 \\ 2 \end{pmatrix} = \begin{pmatrix} -1 \\ -4 \\ 3 \end{pmatrix} \qquad \overrightarrow{BC} = \begin{pmatrix} 6 \\ 7 \\ 8 \end{pmatrix} - \begin{pmatrix} 2 \\ 0 \\ 5 \end{pmatrix} = \begin{pmatrix} 4 \\ 7 \\ 3 \end{pmatrix}$$

$$\Rightarrow \overrightarrow{AB} \times \overrightarrow{BC} = \begin{pmatrix} -1 \\ -4 \\ 3 \end{pmatrix} \times \begin{pmatrix} 4 \\ 7 \\ 3 \end{pmatrix} = \begin{pmatrix} -33 \\ 15 \\ 9 \end{pmatrix} = -3\begin{pmatrix} 11 \\ -5 \\ -3 \end{pmatrix}$$

so $\mathbf{n} = \begin{pmatrix} 11 \\ -5 \\ -3 \end{pmatrix}$ is a vector perpendicular to plane ABC.

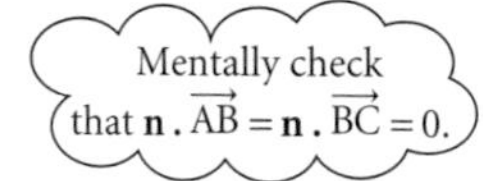

Plane ABC has equation $11x - 5y - 3z = \text{constant}$. You can find the value of the constant by substituting the co-ordinates of A or B or C, obtaining 7.

The cartesian equation of plane ABC is $11x - 5y - 3z = 7$.

Note how it was helpful to remove common factors from the components of $\overrightarrow{AB} \times \overrightarrow{BC}$ so as to produce the simplest possible equation.

Finally, here is an example where we are not expressing the vectors in terms of their components.

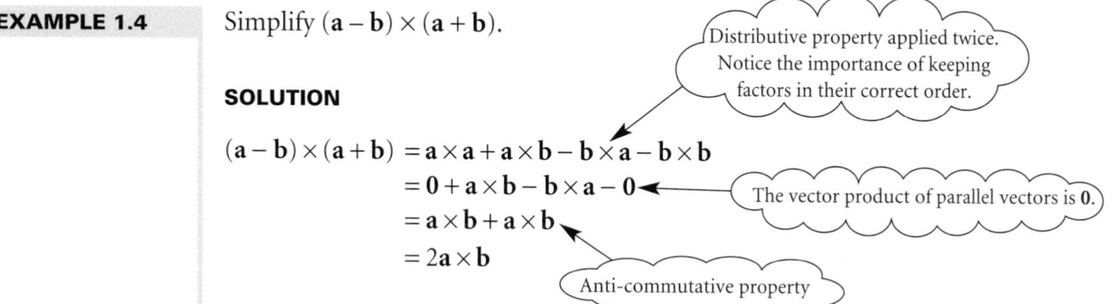

Distributive property applied twice. Notice the importance of keeping factors in their correct order.
The vector product of parallel vectors is $\mathbf{0}$.
Anti-commutative property

EXAMPLE 1.4

Simplify $(\mathbf{a} - \mathbf{b}) \times (\mathbf{a} + \mathbf{b})$.

SOLUTION

$$\begin{aligned}(\mathbf{a} - \mathbf{b}) \times (\mathbf{a} + \mathbf{b}) &= \mathbf{a} \times \mathbf{a} + \mathbf{a} \times \mathbf{b} - \mathbf{b} \times \mathbf{a} - \mathbf{b} \times \mathbf{b} \\ &= \mathbf{0} + \mathbf{a} \times \mathbf{b} - \mathbf{b} \times \mathbf{a} - \mathbf{0} \\ &= \mathbf{a} \times \mathbf{b} + \mathbf{a} \times \mathbf{b} \\ &= 2\mathbf{a} \times \mathbf{b}\end{aligned}$$

Historical note

The Irish mathematician William Rowan Hamilton (1805–1865) was appointed Professor of Astronomy at Trinity College, Dublin, at the age of 21, a post he held till the year of his death. Hamilton set out to create an algebra which was related to the rotation of three-dimensional space in much the same way that the algebra of complex numbers is related to the rotation of the plane. He defined a 'quaternion' as the sum of a real number and a 'triplet', a triplet being what we call a vector. For many years he was hampered because he expected to preserve the commutative property of multiplication; this turned out to be impossible in an algebra of three-dimensional rotations, and he finally defined multiplication in such a way that $\mathbf{a} \times \mathbf{b} = -\mathbf{b} \times \mathbf{a}$, though it appears that Carl Friedrich Gauss (1777–1855) had reached similar results about 30 years previously. Also in Germany, Hermann Günther Grassmann (1809–1877) independently developed similar ideas. Quaternions did not long survive Hamilton, but vectors became a major tool for physicists, though not all considered them useful. Even the eminent Lord Kelvin (1824–1907) wrote: 'Vector is a useless survival or off-shoot from quaternion and has never been of the slightest use to any creature.' See Exercise 4H, Question 10 on page 167.

EXERCISE 1A

1 Calculate each of the following vector products.

(i) $\begin{pmatrix}3\\5\\2\end{pmatrix}\times\begin{pmatrix}2\\4\\-3\end{pmatrix}$ **(ii)** $\begin{pmatrix}7\\-4\\-5\end{pmatrix}\times\begin{pmatrix}-4\\5\\-3\end{pmatrix}$

(iii) $\begin{pmatrix}5\\-2\\4\end{pmatrix}\times\begin{pmatrix}1\\5\\-6\end{pmatrix}$ **(iv)** $(3\mathbf{i}-7\mathbf{k})\times(2\mathbf{i}+3\mathbf{j}+5\mathbf{k})$

2 The distributive property of vector product over vector addition states that

$$\mathbf{a}\times(\mathbf{b}+\mathbf{c})=\mathbf{a}\times\mathbf{b}+\mathbf{a}\times\mathbf{c} \quad \text{and} \quad (\mathbf{a}+\mathbf{b})\times\mathbf{c}=\mathbf{a}\times\mathbf{c}+\mathbf{b}\times\mathbf{c}.$$

Check that these are both true when

$$\mathbf{a}=3\mathbf{i}+4\mathbf{j}+6\mathbf{k} \quad \mathbf{b}=8\mathbf{i}+2\mathbf{j}+5\mathbf{k} \quad \mathbf{c}=7\mathbf{i}-3\mathbf{j}+9\mathbf{k}.$$

3 Find vectors perpendicular to the following pairs of vectors.

(i) $\begin{pmatrix}2\\0\\5\end{pmatrix},\begin{pmatrix}3\\-1\\-2\end{pmatrix}$ **(ii)** $\begin{pmatrix}12\\3\\-2\end{pmatrix},\begin{pmatrix}7\\1\\4\end{pmatrix}$ **(iii)** $\begin{pmatrix}2\\3\\4\end{pmatrix},\begin{pmatrix}3\\6\\7\end{pmatrix}$ **(iv)** $\begin{pmatrix}3\\-4\\6\end{pmatrix},\begin{pmatrix}8\\5\\-3\end{pmatrix}$

4 Find a unit vector perpendicular to both $\mathbf{i}+2\mathbf{j}+7\mathbf{k}$ and $3\mathbf{i}-\mathbf{j}+6\mathbf{k}$.

5 Find the cartesian equations of the planes containing the three points given.

(i) M(1, 4, 2), E(5, 1, 3), I(1, 0, 0)
(ii) T(5, −3, 4), J(0, 1, 0), H(6, 2, 5)
(iii) D(6, 2, −2), R(1, 4, 3), M(−5, 7, 1)
(iv) C(4, 2, −1), L(8, 2, 4), S(5, 8, −7)

6 The angle between $\mathbf{p}=\begin{pmatrix}5\\-3\\1\end{pmatrix}$ and $\mathbf{q}=\begin{pmatrix}-2\\-5\\2\end{pmatrix}$ is θ.

(i) Calculate $\mathbf{p}\times\mathbf{q}$ and $|\mathbf{p}\times\mathbf{q}|$ and hence find the value of $\sin\theta$.
(ii) Calculate $\mathbf{p}\,.\,\mathbf{q}$ and hence find the value of $\cos\theta$.
(iii) Show that the results you obtained in parts **(i)** and **(ii)** fit the identity $\sin^2\theta+\cos^2\theta\equiv 1$.
(iv) If you want to find the angle between two vectors it is usually quicker to use the scalar product rather than the vector product. Give another reason why the scalar product method is preferable.

7 What can you say about **a** and **b** if $\mathbf{a}\times\mathbf{c}=\mathbf{b}\times\mathbf{c}$?

8 Explain why $\mathbf{a}\,.\,(\mathbf{a}\times\mathbf{b})=0$.

9 **v** and **w** are non-parallel vectors.

Show that $(\mathbf{v}+2\mathbf{w})\times(\mathbf{v}-3\mathbf{w})=k(\mathbf{v}\times\mathbf{w})$, where the real number k is to be found.

[MEI, *part*]

10 In triangle ABC, let $\overrightarrow{BC}$, $\overrightarrow{CA}$ and $\overrightarrow{AB}$ be denoted by **a**, **b** and **c**, as illustrated. Show that $\mathbf{a}\times\mathbf{b}=\mathbf{b}\times\mathbf{c}=\mathbf{c}\times\mathbf{a}$, and use this result to complete an alternative proof of the sine rule.

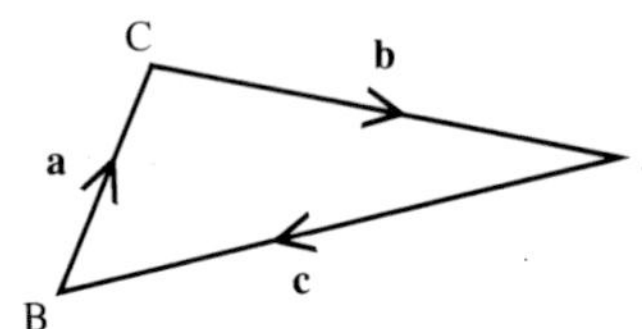

11 The moment of a force $\mathbf{F}$ about the origin O is $\mathbf{r} \times \mathbf{F}$, where $\mathbf{r}$ is the position vector of any point R on the line of action of $\mathbf{F}$. Prove that the moment of a force about O is independent of the choice of the point R, provided R is on the line of action of $\mathbf{F}$.

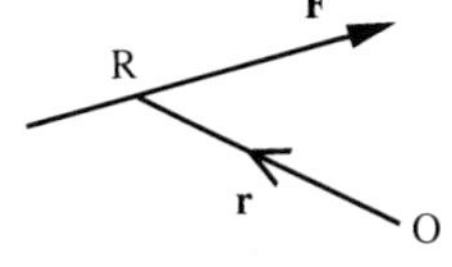

12 If a body is rotating at angular speed ω about an axis through O (see below) then the angular velocity is represented by the vector $\boldsymbol{\omega}$, defined to have magnitude ω and be parallel to the axis such that a right-handed corkscrew attached to the body would move in the direction indicated by $\boldsymbol{\omega}$.

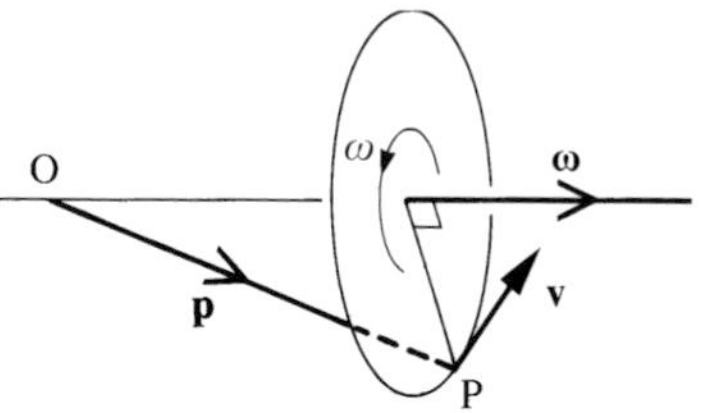

Show that the velocity $\mathbf{v}$ of a point P on the rotating body is given by $\mathbf{v} = \boldsymbol{\omega} \times \mathbf{p}$, where $\mathbf{p}$ is the position vector of P.

The intersection of two planes

If you look around you will find objects which can be used to represent planes – walls, floors, ceilings, doors, roofs, and so on. You will see that the intersection of two planes is a straight line.

EXAMPLE 1.5

Find ℓ, the line of intersection of the two planes

$$3x + 2y - 3z = -18 \quad \text{and} \quad x - 2y + z = 12.$$

SOLUTION 1

This solution depends on finding two points on ℓ.

You can find one point by arbitrarily choosing to put $y = 0$ into the equations of the planes and solving simultaneously:

Figure 1.6

$$\left.\begin{array}{r} 3x - 3z = -18 \\ x + y = 12 \end{array}\right\} \Leftrightarrow \left\{\begin{array}{l} x - z = -6 \\ x + z = 12 \end{array}\right\} \Leftrightarrow x = 3,\ z = 9.$$

So P with co-ordinates $(3, 0, 9)$ is a point on ℓ.

(You could run into difficulties putting $y = 0$ as it is possible that the line has no points where $y = 0$. In this case your simultaneous equations for x and z would be inconsistent; you would then choose a value for x or z instead.)

Choosing to put $z = 1$ into the equations gives

$$\left.\begin{aligned}3x + 2y &= -15\\ x - 2y &= 11\end{aligned}\right\} \Leftrightarrow \left\{\begin{aligned}4x &= -4\\ 2y &= x - 11\end{aligned}\right\} \Leftrightarrow x = -1,\ y = -6$$

so Q with co-ordinates $(-1, -6, 1)$ is a point on ℓ.

$$\overrightarrow{PQ} = \begin{pmatrix}-1\\-6\\1\end{pmatrix} - \begin{pmatrix}3\\0\\9\end{pmatrix} = \begin{pmatrix}-4\\-6\\-8\end{pmatrix} = -2\begin{pmatrix}2\\3\\4\end{pmatrix}.$$

Removing factor −2 makes the arithmetic simpler.

Use $\begin{pmatrix}2\\3\\4\end{pmatrix}$ as the direction vector for ℓ.

A vector equation for ℓ is $\mathbf{r} = \begin{pmatrix}-1\\-6\\1\end{pmatrix} + t\begin{pmatrix}2\\3\\4\end{pmatrix}$.

You can give the cartesian form of the equations: $\dfrac{x+1}{2} = \dfrac{y+6}{3} = \dfrac{z-1}{4}$

or the parametric form: $\begin{cases}x = 2t - 1\\ y = 3t - 6.\\ z = 4t + 1\end{cases}$

SOLUTION 2

The planes have normals $\mathbf{n}_1 = \begin{pmatrix}3\\2\\-3\end{pmatrix}$ and $\mathbf{n}_2 = \begin{pmatrix}1\\-2\\1\end{pmatrix}$.

As line ℓ is in each plane (see figure 1.7) it must be perpendicular to both $\mathbf{n}_1$ and $\mathbf{n}_2$, so

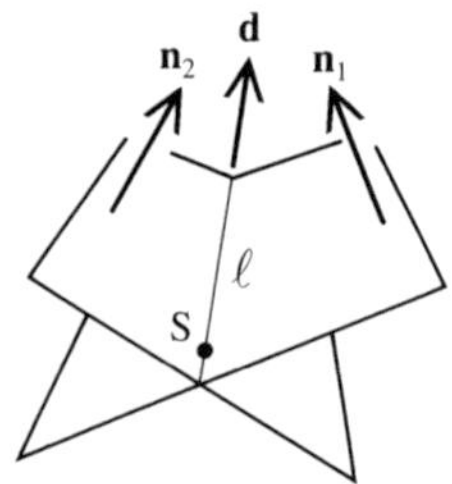

Figure 1.7

$$\mathbf{n}_1 \times \mathbf{n}_2 = \begin{pmatrix}-4\\-6\\-8\end{pmatrix} = -2\begin{pmatrix}2\\3\\4\end{pmatrix}$$

Removing factor −2 makes the arithmetic simpler.

gives a vector in the direction of ℓ.

Use $\mathbf{d} = \begin{pmatrix}2\\3\\4\end{pmatrix}$ as the direction vector for ℓ.

Mentally check that $\mathbf{d}.\mathbf{n}_1 = \mathbf{d}.\mathbf{n}_2 = 0$.

Now you only need to find a point S on ℓ.

Choosing to put $x = 1$ into the equations gives

$$\left.\begin{aligned}2y - 3z &= -21\\ -2y + z &= 11\end{aligned}\right\} \Leftrightarrow \left\{\begin{aligned}-2z &= -10\\ 2y &= 3z - 21\end{aligned}\right\} \Leftrightarrow z = 5,\ y = -3$$

so S with co-ordinates $(1, -3, 5)$ is a point on line ℓ.

The cartesian equations of ℓ are $\dfrac{x-1}{2} = \dfrac{y+3}{3} = \dfrac{z-5}{4}$, though you could give

the parametric form $\begin{cases}x = 2t + 1\\ y = 3t - 3\\ z = 4t + 5\end{cases}$ or the vector form $\mathbf{r} = \begin{pmatrix}1\\-3\\5\end{pmatrix} + t\begin{pmatrix}2\\3\\4\end{pmatrix}$.

Note

The equations in Solution 2 do not look the same as the equations in Solution 1 because S(1, −3, 5) was used instead of Q(−1, −6, 1) as the 'starting point' for the line. There are infinitely many 'starting points' available. Putting $x=-1$ in the equations obtained at the end of Solution 2 gives $t=-1$, $y=-6$, $z=1$, showing that the line does go through the point Q(−1, −6, 1): these two solutions are equivalent as they have a common point and the same direction vector.

SOLUTION 3

In this solution the original two equations in x, y and z are solved, expressing each of x, y and z in terms of some parameter.

Put $x=\lambda$ into $\begin{cases} 3x+2y-3z=-18 \\ x-2y+z=12 \end{cases}$ and solve simultaneously for y and z:

$$\left.\begin{cases} 2y-3z=-18-3\lambda \\ -2y+z=12-\lambda \end{cases}\right\} \Rightarrow -2z=-6-4\lambda \Rightarrow z=2\lambda+3.$$

so that $2y=3z-18-3\lambda=3(2\lambda+3)-18-3\lambda=3\lambda-9$ and $y=\frac{3}{2}\lambda-\frac{9}{2}$.

Thus the parametric equations for ℓ are

$$\begin{cases} x=\lambda \\ y=\frac{3}{2}\lambda-\frac{9}{2} \\ z=2\lambda+3 \end{cases} \quad \text{or} \quad \begin{pmatrix} x \\ y \\ z \end{pmatrix}=\begin{pmatrix} 0 \\ -\frac{9}{2} \\ 3 \end{pmatrix}+\lambda\begin{pmatrix} 1 \\ \frac{3}{2} \\ 2 \end{pmatrix}.$$

Note

Again this set of equations is different from but equivalent to the earlier equations. The equivalence is most easily seen by substituting $2\mu-1$ for λ, obtaining

$$\begin{cases} x=2\mu-1 \\ y=\frac{3}{2}(2\mu-1)-\frac{9}{2}=3\mu-6 \\ z=2(2\mu-1)-3=4\mu+1 \end{cases}$$

Notice that cartesian equations of a line, such as $\frac{x-1}{5}=\frac{y-3}{7}=\frac{z-4}{2}$, are equivalent to the pair of equations

$$\frac{x-1}{5}=\frac{y-3}{7} \quad \text{and} \quad \frac{y-3}{7}=\frac{z-4}{2}.$$

These can be rearranged as $\begin{cases} 7x-5y=-8 \\ 2y-7z=-22 \end{cases}$ which are the equations of planes.

You can always convert the cartesian equations of a line into the equations of two planes and regard the line as the intersection of these planes.

The angle between two planes

The angle between two planes can be found by using the scalar product. As figures 1.8 and 1.9 make clear, the angle between planes π_1 and π_2 is the same as the angle between their normals, $\mathbf{n}_1$ and $\mathbf{n}_2$.

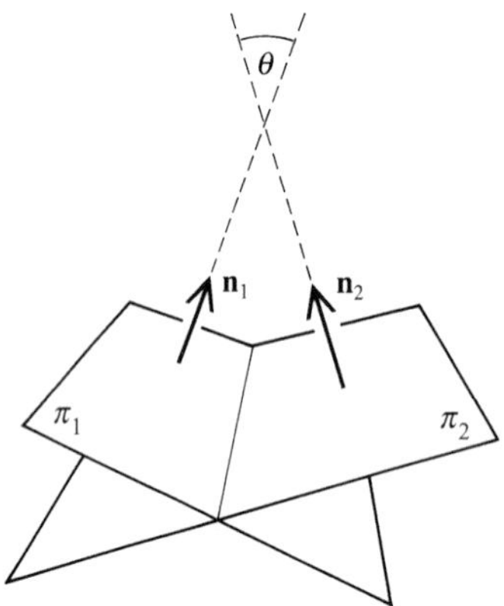

Figure 1.8

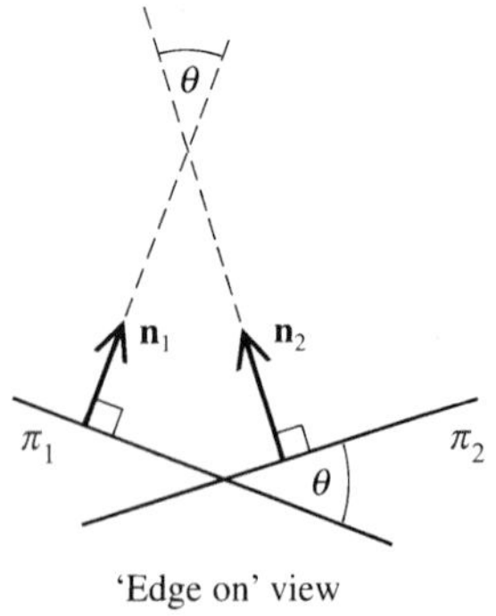

θ n1 n2 π1 π2 θ

'Edge on' view

Figure 1.9

EXAMPLE 1.6

Find the acute angle between the planes π_1: $2x + 3y + 5z = 8$ and π_2: $5x + y - 4z = 12$.

SOLUTION

The planes have normals $\mathbf{n}_1 = \begin{pmatrix} 2 \\ 3 \\ 5 \end{pmatrix}$ and $\mathbf{n}_2 = \begin{pmatrix} 5 \\ 1 \\ -4 \end{pmatrix}$, so $\mathbf{n}_1 \cdot \mathbf{n}_2 = 10 + 3 - 20 = -7$.

The angle between the normals is θ, where

$$\cos\theta = \frac{\mathbf{n}_1 \cdot \mathbf{n}_2}{|\mathbf{n}_1||\mathbf{n}_2|} = \frac{-7}{\sqrt{38}\sqrt{42}} \Rightarrow \theta \approx 100°.$$

Therefore the acute angle between the planes is about 80°.

Sheaf of planes

When several planes share a common line the arrangement is known as a *sheaf of planes* (figure 1.10). The next example shows how you can find the equation of a plane which contains the line ℓ common to two given planes, π_1 and π_2, without having to find the equation of ℓ itself, or any points on ℓ.

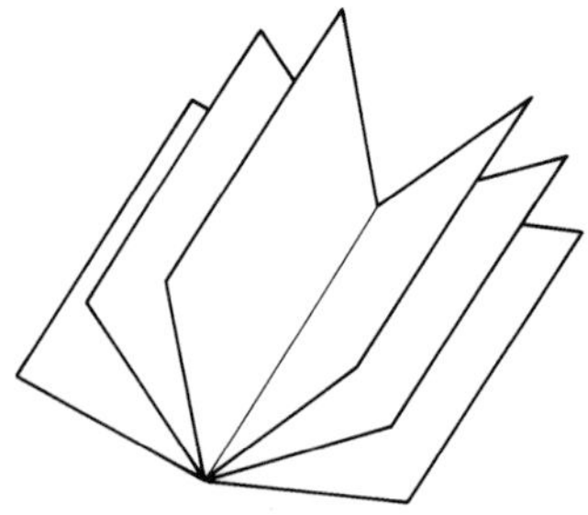

Figure 1.10

EXAMPLE 1.7

Find the equation of the plane which passes through the point $(1, 2, 3)$ and contains the common line of the planes π_1: $2x + 2y + z + 3 = 0$ and π_2: $2x + 3y + z + 13 = 0$.

SOLUTION

The equation

$$p(2x + 2y + z + 3) + q(2x + 3y + z + 13) = 0 \qquad ①$$

can be rearranged in the form $ax + by + cz + d = 0$, where not all of a, b, c, d are zero provided p and q are not both zero. Therefore equation ① represents a plane. Further, any point (x, y, z) which satisfies both π_1 and π_2 will also satisfy equation ①. Thus equation ① represents a plane containing the common line of planes π_1 and π_2. Substituting $(1, 2, 3)$ into ① gives

$$12p + 24q = 0 \quad \Leftrightarrow \quad p = -2q.$$

The required equation is

$$-2q(2x + 2y + z + 3) + q(2x + 3y + z + 13) = 0$$
$$\Leftrightarrow \qquad -q(2x + y + z - 7) = 0$$

so that the required plane has equation $2x + y + z - 7 = 0$.

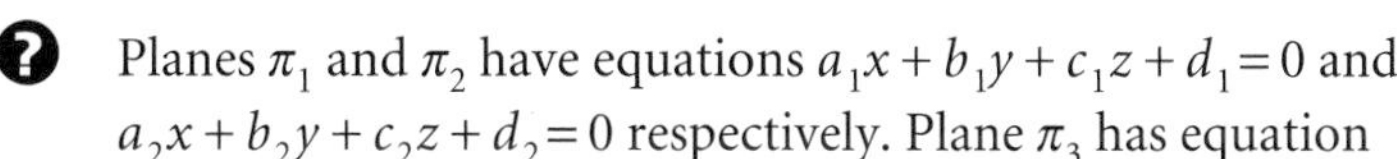

? Planes π_1 and π_2 have equations $a_1x + b_1y + c_1z + d_1 = 0$ and $a_2x + b_2y + c_2z + d_2 = 0$ respectively. Plane π_3 has equation

$$p(a_1x + b_1y + c_1z + d_1) + q(a_2x + b_2y + c_2z + d_2) = 0.$$

How is π_3 related to π_1 and π_2 if π_1 and π_2 are parallel?

EXERCISE 1B

1 Find cartesian equations of the line of intersection of these pairs of planes.

(i) $x + y - 6z = 4,\ 5x - 2y - 3z = 13$
(ii) $5x - y + z = 8,\ x + 3y + z = -4$
(iii) $3x + 2y - 6z = 4, x + 5y - 7z = 2$
(iv) $5x + 2y - 3z = -2,\ 3x - 3y - z = 2$

2 Find the acute angle between each pair of planes in Question 1.

3 Find cartesian equations of the line which passes through the given point and which is parallel to the line of intersection of the two planes.

(i) $(-2, 3, 5),\ 4x - y + 3z = 5,\ 3x - y + 2z = 7$
(ii) $(4, -3, 2),\ 2x + 3y + 2z = 6,\ 4x - 3y + z = 11$

4 Find the equation of the plane which goes through $(3, 2, -2)$ and which contains the common line of $x + 7y - 2z - 3 = 0$ and $2x - 3y + 2z - 1 = 0$.

5 Find the equation of the plane which contains the point $(1, -2, 3)$ and which is perpendicular to the common line of $5x - 3y - 4z = 2$ and $2x + y + 5z = 7$.

6 Find the equation of the line which goes through $(4, -2, -7)$ and which is parallel to both $2x - 5y - 2z = 8$ and $x + 3y - 3z = 12$.

7 The diagram shows the co-ordinates of the corners of parts of the roof of a warehouse.

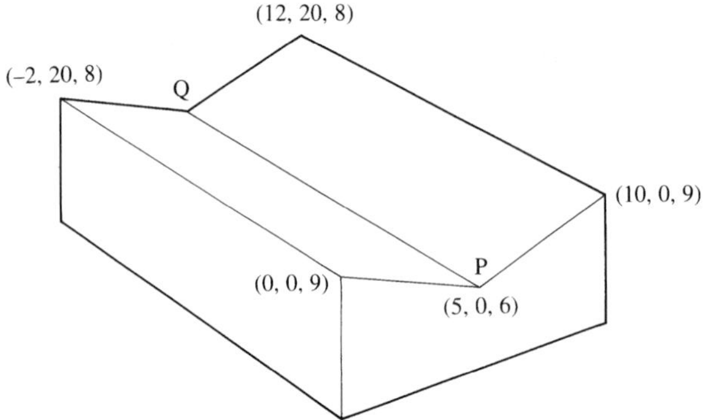

Find the equations of both roof sections, and the vector equation of the line PQ. Assuming that the z axis is vertical, what angle does PQ make with the horizontal?

8 Test drilling in the Namibian desert has shown the existence of gold deposits at $(400, 0, -400)$, $(-50, 500, -250)$, $(-200, -100, -200)$, where the units are in metres, the x axis points east, the y axis points north, and the z axis points up. Assume that these deposits are part of the same seam, contained in plane π.

(i) Find the equation of plane π.
(ii) Find the angle at which π is tilted to the horizontal.

The drilling positions $(400, 0, 3)$, $(-50, 500, 7)$, $(-200, -100, 5)$ are on the desert floor. Take the desert floor as a plane, Π.

(iii) Find the equation of Π.
(iv) Find the equation of the line where the plane containing the gold seam intersects the desert floor.
(v) How far south of the origin does the line found in part **(iv)** pass?

The intersection of lines

Hold a pen and a pencil to represent two distinct straight lines as follows:

- hold them to represent parallel lines;
- hold them to represent intersecting lines;
- hold them to represent lines which are not parallel and which do not intersect (even if you extend them).

In three-dimensional space two or more straight lines which are not parallel and which do not meet are known as *skew* lines. In a plane two distinct lines are either parallel or intersecting, but in three dimensions there are three possibilities: the lines may be parallel, or intersecting, or skew. The next example illustrates a method of finding whether two lines meet, and, if they do meet, the co-ordinates of the point of intersection. A very similar method can be used if the lines are specified by their vector equations instead of their cartesian equations.

EXAMPLE 1.8

The lines ℓ_1 and ℓ_2 are represented by the equations

$$\ell_1: \frac{x-1}{1} = \frac{y+6}{2} = \frac{z+1}{3} \qquad \ell_2: \frac{x-9}{2} = \frac{y-7}{3} = \frac{z-2}{-1}.$$

Find whether the lines meet, and, if so, the co-ordinates of their common point.

SOLUTION

If there is a point (X, Y, Z) common to both lines then

$$\frac{X-1}{1} = \frac{Y+6}{2} = \frac{Z+1}{3} = \lambda, \text{ say, and } \frac{X-9}{2} = \frac{Y-7}{3} = \frac{Z-2}{-1} = \mu, \text{ say.}$$

Writing X, Y and Z in terms of the parameters λ and μ, gives

$$X = \lambda + 1 = 2\mu + 9 \qquad ①$$

$$Y = 2\lambda - 6 = 3\mu + 7 \qquad ②$$

$$Z = 3\lambda - 1 = -\mu + 2 \qquad ③$$

Now solve any two of the three equations above simultaneously.

In this example we use ① and ②:

$$\left.\begin{matrix} \lambda - 2\mu = 8 \\ 2\lambda - 3\mu = 13 \end{matrix}\right\} \Leftrightarrow \left\{\begin{matrix} 2\lambda - 4\mu = 16 \\ 2\lambda - 3\mu = 13 \end{matrix}\right\} \Leftrightarrow \mu = -3, \lambda = 2.$$

If these solutions satisfy the previously unused equation (equation ③ here) then the lines do meet, and the value of λ (or value of μ) substituted into equations ①, ② and ③ gives us the co-ordinates (X, Y, Z) of the common point.

If the values of λ and μ do not fit the third (previously unused) equation then the lines do not meet.

As $\lambda = 2 \Rightarrow Z = 3\lambda - 1 = 5$ and $\mu = -3 \Rightarrow Z = -\mu + 2 = 5$, the values $\lambda = 2$ and $\mu = -3$ satisfy equation ③, as well as equations ① and ②, proving that the lines meet.

Using $\lambda = 2$ or $\mu = -3$ in equations ①, ② and ③ gives $X = 3$, $Y = -2$, $Z = 5$. The lines meet at the point $(3, -2, 5)$.

The cartesian equations of line ℓ_2 in the last example were

$$\frac{x-9}{2} = \frac{y-7}{3} = \frac{z-2}{-1}.$$

If you replace $y - 7$ by $y - 8$ in the equations, you translate line ℓ_2 one unit parallel to the y axis, forming line ℓ_3 (figure 1.11). You would not expect lines ℓ_1 and ℓ_3 to intersect.

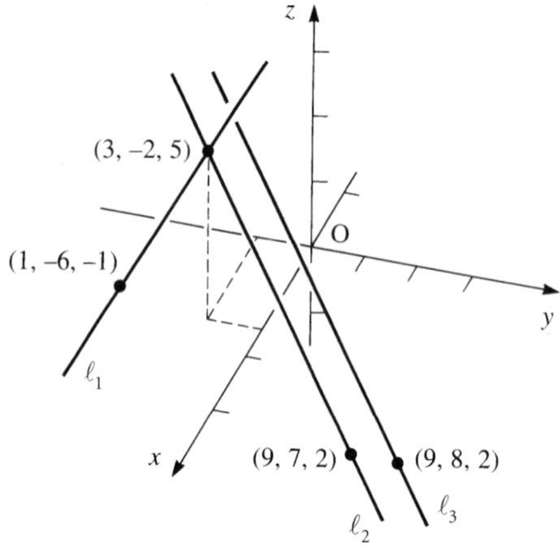

Figure 1.11

EXAMPLE 1.9

Prove that the lines ℓ_1 and ℓ_3 do not meet, where

$$\ell_1\text{: } \frac{x-1}{1} = \frac{y+6}{2} = \frac{z+1}{3} \qquad \ell_3\text{: } \frac{x-9}{2} = \frac{y-8}{3} = \frac{z-2}{-1}.$$

SOLUTION

If there is a point (X, Y, Z) common to both lines then

$$\frac{X-1}{1} = \frac{Y+6}{2} = \frac{Z+1}{3} = \lambda\text{, say, and } \frac{X-9}{2} = \frac{Y-8}{3} = \frac{Z-2}{-1} = \mu\text{, say.}$$

Writing X, Y and Z in terms of the parameters λ and μ:

$$X = \lambda + 1 = 2\mu + 9 \quad ①$$
$$Y = 2\lambda - 6 = 3\mu + 8 \quad ②$$
$$Z = 3\lambda - 1 = -\mu + 2 \quad ③$$

Solving equations ① and ② simultaneously:

$$\begin{Bmatrix} \lambda - 2\mu = 8 \\ 2\lambda - 3\mu = 14 \end{Bmatrix} \Leftrightarrow \begin{Bmatrix} 2\lambda - 4\mu = 16 \\ 2\lambda - 3\mu = 14 \end{Bmatrix} \Leftrightarrow \mu = -2, \lambda = 4.$$

As $\lambda = 4 \Rightarrow Z = 3\lambda - 1 = 11$, but $\mu = -2 \Rightarrow Z = -\mu + 2 = 4$, the values $\lambda = 4$ and $\mu = -2$ do not satisfy equation ③, although they satisfy equations ① and ②, proving that the lines ℓ_1 and ℓ_3 do not meet.

EXERCISE 1C

1 Decide whether the following pairs of lines intersect or not. If they do intersect, find the co-ordinates of the point of intersection.

(i) $\dfrac{x-6}{1}=\dfrac{y+4}{-2}=\dfrac{z-2}{5}, \dfrac{x-1}{1}=\dfrac{y-4}{-1}=\dfrac{z+17}{2}$

(ii) $\dfrac{x+1}{2}=\dfrac{y-2}{0}=\dfrac{z-4}{3}, \dfrac{x+4}{5}=\dfrac{y-4}{-2}=\dfrac{z-6}{1}$

(iii) $\dfrac{x}{5}=\dfrac{y+1}{3}=\dfrac{z-4}{-3}, \dfrac{x-2}{4}=\dfrac{y-5}{-3}=\dfrac{z+1}{2}$

(iv) $\mathbf{r}=\begin{pmatrix}9\\3\\-4\end{pmatrix}+t\begin{pmatrix}1\\2\\-3\end{pmatrix}, \mathbf{r}=\begin{pmatrix}1\\-4\\5\end{pmatrix}+t\begin{pmatrix}1\\-1\\2\end{pmatrix}$

(v) $\mathbf{r}=\begin{pmatrix}2\\3\\1\end{pmatrix}+t\begin{pmatrix}1\\1\\-2\end{pmatrix}, \mathbf{r}=\begin{pmatrix}-1\\-3\\-1\end{pmatrix}+t\begin{pmatrix}1\\3\\2\end{pmatrix}$

2 To support a tree damaged in a gale a tree surgeon attaches wire guys to four of the branches (see the diagram). He joins (2, 0, 3) to (−1, 2, 6) and (0, 3, 5) to (−2, −2, 4). Do the guys, assumed straight, meet?

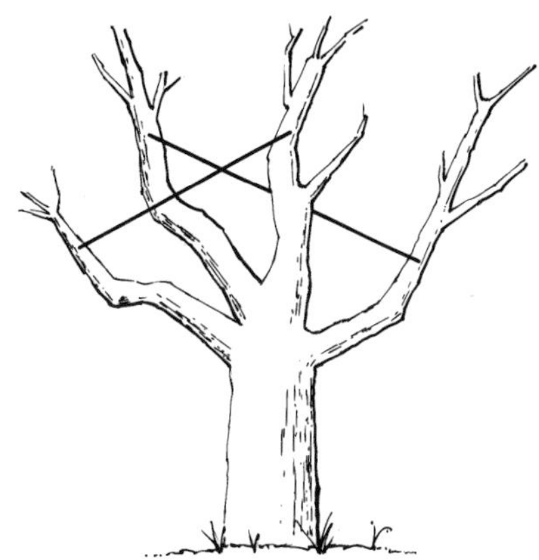

3 The line with cartesian equations $\dfrac{x+4}{2}=\dfrac{y-4}{-10}=\dfrac{z+12}{11}$ meets $\dfrac{x-4}{2}=\dfrac{y+15}{-3}=\dfrac{z+16}{-5}$ at A and meets $\dfrac{x+1}{1}=\dfrac{y+29}{1}=\dfrac{z+3}{8}$ at B. Find the co-ordinates of A and the length of AB.

4 Show that the three lines $\dfrac{x+7}{4}=\dfrac{y-24}{-7}=\dfrac{z+4}{4}, \dfrac{x-3}{2}=\dfrac{y+10}{2}=\dfrac{z-15}{-1}$, $\dfrac{x+3}{8}=\dfrac{y-6}{-3}=\dfrac{z-6}{2}$ form a triangle, and find the lengths of its sides.

5 The co-ordinates of four points are as follows:

$$\mathrm{A}(2,-9,-5),\ \mathrm{B}(5,-4,-4),\ \mathrm{C}(8,15,4) \text{ and } \mathrm{D}(7,18,6).$$

(i) Calculate the vector product $\overrightarrow{\mathrm{AB}}\times\overrightarrow{\mathrm{CD}}$.

(ii) Show that the lines AB and CD intersect, and find the co-ordinates of the point of intersection.

(iii) Find, in the form $ax+by+cz+d=0$, the equation of the plane P which contains the points A, B, C and D.

(iv) Find the equation of the plane which contains the line AB and is perpendicular to the plane P.

[MEI]

6 (i) Calculate the vector product $\mathbf{a} \times \mathbf{b}$ when $\mathbf{a} = 6\mathbf{i} - 8\mathbf{j} - 3\mathbf{k}$ and $\mathbf{b} = -6\mathbf{i} + 5\mathbf{j} + 2\mathbf{k}$.

Two straight lines L and M are given by the equations

$$\text{L: } \frac{x-1}{6} = \frac{y+2}{-8} = \frac{z-5}{-3} \qquad \text{and} \qquad \text{M: } \frac{x-7}{-6} = \frac{y-2}{5} = \frac{z-h}{2}$$

where (x, y, z) are cartesian co-ordinates and h is a constant.
The lines L and M intersect.

(ii) Find the value of h and the co-ordinates of the point of intersection of L and M.

(iii) Find, in the form $ax + by + cz + d = 0$, the equation of the plane P containing the lines L and M.
(You may find your answer to part **(i)** helpful.)

(iv) Explain why the line with equation $\frac{x-12}{6} = \frac{y+4}{-8} = \frac{z-9}{-3}$ is parallel to the plane P, and calculate the shortest distance between this line and the plane. [MEI]

7 Lines ℓ_1 and ℓ_2 are skew, and X is a point on neither ℓ_1 nor ℓ_2. By considering the plane containing both ℓ_1 and X, or otherwise, prove that if there is a line through X intersecting both ℓ_1 and ℓ_2, then it is unique.

8 (i) Show that the lines ℓ_1: $\frac{x+1}{3} = \frac{y+4}{-4} = \frac{z-5}{7}$ and ℓ_2: $\frac{x-12}{0} = \frac{y}{2} = \frac{z-2}{-3}$ are skew.

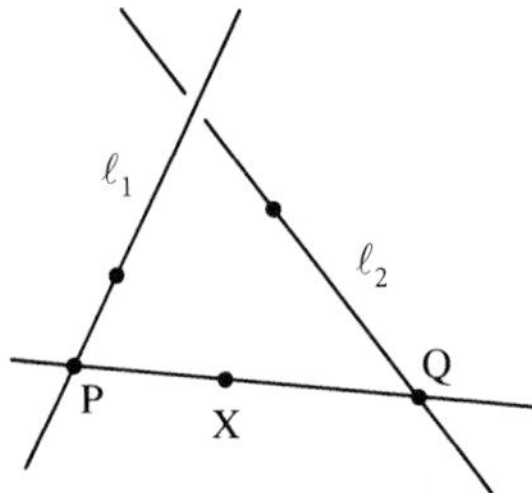

(ii) The points P and Q are on lines ℓ_1 and ℓ_2 respectively. Write down the co-ordinates of P and Q in terms of parameters p and q respectively.

(iii) The line PQ passes through the point X(8, 6, –8). Use the fact that $\overrightarrow{XP} = \lambda\overrightarrow{XQ}$ to find the equation of PQ (in any form).

(iv) Find the co-ordinates of P and Q.

9 (i) A cube has side a. Show that the vertices are $\frac{1}{2}a\sqrt{3}$ from the centre of the cube.

(ii) Points A and B have co-ordinates (3, 3, 3) and (5, –1, –1) respectively. Show that $OA = OB = \frac{1}{2}\sqrt{3}AB$.

(iii) A and B are adjacent vertices of a cube which has its centre at the origin. Find the co-ordinates of the other vertices.

10 (i) Show that the lines ℓ_1: $\frac{x-11}{2} = \frac{y+9}{1} = \frac{z-25}{2}$ and ℓ_2: $\frac{x-4}{2} = \frac{y-15}{-6} = \frac{z-5}{-5}$ are skew.

(ii) The points P and Q are on lines ℓ_1 and ℓ_2 respectively, such that PQ is perpendicular to both ℓ_1 and ℓ_2. Find a vector parallel to PQ and a vector perpendicular to both PQ and ℓ_2.

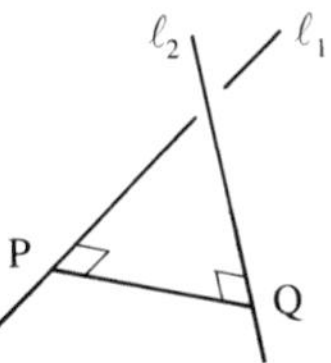

(iii) Find the equation of the plane π that contains both PQ and ℓ_2.

(iv) Find where ℓ_1 meets π.

(v) Find the cartesian equations of PQ.

(vi) Find the co-ordinates of Q and the shortest distance between lines ℓ_1 and ℓ_2.

11 In a chemical plant a straight pipe connects A(−2, 32, −3) and B(23, 57, −23) and a second straight pipe connects C(25, 3, 14) and D(49, 30, −1), where axes are scaled in metres. Use the methods described in Question 10 to find the length of the shortest straight pipe that would connect AB to CD, and the co-ordinates of the necessary junction points.

Calculating distances

The distance of a point from a line

Building works at an airport require the use of a crane near the end of the runway.

How far is it from the top of the crane to the flight path of the plane?

Figure 1.12

To answer this question you need to know the flight path and the position of the top of the crane. Working in metres, suppose planes take off along the line $\ell: \frac{x+10}{5} = \frac{y-20}{4} = \frac{z-2}{3}$ and that the top of the crane is at P(70, 30, 22), as illustrated in figure 1.13.

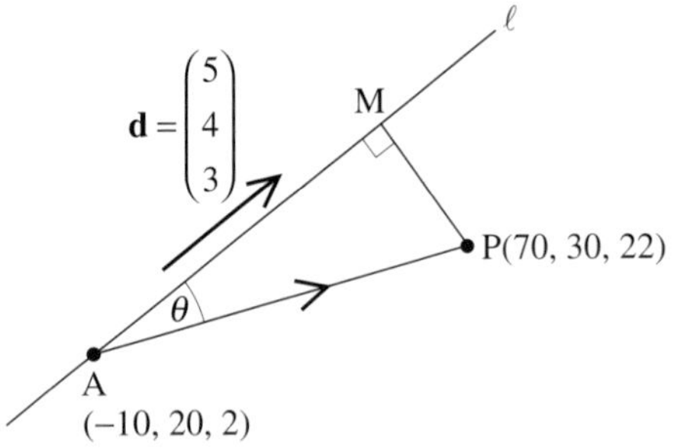

Figure 1.13

The shortest distance from a point P to a straight line ℓ is measured along the line which is perpendicular to ℓ. This distance, PM in figure 1.13, is the distance from the point P to the line ℓ. The vector product provides a convenient way of calculating such distances.

Since PM is perpendicular to ℓ

$$\begin{aligned} \text{PM} &= \text{AP} \sin \text{PAM} \\ &= |\overrightarrow{\text{AP}} \times \hat{\mathbf{d}}| \end{aligned}$$

where $\hat{\mathbf{d}}$ is the unit vector parallel to $\mathbf{d}$.

> $\mathbf{a} \times \mathbf{b} = |\mathbf{a}|\,|\mathbf{b}| \sin \theta \hat{\mathbf{n}}$, where $\hat{\mathbf{n}}$ is a unit vector perpendicular to **a** and **b**.

Using the convention that **a** and **p** represent the position vectors of A and P respectively, you can write:

$$\text{PM} = |(\mathbf{p} - \mathbf{a}) \times \hat{\mathbf{d}}|.$$

Since $\mathbf{d} = |\mathbf{d}|\hat{\mathbf{d}}$, you can also write:

$$\text{PM} = \frac{|(\mathbf{p} - \mathbf{a}) \times \mathbf{d}|}{|\mathbf{d}|}$$

a result which is harder to remember but easier to use.

Returning to calculating the distance from the top of the crane to the flight path:

$$\mathbf{p} = \begin{pmatrix} 70 \\ 30 \\ 22 \end{pmatrix}, \mathbf{a} = \begin{pmatrix} -10 \\ 20 \\ 2 \end{pmatrix} \text{ and } \mathbf{d} = \begin{pmatrix} 5 \\ 4 \\ 3 \end{pmatrix} \text{ so that}$$

$$\overrightarrow{AP} = \mathbf{p} - \mathbf{a} = \begin{pmatrix} 70 \\ 30 \\ 22 \end{pmatrix} - \begin{pmatrix} -10 \\ 20 \\ 2 \end{pmatrix} = \begin{pmatrix} 80 \\ 10 \\ 20 \end{pmatrix} = 10\begin{pmatrix} 8 \\ 1 \\ 2 \end{pmatrix} \text{ and}$$

$$\begin{pmatrix} a_1 \\ a_2 \\ a_3 \end{pmatrix} \times \begin{pmatrix} b_1 \\ b_2 \\ b_3 \end{pmatrix} = \begin{pmatrix} a_2b_3 - a_3b_2 \\ a_3b_1 - a_1b_3 \\ a_1b_2 - a_2b_1 \end{pmatrix}$$

$$\overrightarrow{AP} \times \mathbf{d} = 10\begin{pmatrix} 8 \\ 1 \\ 2 \end{pmatrix} \times \begin{pmatrix} 5 \\ 4 \\ 3 \end{pmatrix} = 10\begin{pmatrix} 3 - 8 \\ 10 - 24 \\ 32 - 5 \end{pmatrix} = 10\begin{pmatrix} -5 \\ -14 \\ 27 \end{pmatrix}.$$

Therefore:

$$|\overrightarrow{AP} \times \mathbf{d}| = 10\sqrt{-5^2 + -14^2 + 27^2} = 10\sqrt{950} = 10\sqrt{25 \times 38} = 50\sqrt{38}$$

while $$|\mathbf{d}| = \sqrt{5^2 + 4^2 + 3^2} = \sqrt{50} = 5\sqrt{2}.$$

Therefore the (shortest) distance from P to ℓ is:

$$\text{PM} = \frac{50\sqrt{38}}{5\sqrt{2}} = 10\sqrt{19} \approx 43.6 \text{ metres.}$$

The technique just illustrated does not tell you which point on line ℓ is closest to P. In such situations the scalar product provides a way of finding the position of M, the foot of the perpendicular from P to ℓ. In figure 1.14, A, with position vector **a**, is any (known) point on ℓ, and **d** is any vector parallel to ℓ. The position vector of M is:

$$\begin{aligned} \mathbf{m} &= \mathbf{a} + \overrightarrow{AM} \\ &= \mathbf{a} + \lambda\mathbf{d} \end{aligned}$$

where λ is a measure of the length of AM.

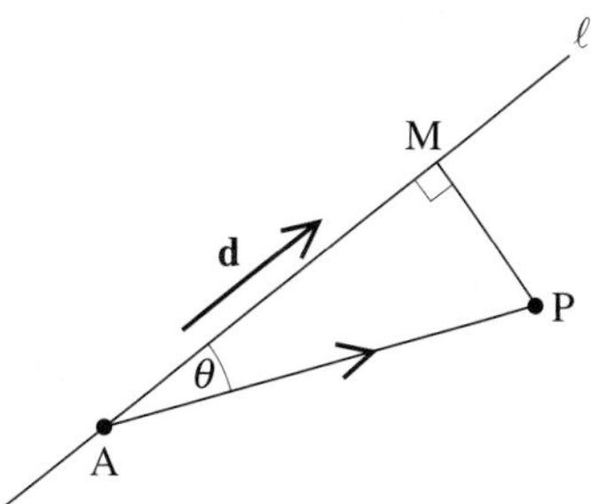

Figure 1.14

Now the length of AM is AP cos PAM $= |\overrightarrow{AP} \,.\, \hat{\mathbf{d}}|$. The modulus function is needed here because $\overrightarrow{AP} \,.\, \hat{\mathbf{d}}$ is only positive when $\overrightarrow{AM}$ and **d** have the same sense (i.e. point in the same direction, as illustrated). When $\overrightarrow{AM}$ and **d** have opposite senses $\overrightarrow{AP} \,.\, \hat{\mathbf{d}}$ is negative. In both cases, $\overrightarrow{AM} = (\overrightarrow{AP} \,.\, \hat{\mathbf{d}})\hat{\mathbf{d}}$, which may also be written as

$\dfrac{\overrightarrow{\mathrm{AP}}.\mathbf{d}}{|\mathbf{d}|^2}\mathbf{d}$ since $\mathbf{d} = |\mathbf{d}|\,\hat{\mathbf{d}}$. Thus the foot of the perpendicular from the point P to the line $\mathbf{r} = \mathbf{a} + \lambda\mathbf{d}$ is $\mathbf{a} + (\overrightarrow{\mathrm{AP}}.\hat{\mathbf{d}})\hat{\mathbf{d}}$. You may prefer to write this as:

$$\mathbf{a} + ((\mathbf{p}-\mathbf{a}).\hat{\mathbf{d}})\hat{\mathbf{d}} \quad \text{or} \quad \mathbf{a} + \frac{\overrightarrow{\mathrm{AP}}.\mathbf{d}}{|\mathbf{d}|^2}\mathbf{d} \quad \text{or} \quad \mathbf{a} + \frac{(\mathbf{p}-\mathbf{a}).\mathbf{d}}{|\mathbf{d}|^2}\mathbf{d}.$$

EXAMPLE 1.10

Find the co-ordinates of M, the foot of the perpendicular from the top of the crane, P(70, 30, 22) to the line ℓ, $\dfrac{x+10}{5} = \dfrac{y-20}{4} = \dfrac{z-2}{3}$, representing the flight path.

SOLUTION

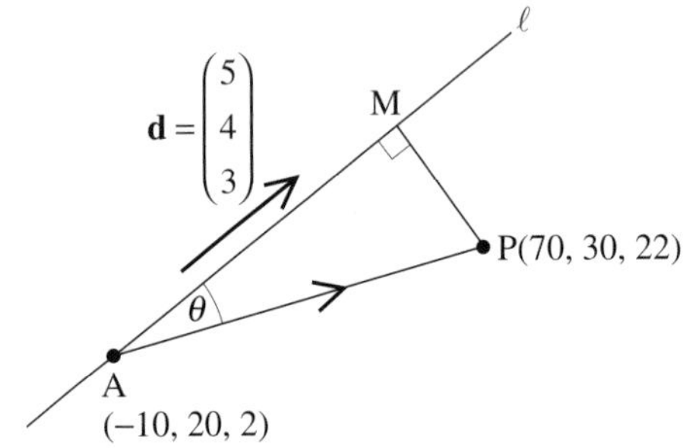

Figure 1.15

From the cartesian equations of ℓ you may, as before, take A as the point (−10, 20, 2) and the direction vector for ℓ as $\mathbf{d} = \begin{pmatrix}5\\4\\3\end{pmatrix}$. Then $\overrightarrow{\mathrm{AP}} = \mathbf{p} - \mathbf{a} = 10\begin{pmatrix}8\\1\\2\end{pmatrix}$ and $|\mathbf{d}| = \sqrt{50}$.

Now $\overrightarrow{\mathrm{AP}}.\mathbf{d} = 10\begin{pmatrix}8\\1\\2\end{pmatrix}.\begin{pmatrix}5\\4\\3\end{pmatrix} = 10(40+4+6) = 500$ so that:

$$\frac{\overrightarrow{\mathrm{AP}}.\mathbf{d}}{|\mathbf{d}|^2} = \frac{500}{(\sqrt{50})^2} = 10 \quad \text{and} \quad \overrightarrow{\mathrm{AM}} = \frac{\overrightarrow{\mathrm{AP}}.\mathbf{d}}{|\mathbf{d}|^2}\mathbf{d} = 10\mathbf{d} = \begin{pmatrix}50\\40\\30\end{pmatrix}.$$

So $\mathbf{m} = \mathbf{a} + \overrightarrow{\mathrm{AM}} = \begin{pmatrix}-10\\20\\2\end{pmatrix} + \begin{pmatrix}50\\40\\30\end{pmatrix} = \begin{pmatrix}40\\60\\32\end{pmatrix}$ and M is (40, 60, 32).

Knowing the co-ordinates of both M and P allows you to use an alternative method of finding the length of PM:

$$\mathrm{PM} = \sqrt{(40-70)^2 + (60-30)^2 + (32-22)^2} = \sqrt{1900} \approx 43.6 \text{ metres.}$$

ALTERNATIVE SOLUTION

M lies on $\ell \Rightarrow$ M is of the form $(-10+5\lambda, 20+4\lambda, 2+3\lambda)$

$$\Rightarrow \overrightarrow{PM} = \begin{pmatrix} -80+5\lambda \\ -10+4\lambda \\ -20+3\lambda \end{pmatrix};$$

$$\overrightarrow{PM} \text{ is perpendicular to } \ell \Rightarrow \begin{pmatrix} -80+5\lambda \\ -10+4\lambda \\ -20+3\lambda \end{pmatrix} . \begin{pmatrix} 5 \\ 4 \\ 3 \end{pmatrix} = 0$$

$$\Rightarrow -400+25\lambda-40+16\lambda-60+9\lambda = 0$$

$$\Rightarrow \lambda = 10 \Rightarrow \text{M is } (40, 60, 32).$$

The distance from the point P, with position vector **p**, to the line $\mathbf{r} = \mathbf{a} + \lambda\mathbf{d}$ may be written in any of the following ways:

$$|\overrightarrow{AP} \times \hat{\mathbf{d}}| = |(\mathbf{p}-\mathbf{a}) \times \hat{\mathbf{d}}| = \frac{|(\mathbf{p}-\mathbf{a}) \times \mathbf{d}|}{|\mathbf{d}|}.$$

As the vector product of vectors **a** and **b** is a vector perpendicular to both **a** and **b** these results presuppose that you are working in three dimensions. When you are working in two dimensions (in which case vectors have only two components) you can either quote the formula obtained in part **(iii)** of Activity 1.3 below or adapt the process described in that activity.

ACTIVITY 1.3

Let points in the plane $z = 0$ correspond to points of two-dimensional space, so that the point $R'(x, y, 0)$ in three-dimensional space corresponds to the point $R(x, y)$ in two-dimensional space. Use the following steps to find the distance from $P(x_1, y_1)$ to the line $ax + by + c = 0$.

(i) The point A′ in three-dimensional space corresponds to $A\left(0, -\frac{c}{b}\right)$.

Write down the co-ordinates of A′.

(ii) Find p, q, r so that $p\mathbf{i} + q\mathbf{j} + r\mathbf{k}$ is parallel to the line in three-dimensional space which corresponds to the line $ax + by + c = 0$ in two-dimensional space.

(iii) Use the formula $\frac{|(\mathbf{p}-\mathbf{a}) \times \mathbf{d}|}{|\mathbf{d}|}$ to show that the distance from $P(x_1, y_1)$ to the line $ax + by + c = 0$ is $\left|\frac{ax_1 + by_1 + c}{\sqrt{a^2 + b^2}}\right|$.

(iv) Show that the expression $\frac{ax_1 + by_1 + c}{\sqrt{a^2 + b^2}}$ changes sign if the point (x_1, y_1) is moved to the opposite side of the line $ax + by + c = 0$.

The shortest distance between two skew lines

The shortest distance between two skew lines, ℓ_1 and ℓ_2, is measured along a line which is perpendicular to both ℓ_1 and ℓ_2. Figure 1.16 shows lines ℓ_1 and ℓ_2. Let π be the plane containing ℓ_2 and parallel to ℓ_1. Drop perpendiculars from points on ℓ_1 to π to form ℓ_1', the projection of ℓ_1 on π. The common perpendicular of ℓ_1 and ℓ_2 is the perpendicular from ℓ_1 that passes through Q, the point of intersection of ℓ_2 and ℓ_1', shown as PQ in the diagram.

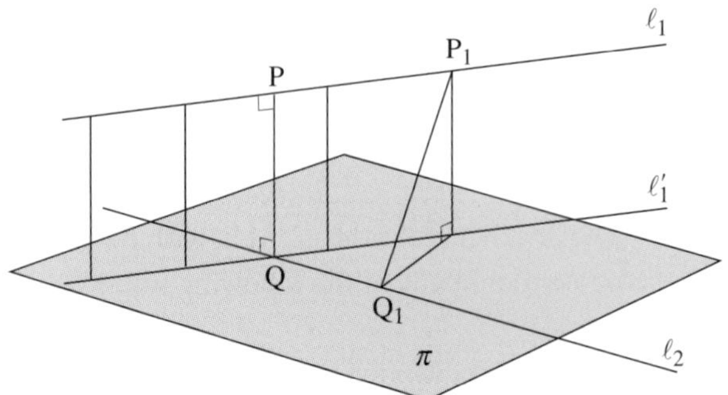

Figure 1.16

ACTIVITY 1.4 Explain why PQ is shorter than any other line (such as P_1Q_1) joining lines ℓ_1 and ℓ_2.

If ℓ_1 and ℓ_2 have equations $\mathbf{r} = \mathbf{a} + t\mathbf{d}$ and $\mathbf{r} = \mathbf{b} + t\mathbf{e}$ respectively, and you want to find the length of the common perpendicular PQ, it is tempting to start with the known result $PQ = |\overrightarrow{AP} \times \hat{\mathbf{d}}|$, but this time you do not know the position of P. However, you do know a point on each line, A and B, and a vector parallel to each line, **d** and **e** respectively.

Figure 1.17 shows lines ℓ_1 and ℓ_2 and two parallel planes:

π_1 contains ℓ_1 and is parallel to ℓ_2
π_2 contains ℓ_2 and is parallel to ℓ_1.

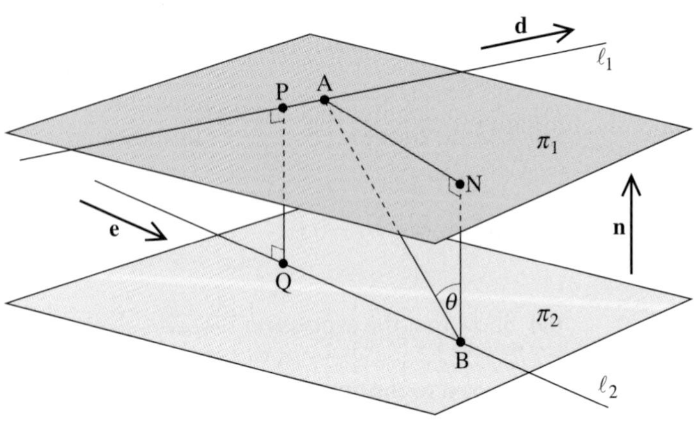

Figure 1.17

Then PQ, the common perpendicular of ℓ_1 and ℓ_2, has the same length as any other perpendicular between the two planes, such as BN, where B is a point on ℓ_2. If A is any point on ℓ_1 and angle ABN = θ then

$$\text{PQ} = \text{BN} = \text{BA}\cos\theta = |\overrightarrow{\text{BA}}\,.\,\hat{\mathbf{n}}|$$

where $\hat{\mathbf{n}}$ is a unit vector parallel to BN, i.e. perpendicular to both planes. The modulus function is used to ensure a positive answer: the vector $\hat{\mathbf{n}}$ may be directed from π_1 towards π_2, making $\overrightarrow{\text{BA}}\,.\,\hat{\mathbf{n}}$ negative.

Since π_1 and π_2 are parallel to ℓ_1 and ℓ_2, which are parallel to **d** and **e** respectively, you may take $\mathbf{d}\times\mathbf{e}$ as **n**, with $\hat{\mathbf{n}} = \dfrac{(\mathbf{d}\times\mathbf{e})}{|\mathbf{d}\times\mathbf{e}|}$. Then:

$$\text{PQ} = \text{BN} = |\overrightarrow{\text{BA}}\,.\,\hat{\mathbf{n}}| = \left|\frac{\overrightarrow{\text{BA}}\,.(\mathbf{d}\times\mathbf{e})}{|\mathbf{d}\times\mathbf{e}|}\right| = \left|\frac{(\mathbf{a}-\mathbf{b})\,.(\mathbf{d}\times\mathbf{e})}{|\mathbf{d}\times\mathbf{e}|}\right|.$$

The final result is just a complicated way of expressing BA cos θ!

EXAMPLE 1.11

Find the shortest distance between the lines ℓ_1: $\dfrac{x-8}{1} = \dfrac{y-9}{2} = \dfrac{z+2}{-3}$ and ℓ_2: $\dfrac{x-6}{1} = \dfrac{y}{-1} = \dfrac{z+2}{-2}$.

SOLUTION

As shown in figure 1.18, line ℓ_1 contains the point A(8, 9, −2) and is parallel to $\mathbf{d} = \mathbf{i} + 2\mathbf{j} - 3\mathbf{k}$; line ℓ_2 contains the point B(6, 0, −2) and is parallel to $\mathbf{e} = \mathbf{i} - \mathbf{j} - 2\mathbf{k}$.

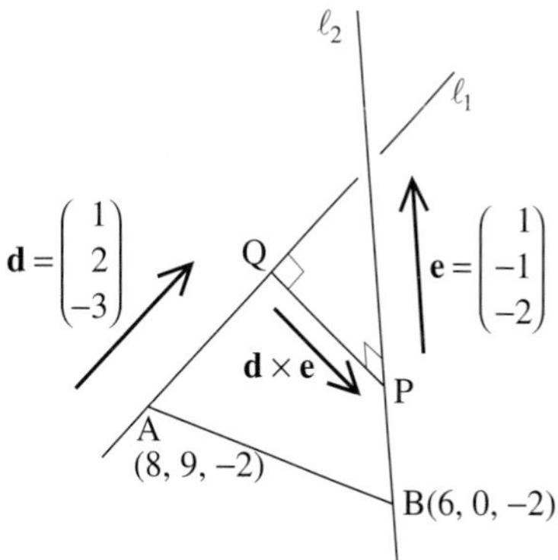

Figure 1.18

Now $\mathbf{a}-\mathbf{b} = \begin{pmatrix} 8 \\ 9 \\ -2 \end{pmatrix} - \begin{pmatrix} 6 \\ 0 \\ -2 \end{pmatrix} = \begin{pmatrix} 2 \\ 9 \\ 0 \end{pmatrix}$

and $\mathbf{d}\times\mathbf{e}=\begin{pmatrix}1\\2\\-3\end{pmatrix}\times\begin{pmatrix}1\\-1\\-2\end{pmatrix}=\begin{pmatrix}-4-3\\-3+2\\-1-2\end{pmatrix}=\begin{pmatrix}-7\\-1\\-3\end{pmatrix}$

so that $(\mathbf{a}-\mathbf{b}).(\mathbf{d}\times\mathbf{e})=\begin{pmatrix}2\\9\\0\end{pmatrix}.\begin{pmatrix}-7\\-1\\-3\end{pmatrix}=-14-9=-23$

and $|\mathbf{d}\times\mathbf{e}|=\sqrt{7^2+1^2+3^2}=\sqrt{59}$.

Therefore the shortest (i.e. perpendicular) distance between ℓ_1 and ℓ_2 is:

$$\left|\frac{(\mathbf{a}-\mathbf{b}).(\mathbf{d}\times\mathbf{e})}{|\mathbf{d}\times\mathbf{e}|}\right|=\frac{23}{\sqrt{59}}\approx 2.99 \text{ units.}$$

As previously, this technique for finding the shortest distance between two skew lines does not tell you the positions of the ends of the shortest line segment joining the two lines. One way of doing that involves the following steps.

1. Express the co-ordinates of the general points P on ℓ_1 and Q on ℓ_2 in terms of parameters such as p and q.
2. Express the vector $\overrightarrow{PQ}$ in terms of p and q.
3. P and Q are the feet of the required common perpendicular if and only if PQ is perpendicular to both ℓ_1 and ℓ_2. Using scalar products, form simultaneous equations in p and q.
4. Solve these equations and find the points P and Q.

The distance of a point from a plane

The distance from the point $P(x_1, y_1, z_1)$ to the plane π with equation $ax+by+cz+d=0$ is PM where M is the foot of the perpendicular from P to the plane. Notice that PM is parallel to $\mathbf{n}=a\mathbf{i}+b\mathbf{j}+c\mathbf{k}$, the normal to plane π. Let R (with position vector $\mathbf{r}$) be any point on plane π.

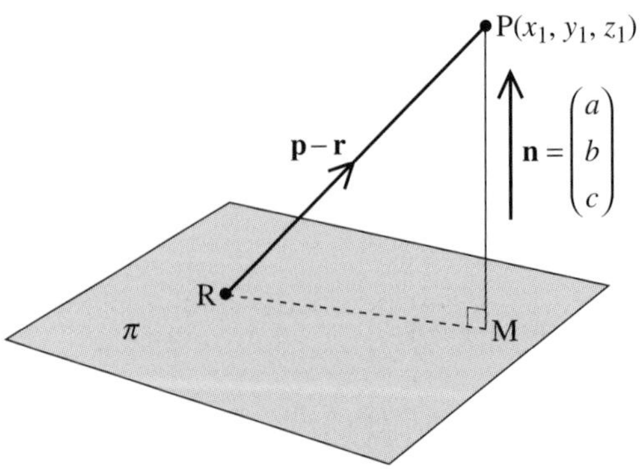

Figure 1.19

If the angle between vectors $\mathbf{p} - \mathbf{r}$ and $\mathbf{n}$ is acute (as illustrated in figure 1.19):

$$\text{PM} = \text{RP} \cos \text{RPM} = \overrightarrow{\text{RP}} \cdot \hat{\mathbf{n}} = (\mathbf{p} - \mathbf{r}) \cdot \hat{\mathbf{n}}.$$

If the angle between $\mathbf{p} - \mathbf{r}$ and $\mathbf{n}$ is obtuse, cos RPM is negative and $\text{PM} = -(\mathbf{p} - \mathbf{r}) \cdot \hat{\mathbf{n}}$. As R is any point on π you may use $\mathbf{r} = -\frac{d}{c}\mathbf{k}$ which means that:

$$(\mathbf{p} - \mathbf{r}) \cdot \mathbf{n} = \begin{pmatrix} x_1 \\ y_1 \\ z_1 + \frac{d}{c} \end{pmatrix} \cdot \begin{pmatrix} a \\ b \\ c \end{pmatrix} = ax_1 + by_1 + cz_1 + d$$

and $\text{PM} = |(\mathbf{p} - \mathbf{r}) \cdot \hat{\mathbf{n}}| = \left| \frac{(\mathbf{p} - \mathbf{r}) \cdot \mathbf{n}}{|\mathbf{n}|} \right| = \left| \frac{ax_1 + by_1 + cz_1 + d}{\sqrt{a^2 + b^2 + c^2}} \right|.$

Notice how the formula for the distance of a point from a plane (in three-dimensional space) resembles the formula given on page 23 for the distance of a point from a line (in two-dimensional space).

ACTIVITY 1.5

It is noticed that $ax_1 + by_1 + cz_1 + d$ and $ax_2 + by_2 + cz_2 + d$ have opposite signs. Explain the significance of this observation.

EXERCISE 1D

1 Calculate the distance from P to the line ℓ.

(i) P(1, –2, 3); $\quad \ell: \begin{cases} x = 2t + 1 \\ y = 2t + 5 \\ z = -t - 1 \end{cases}$

(ii) P(2, 3, –5); $\quad \ell: \mathbf{r} = \begin{pmatrix} 4 \\ 3 \\ 4 \end{pmatrix} + t\begin{pmatrix} 6 \\ -7 \\ 6 \end{pmatrix}$

(iii) P(8, 9, 1); $\quad \ell: \frac{x-6}{12} = \frac{y-5}{-9} = \frac{z-11}{-8}$

2 Find the distance from P to the line ℓ.

(i) P(8, 9); $\quad \ell: 3x + 4y + 5 = 0$
(ii) P(5, –4); $\quad \ell: 6x - 3y + 3 = 0$
(iii) P(4, –4); $\quad \ell: 8x + 15y + 11 = 0$

3 Find the distance from P to plane π.

(i) P(5, 4, 0); $\quad \pi: 6x + 6y + 7z + 1 = 0$
(ii) P(7, 2, –2); $\quad \pi: 12x - 9y - 8z + 3 = 0$
(iii) P(–4, –5, 3); $\quad \pi: 8x + 5y - 3z - 4 = 0$

4 Are P and Q on the same side of the plane π? Justify your answer.

(i) P(1, 1, 3); Q(1, 1, 2); π: $5x - 7y + 2z - 3 = 0$

(ii) P(0, 3, 5); Q(2, −1, 1); π: $11x + 5y + z + 2 = 0$

(iii) P(1, 2, 2); Q(5, −2, 3); π: $4x + 6y - 3z + 1 = 0$

5 Find the shortest distance between lines ℓ and ℓ'.

(i) $\ell: x - 2 = \dfrac{y-3}{2} = \dfrac{z-4}{2}$; $\ell': \dfrac{x-2}{2} = \dfrac{y-9}{-2} = z - 1$

(ii) $\ell: \dfrac{x-8}{4} = \dfrac{y+2}{3} = \dfrac{z-7}{5}$; $\ell': \dfrac{x-2}{2} = \dfrac{y+6}{-6} = \dfrac{z-1}{-9}$

(iii) $\ell: \dfrac{x+5}{8} = \dfrac{y-6}{6} = \dfrac{z-1}{3}$; $\ell': \dfrac{x-5}{5} = y - 8 = z - 3$

6 Find the co-ordinates of the foot of the perpendicular from P to the line ℓ.

(i) P(0, 0, 0); $\ell: x - 14 = -\frac{1}{3}(y + 4) = z - 18$

(ii) P(10, 3, −14); $\ell: x - 11 = 5 - y = z + 1$

(iii) P(13, 4, 2); $\ell: \mathbf{r} = 2\mathbf{i} - 8\mathbf{j} + 21\mathbf{k} + t(\mathbf{i} - 2\mathbf{j} + 3\mathbf{k})$

7 Find the co-ordinates of A on ℓ and B on ℓ' such that AB is as short as possible.

(i) $\ell: \begin{cases} x = 5t - 6 \\ y = 4t \\ z = 3t - 3 \end{cases}$ $\ell': \begin{cases} x = t + 6 \\ y = 2t - 8 \\ z = 3t - 1 \end{cases}$

(ii) $\ell: \dfrac{x-5}{2} = \dfrac{y+2}{-3} = \dfrac{z-3}{-4}$ $\ell': \dfrac{x-10}{3} = \dfrac{y-1}{-1} = \dfrac{z+7}{-6}$

(iii) $\ell: \mathbf{r} = \begin{pmatrix} -5 \\ 10 \\ 12 \end{pmatrix} + t\begin{pmatrix} 3 \\ -1 \\ 4 \end{pmatrix}$ $\ell': \mathbf{r} = \begin{pmatrix} 21 \\ -7 \\ 3 \end{pmatrix} + t\begin{pmatrix} 2 \\ 1 \\ -1 \end{pmatrix}$

8 Two straight lines are said to be *skew* if they do not intersect and are not parallel. Distinct points with position vectors **a** and **b** lie on the first of two such lines and distinct points with position vectors **c** and **d** lie on the second. Find an expression for the shortest distance between the two lines in terms of **a**, **b**, **c** and **d**.

Find the shortest distance between the two skew lines defined by the points $\mathbf{a} = \mathbf{i} - 2\mathbf{j} + 3\mathbf{k}$, $\mathbf{b} = 2\mathbf{i} + 5\mathbf{k}$, $\mathbf{c} = 4\mathbf{i} + \mathbf{j} - \mathbf{k}$, $\mathbf{d} = -2\mathbf{i} + 3\mathbf{j} + 4\mathbf{k}$.

[MEI]

9 The plane π has equation $\mathbf{n}.\mathbf{r} + d = 0$. Reflection in π maps the point P to P′.

Show that $\mathbf{p}' = \mathbf{p} - \dfrac{2}{|\mathbf{n}|^2}(\mathbf{n}.\mathbf{p} + d)\mathbf{n}$.

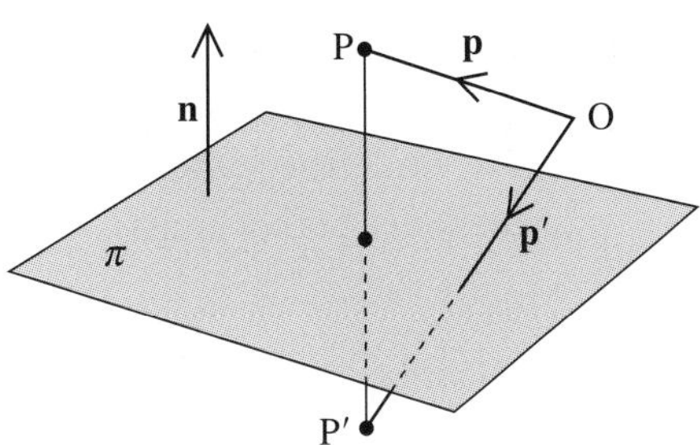

10 The diagram shows skew lines ℓ_1 and ℓ_2. Plane π contains ℓ_1 and is perpendicular to ℓ_2. Line ℓ_2 intersects π at Q, and lines are drawn from Q to $P_1, P_2, P_3, \ldots$ on ℓ_1. Use this as the basis of an explanation as to why the shortest distance between two skew lines is along the common perpendicular.

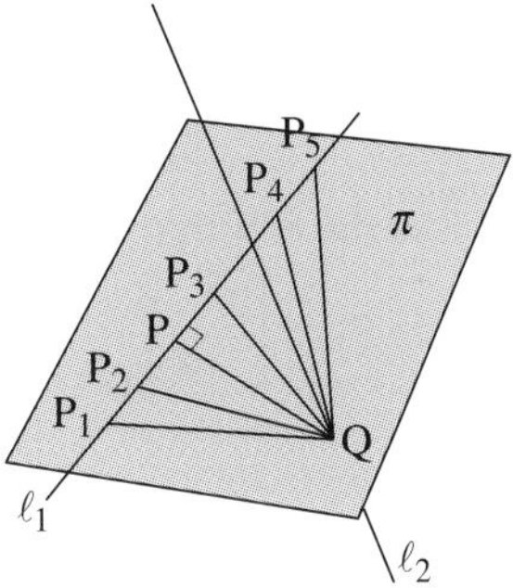

11 **(i)** Lines ℓ and ℓ' are skew, and P is a point on neither ℓ nor ℓ'. By considering the plane containing ℓ and P, or otherwise, prove that there is at most one line through P which intersects both ℓ and ℓ'.

(ii) Lines ℓ and ℓ' have equations

$$x - 5 = -y = z + 1 \quad \text{and} \quad \frac{x-5}{2} = \frac{y-5}{-2} = \frac{z-4}{-3}.$$

Find equations for the line through P(2, 5, 4) which intersects both ℓ and ℓ'.

12 The point P has co-ordinates $(4, k, 5)$, where k is a constant.

The line L has equation $\mathbf{r} = \begin{pmatrix} 1 \\ 0 \\ -4 \end{pmatrix} + t\begin{pmatrix} 1 \\ 2 \\ -2 \end{pmatrix}$.

The line M has equation $\mathbf{r} = \begin{pmatrix} 4 \\ k \\ 5 \end{pmatrix} + t\begin{pmatrix} 7 \\ 3 \\ -4 \end{pmatrix}$.

(i) Show that the shortest distance from the point P to the line L is $\frac{1}{3}\sqrt{5(k^2+12k+117)}$.

(ii) Find (in terms of k) the shortest distance between the lines L and M.

(iii) Find the value of k for which the lines L and M intersect.

(iv) When $k = 12$, show that the distances in parts **(i)** and **(ii)** are equal. In this case, find the equation of the line which is perpendicular to, and intersects, both L and M.

[MEI]

13 Lines ℓ_1 and ℓ_2 have direction vectors $\mathbf{d}$ and $\mathbf{e}$ respectively; A is any point on ℓ_1 and B is any point on ℓ_2; $\hat{\mathbf{n}}$ is a unit vector parallel to the common perpendicular PQ.

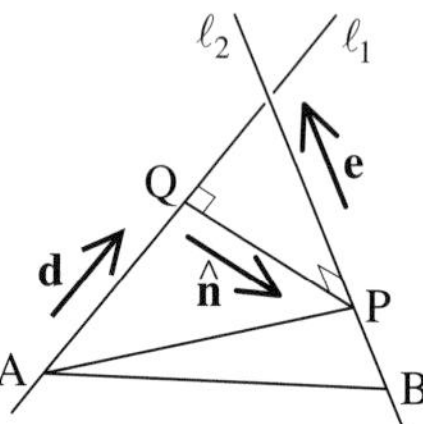

(i) Explain why $PQ = |\overrightarrow{PA}\,.\,\hat{\mathbf{n}}|$.

(ii) Use the fact that $\overrightarrow{PA} = \overrightarrow{PB} + \overrightarrow{BA}$ to show that $\overrightarrow{PA}.\hat{\mathbf{n}} = \overrightarrow{BA}.\hat{\mathbf{n}}$ and deduce that $PQ = \left|\dfrac{\overrightarrow{BA}.(\mathbf{d}\times\mathbf{e})}{|\mathbf{d}\times\mathbf{e}|}\right|$.

14 Two ships are moving with constant, but different, velocities $\mathbf{v}_1$ and $\mathbf{v}_2$. At noon the ships have position vectors $\mathbf{a}_1$ and $\mathbf{a}_2$ respectively with respect to a fixed origin. The distance between the ships is decreasing. Show that

$$(\mathbf{v}_1 - \mathbf{v}_2)\,.\,(\mathbf{a}_1 - \mathbf{a}_2) < 0.$$

The ship with velocity $\mathbf{v}_1$ will sight the second ship if the distance between the ships is, at any time, less than or equal to d, where $d < |\mathbf{a}_1 - \mathbf{a}_2|$. Show that sighting will occur provided

$$d^2 \geqslant |\mathbf{a}_1 - \mathbf{a}_2|^2 - \frac{((\mathbf{v}_1 - \mathbf{v}_2).(\mathbf{a}_1 - \mathbf{a}_2))^2}{|\mathbf{v}_1 - \mathbf{v}_2|^2}.$$

If this condition is just satisfied, find the time after noon when sighting occurs.

[MEI]

15 A and B have position vectors $\mathbf{a}$ and $\mathbf{b}$, and $\hat{\mathbf{n}}$ is a unit vector. Prove that:

(i) $|(\mathbf{a} - \mathbf{b})\,.\,\hat{\mathbf{n}}|$ is the shortest distance from A to π, the plane through B perpendicular to $\hat{\mathbf{n}}$

(ii) $|(\mathbf{a} - \mathbf{b}) \times \hat{\mathbf{n}}|$ is the shortest distance from A to ℓ, the line through B parallel to $\hat{\mathbf{n}}$.

The scalar triple product

In the last section the formula $\left|\dfrac{(\mathbf{a}-\mathbf{b}).(\mathbf{d}\times\mathbf{e})}{|\mathbf{d}\times\mathbf{e}|}\right|$ for the shortest distance between two skew lines was developed. This contains the expression $(\mathbf{a}-\mathbf{b}).(\mathbf{d}\times\mathbf{e})$, an example of a *scalar triple product*. The simplest form of a scalar triple product is $\mathbf{a}.(\mathbf{b}\times\mathbf{c})$.

❓ Does it matter if the brackets are omitted from $\mathbf{a}.(\mathbf{b}\times\mathbf{c})$?

The magnitude of the vector product $\mathbf{b}\times\mathbf{c}$ is $|\mathbf{b}\times\mathbf{c}| = |\mathbf{b}||\mathbf{c}|\sin\theta$ which is the area of the parallelogram OBDC with sides OB and OC, illustrated in figure 1.20.

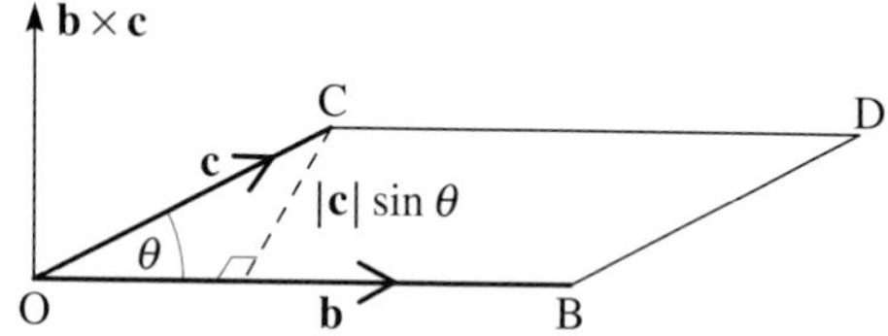

Figure 1.20

A parallelepiped is a polyhedron with six faces, each of which is a parallelogram. The volume of any parallelepiped is the product of its height and the area of its base.

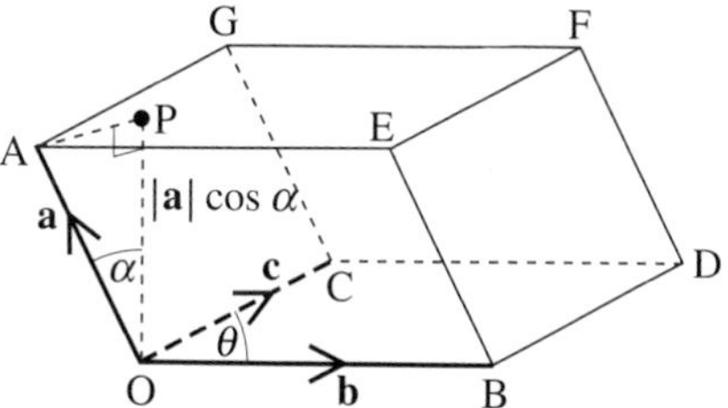

Figure 1.21

Figure 1.21 shows parallelepiped OBDCAEFG, with parallelogram OBDC as base. The area of the base is $|\mathbf{b}\times\mathbf{c}|$. The height of the parallelepiped is OP, where P is the foot of the perpendicular from O to plane AEFG. Using α to denote angle AOP, the length of OP is $|\mathbf{a}|\cos\alpha$, and the volume of parallelepiped OBDCAEFG is

$$V = |\mathbf{a}||\mathbf{b}\times\mathbf{c}|\cos\alpha.$$

If, as illustrated in figure 1.21, $\mathbf{a}$, $\mathbf{b}$, $\mathbf{c}$ is a right-handed set of vectors, $\mathbf{b}\times\mathbf{c}$ has the same direction and sense as $\overrightarrow{OP}$, so that $|\mathbf{a}||\mathbf{b}\times\mathbf{c}|\cos\alpha = \mathbf{a}.(\mathbf{b}\times\mathbf{c})$ and therefore $V = \mathbf{a}.(\mathbf{b}\times\mathbf{c})$.

You will recall that $\mathbf{b}\times\mathbf{c}$ is defined as $|\mathbf{b}||\mathbf{c}|\sin\theta\,\hat{\mathbf{n}}$ where $\hat{\mathbf{n}}$ is a unit vector with the same direction and sense as $\overrightarrow{OP}$; this means that:

$$\mathbf{a}.(\mathbf{b}\times\mathbf{c}) = (\mathbf{a}.\hat{\mathbf{n}})\,|\mathbf{b}||\mathbf{c}|\sin\theta = (\mathbf{a}.\hat{\mathbf{n}})\,|\mathbf{b}\times\mathbf{c}|.$$

However, if **a**, **b**, **c** is a left-handed set of vectors, $\mathbf{b} \times \mathbf{c}$ and $\overrightarrow{OP}$ are parallel but with opposite sense; this means that the angle between **a** and $\mathbf{b} \times \mathbf{c}$ is $\pi - \alpha$, an obtuse angle, so that

$$V = |\mathbf{a}||\mathbf{b} \times \mathbf{c}| \cos \alpha = -\mathbf{a} \cdot (\mathbf{b} \times \mathbf{c}).$$

Therefore the scalar triple product $\mathbf{a} \cdot (\mathbf{b} \times \mathbf{c})$ is the signed volume of the parallelepiped with edges represented by **a**, **b** and **c**.

As the volume of the parallelepiped does not depend on which parallelogram you take as the base:

$$\begin{aligned}\mathbf{a} \cdot (\mathbf{b} \times \mathbf{c}) &= \mathbf{b} \cdot (\mathbf{c} \times \mathbf{a}) = \mathbf{c} \cdot (\mathbf{a} \times \mathbf{b}) \\ &= -\mathbf{a} \cdot (\mathbf{c} \times \mathbf{b}) = -\mathbf{b} \cdot (\mathbf{a} \times \mathbf{c}) = -\mathbf{c} \cdot (\mathbf{b} \times \mathbf{a}).\end{aligned}$$

This shows that cyclic interchange of the vectors does not affect the value of the scalar triple product, but non-cyclic interchange of the vectors multiplies the product by -1.

ACTIVITY 1.6

1 What (if any) difference does interchanging the . and the $\times$ make?

2 Show that:

(i) the volume of the tetrahedron OABC is $\frac{1}{6}|\mathbf{a} \cdot (\mathbf{b} \times \mathbf{c})|$;

(ii) the volume of the tetrahedron PQRS is $\frac{1}{6}|(\mathbf{q} - \mathbf{p}) \cdot ((\mathbf{r} - \mathbf{p}) \times (\mathbf{s} - \mathbf{p}))|$.

Evaluating scalar triple products

This section shows you one way of evaluating a scalar triple product.

If $\mathbf{a} = \begin{pmatrix} a_1 \\ a_2 \\ a_3 \end{pmatrix}$, $\mathbf{b} = \begin{pmatrix} b_1 \\ b_2 \\ b_3 \end{pmatrix}$ and $\mathbf{c} = \begin{pmatrix} c_1 \\ c_2 \\ c_3 \end{pmatrix}$ then

$$\mathbf{a} \cdot (\mathbf{b} \times \mathbf{c}) = \begin{pmatrix} a_1 \\ a_2 \\ a_3 \end{pmatrix} \cdot \left(\begin{pmatrix} b_1 \\ b_2 \\ b_3 \end{pmatrix} \times \begin{pmatrix} c_1 \\ c_2 \\ c_3 \end{pmatrix} \right)$$

$$= \begin{pmatrix} a_1 \\ a_2 \\ a_3 \end{pmatrix} \cdot \begin{pmatrix} b_2c_3 - b_3c_2 \\ b_3c_1 - b_1c_3 \\ b_1c_2 - b_2c_1 \end{pmatrix}$$

These three components may be written as 2 – 2 determinants, e.g. $b_2c_3 - b_3c_2 = \begin{vmatrix} b_2 & c_2 \\ b_3 & c_3 \end{vmatrix}$.

$$= \begin{pmatrix} a_1 \\ a_2 \\ a_3 \end{pmatrix} \cdot \left(\begin{vmatrix} b_2 & c_2 \\ b_3 & c_3 \end{vmatrix} \mathbf{i} - \begin{vmatrix} b_1 & c_1 \\ b_3 & c_3 \end{vmatrix} \mathbf{j} + \begin{vmatrix} b_1 & c_1 \\ b_2 & c_2 \end{vmatrix} \mathbf{k} \right)$$

$$= a_1 \begin{vmatrix} b_2 & c_2 \\ b_3 & c_3 \end{vmatrix} - a_2 \begin{vmatrix} b_1 & c_1 \\ b_3 & c_3 \end{vmatrix} + a_3 \begin{vmatrix} b_1 & c_1 \\ b_2 & c_2 \end{vmatrix}.$$

Note these minus signs.

You may recognise that this final result may be written as the

3×3 determinant $\begin{vmatrix} a_1 & b_1 & c_1 \\ a_2 & b_2 & c_2 \\ a_3 & b_3 & c_3 \end{vmatrix}$ (see *A2 Further Pure Mathematics (FP2)*, Chapter 5).

EXAMPLE 1.12

Evaluate $\mathbf{a}.(\mathbf{b}\times\mathbf{c})$ when $\mathbf{a} = 3\mathbf{i} + 2\mathbf{j} + 5\mathbf{k}$, $\mathbf{b} = 4\mathbf{i} - 3\mathbf{j} + 6\mathbf{k}$ and $\mathbf{c} = 2\mathbf{i} + 3\mathbf{j} + 5\mathbf{k}$, and interpret the result.

SOLUTION

Note the minus sign.

$$\mathbf{a}.(\mathbf{b}\times\mathbf{c}) = \begin{vmatrix} 3 & 4 & 2 \\ 2 & -3 & 3 \\ 5 & 6 & 5 \end{vmatrix} = 3\begin{vmatrix} -3 & 3 \\ 6 & 5 \end{vmatrix} - 2\begin{vmatrix} 4 & 2 \\ 6 & 5 \end{vmatrix} + 5\begin{vmatrix} 4 & 2 \\ -3 & 3 \end{vmatrix}$$

$$= 3\times(-33) - 2\times 8 + 5\times 18$$

$$= -25.$$

The volume of the parallelepiped which has edges given by **a**, **b** and **c** is 25 units. The negative sign indicates that **a**, **b** and **c**, in that order, form a left-handed set of vectors.

Proof that the vector product is distributive over vector addition

The cyclic interchange property of scalar triple products provides a neat way to prove the distributive property of vector product over vector addition.
Let **e** be an arbitrary unit vector. Then

$$\mathbf{e}.(\mathbf{a}\times(\mathbf{b}+\mathbf{c})) = (\mathbf{b}+\mathbf{c}).(\mathbf{e}\times\mathbf{a})$$

Cyclic interchange of the terms **e**, **a** and (**b** + **c**) in the scalar triple product.

$$= \mathbf{b}.(\mathbf{e}\times\mathbf{a}) + \mathbf{c}.(\mathbf{e}\times\mathbf{a})$$

Scalar product is distributive.

$$= \mathbf{e}.(\mathbf{a}\times\mathbf{b}) + \mathbf{e}.(\mathbf{a}\times\mathbf{c})$$

Cyclic interchange of terms in the scalar triple product.

$$= \mathbf{e}.(\mathbf{a}\times\mathbf{b} + \mathbf{a}\times\mathbf{c}).$$

Scalar product is distributive.

Since **e** is any unit vector we may replace **e** with **i**:

$$\mathbf{i}.(\mathbf{a}\times(\mathbf{b}+\mathbf{c})) = \mathbf{i}.(\mathbf{a}\times\mathbf{b} + \mathbf{a}\times\mathbf{c}).$$

This means that the **i** components of the two vectors $\mathbf{a}\times(\mathbf{b}+\mathbf{c})$ and $\mathbf{a}\times\mathbf{b} + \mathbf{a}\times\mathbf{c}$ are equal. A similar argument shows that the **j** components of $\mathbf{a}\times(\mathbf{b}+\mathbf{c})$ and $\mathbf{a}\times\mathbf{b} + \mathbf{a}\times\mathbf{c}$ are equal, and that their **k** components are also equal. Thus

$$\mathbf{a}\times(\mathbf{b}+\mathbf{c}) = \mathbf{a}\times\mathbf{b} + \mathbf{a}\times\mathbf{c}.$$

Geometrical applications of the scalar triple product

To test whether two lines meet

The discussion of the scalar triple product arose from the construction of the formula $\left|\dfrac{(\mathbf{a}-\mathbf{b}).(\mathbf{d}\times\mathbf{e})}{|\mathbf{d}\times\mathbf{e}|}\right|$ for the shortest distance between two skew lines ℓ_1 and ℓ_2, with equations $\mathbf{r} = \mathbf{a} + t\mathbf{d}$ and $\mathbf{r} = \mathbf{b} + t\mathbf{e}$ respectively.

ACTIVITY 1.7 What happens if ℓ_1 and ℓ_2 are parallel?

Clearly, if ℓ_1 and ℓ_2 intersect, the shortest distance between them is zero, so that $\dfrac{(\mathbf{a}-\mathbf{b}).(\mathbf{d}\times\mathbf{e})}{|\mathbf{d}\times\mathbf{e}|} = 0 \Leftrightarrow (\mathbf{a}-\mathbf{b}).(\mathbf{d}\times\mathbf{e}) = 0$, providing an easily applied test as to whether the two lines $\mathbf{r} = \mathbf{a} + t\mathbf{d}$ and $\mathbf{r} = \mathbf{b} + t\mathbf{e}$ intersect or not.

EXAMPLE 1.13

Decide whether the line ℓ_1: $\mathbf{r} = -4\mathbf{i} + 2\mathbf{j} + \mathbf{k} + t(2\mathbf{i} + 3\mathbf{j} + 2\mathbf{k})$ meets the line ℓ_2: $\dfrac{x-2}{3} = \dfrac{y-5}{3} = z+1$.

SOLUTION

The points A(–4, 2, 1) and B(2, 5, –1) are on ℓ_1 and ℓ_2 respectively, so:

$$\mathbf{a}-\mathbf{b} = \begin{pmatrix}-4\\2\\1\end{pmatrix} - \begin{pmatrix}2\\5\\-1\end{pmatrix} = \begin{pmatrix}-6\\-3\\2\end{pmatrix}.$$

The respective direction vectors are $\mathbf{d} = \begin{pmatrix}2\\3\\2\end{pmatrix}$ and $\mathbf{e} = \begin{pmatrix}3\\3\\1\end{pmatrix}$.

$$\text{Therefore } (\mathbf{a}-\mathbf{b}).(\mathbf{d}\times\mathbf{e}) = \begin{pmatrix}-6\\-3\\2\end{pmatrix}.\left(\begin{pmatrix}2\\3\\2\end{pmatrix}\times\begin{pmatrix}3\\3\\1\end{pmatrix}\right)$$

$$= \begin{pmatrix}-6\\-3\\2\end{pmatrix}.\begin{pmatrix}-3\\4\\-3\end{pmatrix}$$

$$= 18 - 12 - 6 = 0$$

proving that ℓ_1 and ℓ_2 meet.

To test whether four points are coplanar

If O, A, B and C are in the same plane the volume of tetrahedron OABC is zero so that $\mathbf{a}\,.\,(\mathbf{b}\times\mathbf{c})=0$. Conversely, if $\mathbf{a}\,.\,(\mathbf{b}\times\mathbf{c})=0$, the volume of tetrahedron OABC is zero, the tetrahedron has collapsed, and the four points O, A, B and C are contained in a single plane. (They may, of course, all fall on one straight line, a special case of being coplanar.)

If you want to test whether the four points P, Q, R and S are coplanar, translate all four points so that one vertex, P say, is moved to the origin. Then the (signed) volume of the tetrahedron PQRS is equal to

$$\tfrac{1}{6}(\mathbf{q}-\mathbf{p}).((\mathbf{r}-\mathbf{p})\times(\mathbf{s}-\mathbf{p}));$$

the points P, Q, R and S are coplanar if and only if this scalar triple product is zero.

EXAMPLE 1.14

Show that the points P(−1, 1, 2), Q(2, 3, −4), R(2, 2, 6) and S(4, 3, 5) are not all contained in a single plane.

SOLUTION

$$\overrightarrow{PQ}=\begin{pmatrix}2\\3\\-4\end{pmatrix}-\begin{pmatrix}-1\\1\\2\end{pmatrix}=\begin{pmatrix}3\\2\\-6\end{pmatrix},\quad \overrightarrow{PR}=\begin{pmatrix}2\\2\\6\end{pmatrix}-\begin{pmatrix}-1\\1\\2\end{pmatrix}=\begin{pmatrix}3\\1\\4\end{pmatrix},$$

$$\overrightarrow{PS}=\begin{pmatrix}4\\3\\5\end{pmatrix}-\begin{pmatrix}-1\\1\\2\end{pmatrix}=\begin{pmatrix}5\\2\\3\end{pmatrix}.$$

$$\text{Therefore } \overrightarrow{PQ}\,.\,(\overrightarrow{PR}\times\overrightarrow{PS})=\begin{pmatrix}3\\2\\-6\end{pmatrix}.\left(\begin{pmatrix}3\\1\\4\end{pmatrix}\times\begin{pmatrix}5\\2\\3\end{pmatrix}\right)$$

$$=\begin{pmatrix}3\\2\\-6\end{pmatrix}.\begin{pmatrix}-5\\11\\1\end{pmatrix}$$

$$=-15+22-6=1.$$

The scalar triple product is not zero so P, Q, R and S are not all in the same plane.

(Notice that the volume of tetrahedron PQRS is $\frac{1}{6}\times 1=\frac{1}{6}$.)

To test whether three vectors form a right- or left-handed set

Assuming you are not double-jointed, if the thumb of your right hand points in the direction of vector **p**, your index finger in the direction of **q**, and your second finger in the direction of **r** then the vectors **p**, **q** and **r** (in that order) form a right-handed set. Figure 1.22 illustrates this and shows other right-handed sets of vectors: in these **p** is drawn to the right across a piece of paper, **q** is drawn 'up' the paper (not necessarily 'straight up') and **r** rises 'up out of' the paper (not necessarily at right angles to the paper).

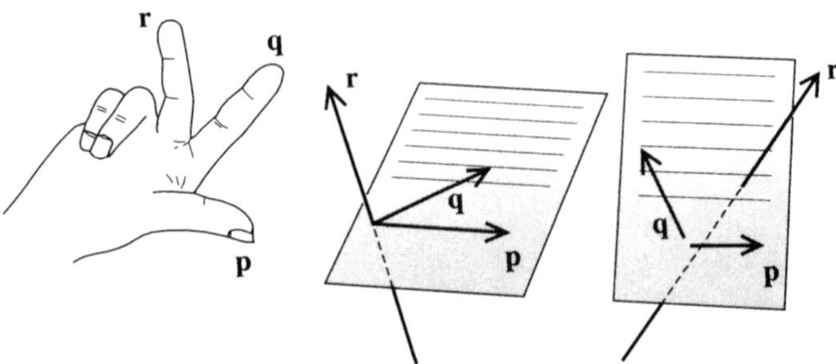

Figure 1.22 Vectors **p**, **q** and **r** form a right-handed set

Figure 1.23 illustrates left-handed sets of vectors, where, as before, **p** points to the right across the paper, **q** points 'up' the paper but now **r** points 'down', again not necessarily at right angles to the paper.

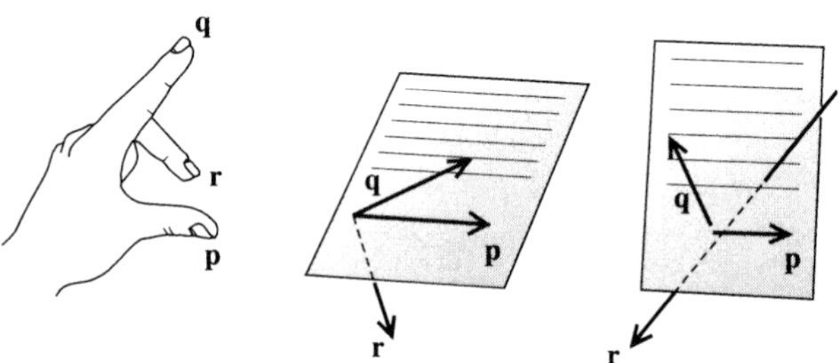

Figure 1.23 Vectors **p**, **q** and **r** form a left-handed set

ACTIVITY 1.8

The vectors **p**, **q** and **r** (in that order) form a right-handed set. Show that **q**, **r**, **p** (in that order) is also a right-handed set but that **p**, **r**, **q** (in that order) is a left-handed set. (This means that cyclical interchange does *not* change the 'handedness' of a set of three vectors, but non-cyclical interchange does change the 'handedness'.)

The vector $\mathbf{a} \times \mathbf{b}$ is defined as being in the direction $\hat{\mathbf{n}}$ such that **a**, **b** and $\hat{\mathbf{n}}$ (in that order) form a right-handed set. When **a**, **b** and **c** (in that order) form a right-handed set the angle between **c** and $\mathbf{a} \times \mathbf{b}$ is acute so that $\mathbf{c}.(\mathbf{a} \times \mathbf{b})$ is positive. When **a**, **b** and **c** (in that order) form a left-handed set the angle between **c** and $\mathbf{a} \times \mathbf{b}$ is obtuse and $\mathbf{c}.(\mathbf{a} \times \mathbf{b})$ is negative. Thus the scalar triple product provides an efficient test of 'handedness'. (As cyclical interchange of the vectors has no effect you can test using $\mathbf{a}.(\mathbf{b} \times \mathbf{c})$ instead of $\mathbf{c}.(\mathbf{a} \times \mathbf{b})$.)

EXERCISE 1E

1 Find $\mathbf{a}.(\mathbf{b}\times\mathbf{c})$ in the following cases.

(i) $\mathbf{a}=\begin{pmatrix}3\\4\\6\end{pmatrix}, \mathbf{b}=\begin{pmatrix}5\\8\\-3\end{pmatrix}, \mathbf{c}=\begin{pmatrix}1\\2\\3\end{pmatrix}$

(ii) $\mathbf{a}=\begin{pmatrix}5\\-2\\2\end{pmatrix}, \mathbf{b}=\begin{pmatrix}3\\1\\5\end{pmatrix}, \mathbf{c}=\begin{pmatrix}3\\1\\-2\end{pmatrix}$

(iii) $\mathbf{a}=\begin{pmatrix}-2\\-5\\1\end{pmatrix}, \mathbf{b}=\begin{pmatrix}4\\3\\2\end{pmatrix}, \mathbf{c}=\begin{pmatrix}2\\3\\2\end{pmatrix}$

2 Does line ℓ meet line ℓ'?

(i) $\ell: \mathbf{r}=\begin{pmatrix}5\\0\\1\end{pmatrix}+t\begin{pmatrix}1\\3\\1\end{pmatrix};$ $\quad \ell': \mathbf{r}=\begin{pmatrix}5\\9\\3\end{pmatrix}+t\begin{pmatrix}4\\3\\2\end{pmatrix}$

(ii) $\ell: \begin{cases}x=2t-2\\y=4-3t;\\z=2t-3\end{cases}$ $\quad \ell': \begin{cases}x=3t-1\\y=3-5t\\z=4-t\end{cases}$

(iii) $\ell: \dfrac{x+1}{5}=y+3=\dfrac{z-1}{7};$ $\quad \ell': \dfrac{x+2}{4}=\dfrac{y-4}{-5}=\dfrac{z-3}{3}$

3 Are A, B, C and D coplanar?

(i) A(1, 2, 3); B(6, 5, 4); C(7, 8, 9); D(12, 11, 10)
(ii) A(−2, −3, 3); B(1, −2, −1); C(4, −1, −5); D(7, 3, 6)
(iii) A(−2, −2, 1); B(−3, −1, 11); C(1, 2, 6); D(3, 2, 5)

4 Decide whether **a**, **b** and **c** (in that order) form a right- or left-handed set.

(i) $\mathbf{a}=-3\mathbf{i}+2\mathbf{j}-3\mathbf{k}, \mathbf{b}=3\mathbf{i}-\mathbf{j}+3\mathbf{k}, \mathbf{c}=2\mathbf{i}+3\mathbf{j}+5\mathbf{k}$
(ii) $\mathbf{a}=2\mathbf{i}+2\mathbf{j}+6\mathbf{k}, \mathbf{b}=\mathbf{i}+\mathbf{j}+2\mathbf{k}, \mathbf{c}=3\mathbf{i}+3\mathbf{j}+4\mathbf{k}$

(iii) $\mathbf{a}=\begin{pmatrix}2\\4\\-5\end{pmatrix}, \mathbf{b}=\begin{pmatrix}-5\\3\\2\end{pmatrix}, \mathbf{c}=\begin{pmatrix}3\\-1\\3\end{pmatrix}$

5 Using the co-ordinates given, find the volume of parallelepiped PQRSP′Q′R′S′.

(i) P(0, 0, 0), Q(1, 2, 5), S(7, 3, 4), P′(2, 3, 4)
(ii) P(3, −2, 4), Q(1, 4, 5), S(6, 2, 7), P′(2, 3, 5)
(iii) P(1, 2, 3), Q(6, 5, 4), S(7, 8, 9), P′(12, 11, 10)
(iv) P(−3, −1, 1), Q(3, 2, 4), S(7, −2, 6), P′(−3, 5, 2)

6 Using the co-ordinates given, find the volume of tetrahedron ABCD.

(i) A(0, 0, 0), B(1, 0, 0), C(1, 2, 0), D(1, 2, 3)
(ii) A(2, 3, 1), B(5, 4, −2), C(3, 6, 5), D(3, 2, −1)
(iii) A(−5, 1, −6), B(7, −3, 5), C(6, 5, 7), D(3, −1, 0)

7 Points A, B and C have position vectors **a**, **b** and **c**. Prove that $(\mathbf{a}\times\mathbf{b}).\mathbf{a}=0$ and show that $\mathbf{b}\times\mathbf{c}+\mathbf{c}\times\mathbf{a}+\mathbf{a}\times\mathbf{b}$ is perpendicular to the plane ABC.

[**Hint:** Use the distributive property of vector product over addition, $\mathbf{p}\times(\mathbf{q}+\mathbf{r})=(\mathbf{p}\times\mathbf{q})+(\mathbf{p}\times\mathbf{r})$.]

8 Show that $(\mathbf{a}\times\mathbf{b}).(\mathbf{c}\times\mathbf{d})=\begin{vmatrix}\mathbf{a}.\mathbf{c} & \mathbf{a}.\mathbf{d}\\ \mathbf{b}.\mathbf{c} & \mathbf{b}.\mathbf{d}\end{vmatrix}$.

9 Two lines have equations $\mathbf{r}=\mathbf{a}+\lambda\mathbf{d}$, $\mathbf{r}=\mathbf{b}+\mu\mathbf{e}$.

(i) Show that the lines intersect if $\mathbf{a}.(\mathbf{d}\times\mathbf{e})=\mathbf{b}.(\mathbf{d}\times\mathbf{e})$.
(ii) Suppose the lines intersect at C. Explain why λ and μ can be found such that $\mathbf{a}+\lambda\mathbf{d}=\mathbf{b}+\mu\mathbf{e}$.

By forming the scalar product of both sides with $\mathbf{a}\times\mathbf{e}$ show that
$$\mathbf{c}=\mathbf{a}+\frac{\mathbf{a}.(\mathbf{b}\times\mathbf{e})}{\mathbf{a}.(\mathbf{d}\times\mathbf{e})}\mathbf{d}.$$

Find a similar expression for **c** in the form $\mathbf{b}+\mu\mathbf{e}$.

10 The diagram shows the plan of five white and four coloured spheres pushed together on a horizontal table. The radius of each sphere is 1 unit. The centres of the spheres are marked, and the x and y axes are shown, with the origin at O, the centre of a coloured sphere.

A second layer is formed by placing four additional coloured spheres, also of unit radius, on top of the first layer in the positions marked U. Each of these spheres touches three spheres in the first layer: C is the centre of the sphere that touches the spheres with centres O, A and B. The second diagram shows both layers.

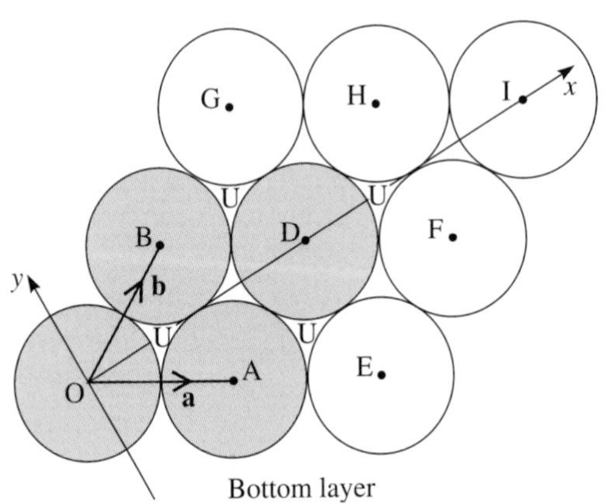

Bottom layer

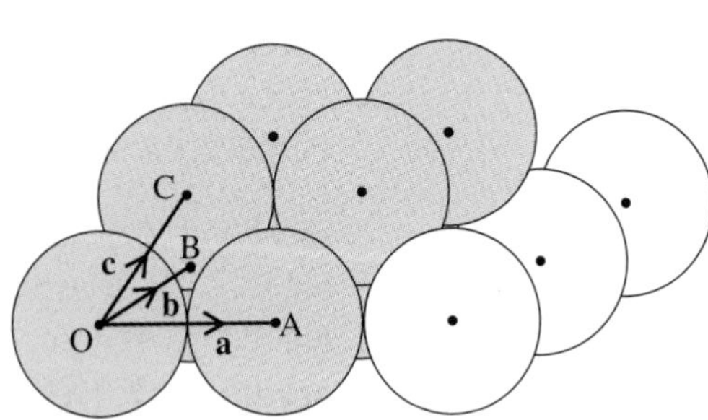

(i) Show that the centres of the eight coloured spheres form the vertices of a parallelepiped with edges given by vectors **a**, **b** and **c**.

(ii) Show that $\mathbf{a} = \sqrt{3}\mathbf{i} - \mathbf{j}$ and express **b** and **c** in terms of **i**, **j** and **k**.

(iii) Find the volume of the parallelepiped with edges given by **a**, **b** and **c**.

(iv) The parallelepiped with edges given by **a**, **b** and **c** contains parts of eight spheres; explain why these parts sum to one whole sphere, and show that the volume of this sphere is just over 74% of the volume of the parallelepiped.

(This stacking arrangement, known as *hexagonal close packing*, is important in crystallography: elements in which the atoms are packed this way include magnesium, titanium, zinc and cobalt.)

EXERCISE 1F

1 **(i)** Find the vector product $(3\mathbf{i} + \mathbf{j} - 2\mathbf{k}) \times (8\mathbf{i} - 9\mathbf{j} - 7\mathbf{k})$.

The two planes with equations $3x + y - 2z = 18$ and $8x - 9y - 7z = 8$ intersect in the line L.

(ii) Show that the point P(2, 4, –4) lies on L, and find the equation of L.

(iii) Find the equation of the straight line in the plane $3x + y - 2z = 18$ which passes through P and is perpendicular to L.

[MEI, *part*]

2 Two straight lines L and M have equations

$$L: \frac{x-7}{8} = \frac{y-13}{6} = \frac{z-14}{1}, \quad M: \frac{x-5}{-2} = \frac{y+8}{5} = \frac{z+9}{3}.$$

(i) Show that the lines L and M do not intersect.

(ii) Find a vector which is perpendicular to both lines L and M.

(iii) Find, in the form $ax + by + cz + d = 0$, the equation of the plane which contains the line L and is parallel to the line M.

[MEI, *part*]

3 Four points have co-ordinates A(12, –5, –5), B(15, 4, –17), C(0, –1, 8) and D(3, 2a, –a).

(i) Find, in terms of a, the volume of the tetrahedron ABCD.

(ii) Show that, provided $a \neq 4$, the shortest distance between the lines AB and CD is $\sqrt{30}$.

(iii) Give a geometrical interpretation of the case $a = 4$, and calculate the shortest distance between the lines AB and CD in this case.

[MEI]

4 Four points A, B, C and D have co-ordinates (0, 5, 0), (3, 10, −4), (7, 0, 24) and (10, k, 20), where k is a constant.

(i) When $k \neq 5$, find the following, giving your answers (in terms of k where appropriate) as simply as possible:

(a) the area of the triangle ABC

(b) the volume of the tetrahedron ABCD

(c) the shortest distance from D to the plane ABC

(d) the shortest distance between the lines AB and CD.

(ii) When $k = 5$, find the shortest distance between the lines AB and CD.

[MEI]

5 Three points A, B and C have co-ordinates (9, 1, 5), (5, −2, 3) and (−3, 10, 8) respectively. The point P($9 + \lambda$, $1 + 3\lambda$, $5 - 4\lambda$), where $\lambda > 0$, is a general point on a straight line starting at A.

(i) Find the volume of the tetrahedron ABCP. State whether $\overrightarrow{AB}$, $\overrightarrow{AC}$, $\overrightarrow{AP}$, (in that order) is a right-handed or left-handed set of vectors.

(ii) Find the shortest distance from P to the plane ABC.

(iii) Find, in terms of λ, the shortest distance between the lines CP and AB. Show that, when λ is small, this distance is approximately 5λ; and show that, when λ is large, this distance is approximately 15.

[MEI]

6 (i) Find the vector product $\begin{pmatrix} 3 \\ -2 \\ -18 \end{pmatrix} \times \begin{pmatrix} 2 \\ 1 \\ -5 \end{pmatrix}$.

(ii) Find the equation of the line of intersection of the two planes

$$3x - 2y - 18z = 6$$

$$2x + y - 5z = 25.$$

You are given the matrix equation

$$\begin{pmatrix} 3 & -2 & -18 \\ 2 & 1 & -5 \\ 7 & k & 2 \end{pmatrix} \begin{pmatrix} x \\ y \\ z \end{pmatrix} = \begin{pmatrix} 6 \\ 25 \\ 20 \end{pmatrix}. \qquad (*)$$

(iii) Solve the equation (*) when $k = -32$.

(iv) Find the value of k for which the equation (*) does not have a unique solution. Determine whether there is no solution or whether there are infinitely many solutions. Give a geometrical interpretation.

[MEI]

KEY POINTS

1 The vector product of **a** and **b** is $\mathbf{a}\times\mathbf{b}=|\mathbf{a}||\mathbf{b}|\sin\theta\,\hat{\mathbf{n}}$, where θ is the angle between **a** and **b**, and $\hat{\mathbf{n}}$ is a unit vector which is perpendicular to both **a** and **b**, and such that **a**, **b**, $\hat{\mathbf{n}}$ is a right-handed set.

2 $\mathbf{a}\times\mathbf{b}=\begin{pmatrix}a_1\\a_2\\a_3\end{pmatrix}\times\begin{pmatrix}b_1\\b_2\\b_3\end{pmatrix}=\begin{pmatrix}a_2b_3-a_3b_2\\a_3b_1-a_1b_3\\a_1b_2-a_2b_1\end{pmatrix}$.

3 The vector product is anti-commutative:

$$\mathbf{a}\times\mathbf{b}=-\mathbf{b}\times\mathbf{a}$$

and distributive over vector addition:

$$\mathbf{a}\times(\mathbf{b}+\mathbf{c})=\mathbf{a}\times\mathbf{b}+\mathbf{a}\times\mathbf{c}.$$

4 To find the equations of ℓ, the line of intersection of the planes

$$a_1x+a_2y+a_3z=a_4 \quad\text{and}\quad b_1x+b_2y+b_3z=b_4$$

- find a point P on ℓ by choosing a value for one of x, y, or z, substituting this into both equations, and then solving simultaneously to find the other two variables;
- *either* find a second point Q on ℓ, as above and use $\overrightarrow{PQ}$ as **d**, the direction vector of ℓ

  or use $\mathbf{a}\times\mathbf{b}$ as **d**, the direction vector of ℓ, where

  $$\mathbf{a}=\begin{pmatrix}a_1\\a_2\\a_3\end{pmatrix} \quad\text{and}\quad \mathbf{b}=\begin{pmatrix}b_1\\b_2\\b_3\end{pmatrix}$$

  are the normals to the two planes;
- then write down the vector equation or the cartesian equations of ℓ.

5 The angle between two planes is the same as the angle between their normals.

6 To find the point of intersection of the lines

$$\frac{x-x_1}{d_1}=\frac{y-y_1}{e_1}=\frac{z-z_1}{f_1} \quad\text{and}\quad \frac{x-x_2}{d_2}=\frac{y-y_2}{e_2}=\frac{z-z_2}{f_2}$$

- express the co-ordinates of points on the lines in terms of parameters λ and μ:

  $$\begin{aligned}x&=d_1\lambda+x_1=d_2\mu+x_2\\y&=e_1\lambda+y_1=e_2\mu+y_2\\z&=f_1\lambda+z_1=f_2\mu+z_2\end{aligned}$$
- solve two of the equations simultaneously for λ and μ, and check whether the solution satisfies the third equation;
- if the values found for λ and μ satisfy all three equations the corresponding values of x, y, z are the co-ordinates of the point where the lines intersect;
- if the values found for λ and μ do not satisfy the third equation the lines do not intersect.

7 The shortest distance from the point P to the line through A parallel to vector **d** is $|\overrightarrow{PA} \times \hat{\mathbf{d}}|$.

8 The shortest distance from (x_1, y_1) to the line $ax + by + c = 0$ is

$$\left|\frac{ax_1 + by_1 + c}{\sqrt{a^2 + b^2}}\right|.$$

9 The shortest distance from (x_1, y_1, z_1) to the plane $ax + by + cz + d = 0$ is

$$\left|\frac{ax_1 + by_1 + cz_1 + d}{\sqrt{a^2 + b^2 + c^2}}\right|.$$

10 The scalar triple product $\mathbf{a} \,.\, (\mathbf{b} \times \mathbf{c})$ is the (signed) volume of a parallelepiped with edges given by the vectors **a**, **b** and **c**.

11 Cyclic interchange of the vectors does not affect the value of the scalar triple product, but non-cyclic interchange of the vectors multiplies the product by -1.

12 The shortest distance between the lines $\mathbf{r} = \mathbf{a} + t\mathbf{d}$ and $\mathbf{r} = \mathbf{b} + t\mathbf{e}$ is

$$\left|\frac{(\mathbf{a} - \mathbf{b}) \,.\, (\mathbf{d} \times \mathbf{e})}{|\mathbf{d} \times \mathbf{e}|}\right|.$$

The lines intersect if and only if $(\mathbf{a} - \mathbf{b}) \,.\, (\mathbf{d} \times \mathbf{e}) = 0$.

13 The volume of the tetrahedron OABC is $\frac{1}{6}|\mathbf{a} \,.\, (\mathbf{b} \times \mathbf{c})|$.

14 The vectors **p**, **q** and **r** (in that order):

form a right-handed set $\Leftrightarrow \mathbf{p} \,.\, (\mathbf{q} \times \mathbf{r}) > 0$

form a left-handed set $\Leftrightarrow \mathbf{p} \,.\, (\mathbf{q} \times \mathbf{r}) < 0$.

2 Multivariable calculus

O neglectful Nature, wherefore art thou thus partial...?

Leonardo da Vinci (1452–1519)

Functions of more than one variable

If you know the radius r of a circle you can easily calculate the area A by using the formula $A = \pi r^2$. Here A depends on the single variable r and this relationship can be written as $A = \mathrm{f}(r)$, where $\mathrm{f}(r) = \pi r^2$. To find the volume V of a cylinder you need to know both the radius r and the height h, since $V = \pi r^2 h$. In this case V depends on the two variables r and h, and this can be shown by writing $V = \mathrm{g}(r, h)$, where $\mathrm{g}(r, h) = \pi r^2 h$. The order of the variables matters, since for example $\mathrm{g}(2, 5) = 20\pi$ whereas $\mathrm{g}(5, 2) = 50\pi$, and these are not the same.

Similarly the formula $\triangle = \frac{1}{2}ab \sin C$ shows how the area $\triangle$ of triangle ABC depends on the sides a, b and the angle C:

$$\triangle = \mathrm{h}(a, b, C), \text{ where } \mathrm{h}(a, b, C) = \tfrac{1}{2}ab \sin C.$$

In these three examples, f is a function of one variable, g is a function of two variables and h is a function of three variables. An important reason for studying functions of more than one variable is that in many applications the value of the quantity you want to know depends on the values of several other quantities. For example, in weather forecasting, atmospheric pressure depends on position (three space co-ordinates) and time, a total of four variables, and in agriculture the cost of wheat depends on such things as the yield, demand, costs of seed, fertiliser and labour, and subsidies. All these situations may be modelled using functions of more than one variable, and then questions arise about how to deal with local approximations (small changes), rates of change and greatest or least values with such functions. Although a realistic model may use dozens of variables, this chapter will concentrate on functions of two or three variables, since the main conceptual step is from 'one' to 'more than one'.

Note

An example of the use of many variables is the Treasury model of the British economy, which started in 1970 with about 200 variables. The number of variables had grown to 1275 by 1989, when it was reduced to 530. In 1995 the model underwent further substantial slimming, and it now has 357 variables which are connected by about 30 functions.

Representing a function of two variables

Just as a function f of one variable is often represented by the curve with equation $y = f(x)$, so the most natural way to represent a function g of two variables x, y is as a *surface*. Take mutually perpendicular x, y and z axes with the z axis vertical. Each pair of values (x, y) can be used to work out $z = g(x, y)$. Then as the point $(x, y, 0)$ varies over the x–y plane (or part of it, if the domain of g is restricted) so the set of points (x, y, z) forms the surface representing the function, as in figure 2.1.

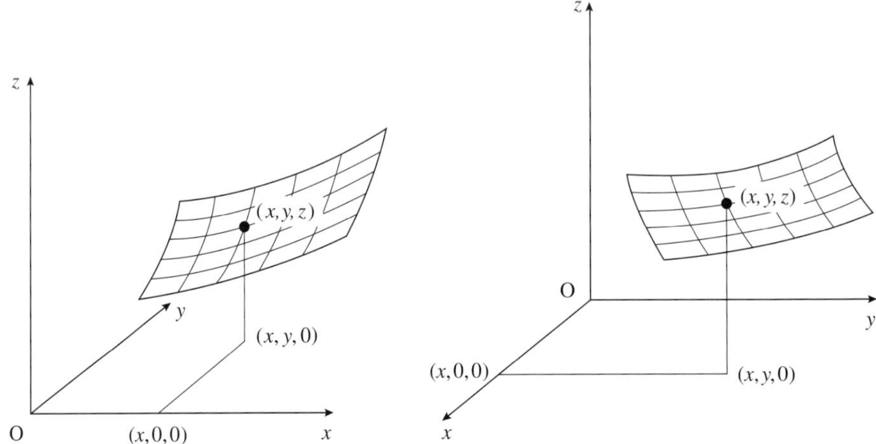

Figure 2.1 Note the two conventional viewing angles

The difficulty is that this representation is three-dimensional, and it is not usually feasible to construct the surface. Various compromises are possible.

1 Use a two-dimensional perspective drawing of the surface. Many modern computer packages will do this very realistically, and it may even be possible to animate the display so that you can 'walk around' the surface.

2 Just write the appropriate values of z at points in the x–y plane. This is the way the depth of the ocean is given in naval charts of coastal waters.

3 Use colour or shading to indicate the value of z. This is common in atlases, and also when showing temperature on weather maps. With the use of conventional colour codes (such as 'blue = cold, red = hot') this method is good for giving a quick impression when not much detail is needed. It is also perhaps a more natural way to represent a temperature distribution than the abstract idea of a 'temperature surface'.

4 Join all the points (x, y) for which $f(x, y)$ takes a particular value, to give a *contour* or *level curve*, as on an Ordnance Survey map. This is often done in addition to **2** or **3** to add precision and ease of reading to the graph. The same terms are also used for the set of points (x, y, c) in three dimensions for which $f(x, y) = c$: thus the water's edge of a reservoir and its representation on a map are both called *contours*. Some contours have special names: an *isobar* is a pressure contour, an *isotherm* is a temperature contour.

EXAMPLE 2.1 Draw contour lines and a perspective sketch of the surface $z = 2\cos x - y^2$.

SOLUTION

The equation of the surface can be rearranged as $y^2 = 2\cos x - z$ and so the contour $z = k$ has equation $y^2 = 2\cos x - k$. This is of the form $y^2 = \mathrm{f}(x)$, which is equivalent to $y = \pm\sqrt{\mathrm{f}(x)}$. Therefore the contour exists only where $\mathrm{f}(x) \geqslant 0$, and is symmetrical about the x axis. Figure 2.2 shows the case $k = 1$: you first sketch the graph $y = 2\cos x - 1$, shown with a broken line, and then use it to draw the contour.

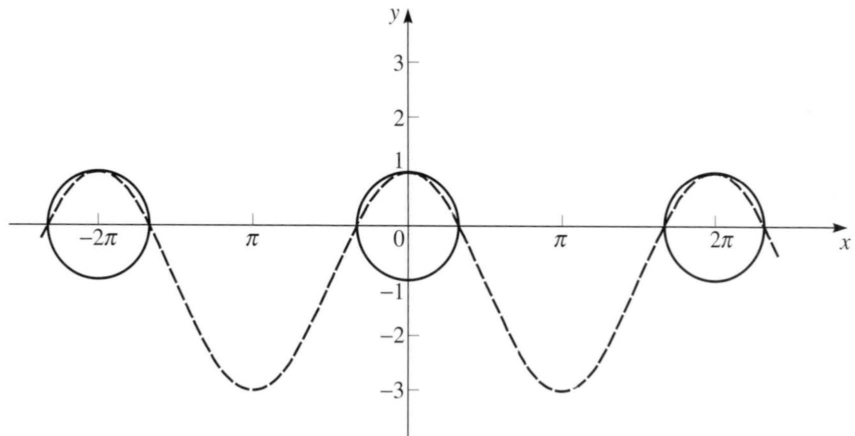

Figure 2.2

Taking the values $k = 2, 1, 0, -1, -2, -3$ gives the set of contours shown in figure 2.3.

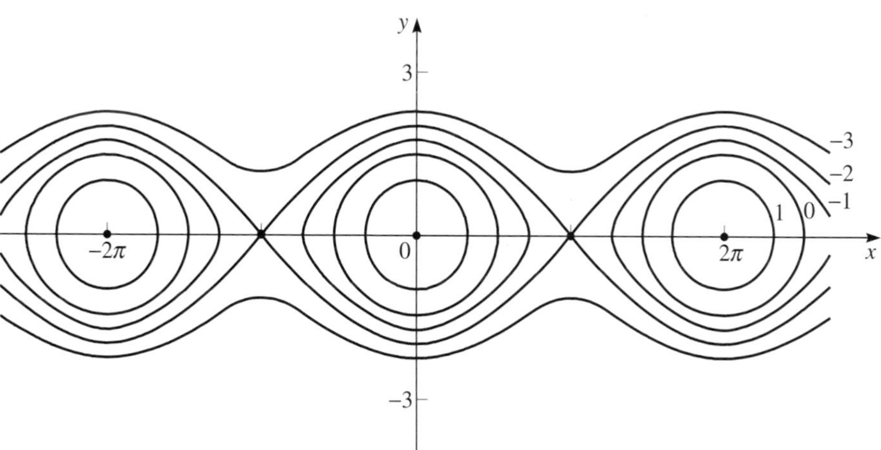

Figure 2.3

Note that:

(i) there are no points of the surface for which $z > 2$, since this would give $y^2 < 0$, which is impossible.
(ii) when $k = 2$ the contour is the set of isolated points $(2m\pi, 0)$
(iii) when $k = -2$ the contour is $y^2 = 2\cos x + 2 = 4\cos^2\left(\frac{1}{2}x\right) \Leftrightarrow y = \pm 2\cos\left(\frac{1}{2}x\right)$, a pair of cosine curves crossing on the x axis.
(iv) when $k < -2$ the contours do not meet the x axis.

From these contours you can see that the surface has a chain of peaks at the points $(2m\pi, 0, 2)$, as drawn in perspective in figure 2.4.

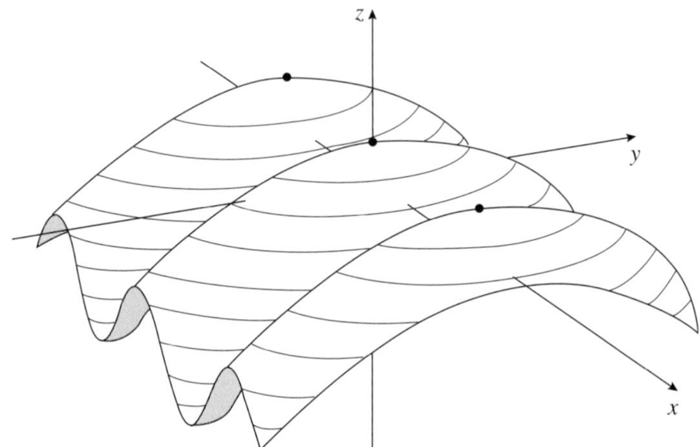

Figure 2.4

EXERCISE 2A

1 The following table shows the varying length of day with latitude in the Northern hemisphere. The length of day (i.e. the period between sunrise and sunset, not including twilight) is given in hours, correct to one decimal place, on the 15th day of each month.

Month	Equator	10°	20°	30°	40°	50°	60°	70°	80°	N. pole
Jan	12.1	11.6	11.0	10.4	9.6	8.5	6.6	0.0	0.0	0.0
Feb	12.1	11.8	11.4	11.2	10.7	10.1	9.2	7.3	0.0	0.0
Mar	12.1	12.1	12.0	12.0	11.9	11.8	11.7	11.5	10.9	0.0
Apr	12.1	12.4	12.6	12.9	13.2	13.7	14.5	16.1	24.0	24.0
May	12.1	12.6	13.1	13.6	14.4	15.4	17.1	22.2	24.0	24.0
Jun	12.1	12.7	13.3	14.1	15.0	16.4	18.8	24.0	24.0	24.0
Jul	12.1	12.7	13.3	13.9	14.8	15.6	17.5	24.0	24.0	24.0
Aug	12.1	12.5	12.8	13.3	13.8	14.6	15.8	18.4	24.0	24.0
Sep	12.1	12.2	12.3	12.4	12.5	12.7	13.0	13.6	15.3	24.0
Oct	12.1	11.9	11.7	11.5	11.2	10.8	10.2	9.1	5.2	0.0
Nov	12.1	11.7	11.2	10.7	10.0	9.1	7.6	3.1	0.0	0.0
Dec	12.1	11.5	10.9	10.2	9.3	8.1	5.9	0.0	0.0	0.0

(i) Draw axes representing the date D (ignore differences in the lengths of months) and the latitude λ. Sketch on these the contours for the duration of the day, T hours, from $T = 0$ to $T = 24$ at intervals of 4 hours.

(ii) Draw (or use a computer to draw) a perspective sketch of the surface representing T as a function of D and λ. Comment on any unusual features of this surface, and say why they occur.

2 The diagram shows a contour map of a hillside with two paths, A and B.

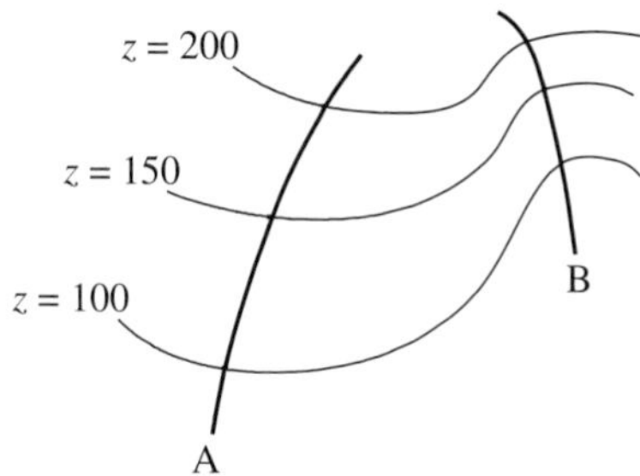

(i) On which path will you have the steeper climb?

(ii) On which path will you probably have the better views?

(iii) On which path are you more likely to be near a stream?

3 Sketch a contour diagram for the surface $V = \pi r^2 h$ showing the contours $V = 0, \pi, 2\pi$ and 3π for $r \geqslant 0$ and $h \geqslant 0$. Then sketch a perspective view of the surface.

4 Explain why all the contours of the surface $z = \mathrm{f}(x^2 + y^2)$ are circles. For each of the following surfaces sketch a contour diagram with at least three labelled contours, and sketch the surface.

(i) $z = x^2 + y^2$ **(ii)** $z = \dfrac{1}{x^2 + y^2}$

(iii) $z = \sqrt{x^2 + y^2}$ **(iv)** $z = \mathrm{e}^{-(x^2 + y^2)}$

5 Show that all but one of the contours of the surface $z = \dfrac{x + 2y}{x^2 + y^2}$ are circles through the origin O with the point O omitted, and describe the exception. Sketch the contours of this surface.

6 Describe these three-dimensional surfaces.

(i) $z = x^2$ **(ii)** $z = y^3$ **(iii)** $z = x^2 + y^3$

7 Sketch the contours of the surface $z = 3x - x^3 - y^2$ for $z = -4, -2, 0, 2, 4$. If $z = 0$ is sea level, describe the geographical feature which might be represented by this surface.

8 With the help of contours and perspective diagrams describe the following surfaces.

(i) $z = \cos(x + y)$ **(ii)** $z = \cos(x - y)$ **(iii)** $z = \cos(x^2 - y)$

9 In a simple model of an anticyclone the pressure p at the point (x, y, z) at time t is given by $p = a\{b^2 - (x - ct)^2 - 4(y - ct)^2\}e^{-kz}$, where z is the height above sea level and a, b, c and k are constants.

(i) Where is the point of highest pressure?

(ii) In what direction is the anticyclone moving?

(iii) What shape are the isobars at sea level?

(iv) What is the purpose of the factor e^{-kz}?

10 The *Wind Chill Index*, developed from experiments in the Antarctic, gives an indication of how the combination of temperature and wind affects the comfort and safety of a suitably-clothed person outdoors. The unit of wind chill is the rate of loss of heat from the body in kg cal m^{-2} h^{-1}.

Using readings from the diagram, draw a new diagram showing the same information presented as wind chill contours plotted against axes representing temperature (in °C) and wind speed (in k.p.h.).

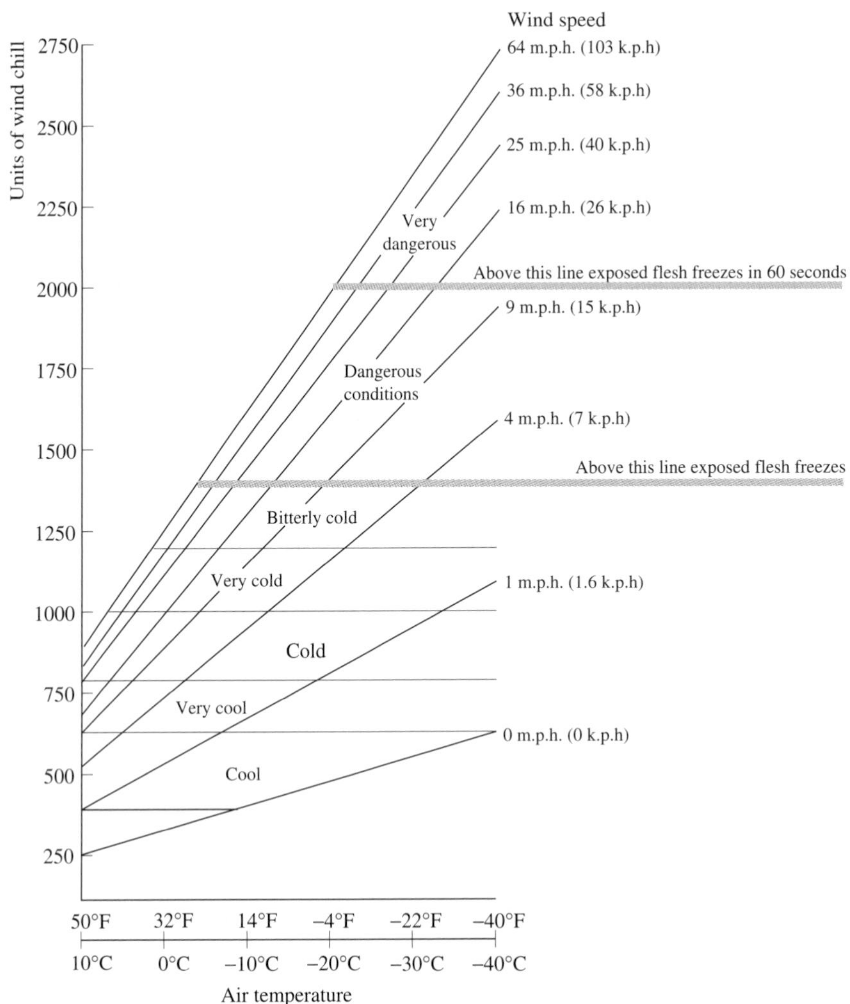

Sections

Another way to give information about a surface is to use the *section* in which a vertical plane cuts the surface. The plane may have any orientation, but it is best to concentrate first on sections parallel to the x or y axis.

A section parallel to the x axis is obtained by fixing the value of y (at $y = b$, say). Then the section is the curve $z = \mathrm{f}(x, b)$ in the plane $y = b$. Similarly, a section parallel to the y axis is a curve $z = \mathrm{f}(a, y)$ in the plane $x = a$ (see figure 2.5).

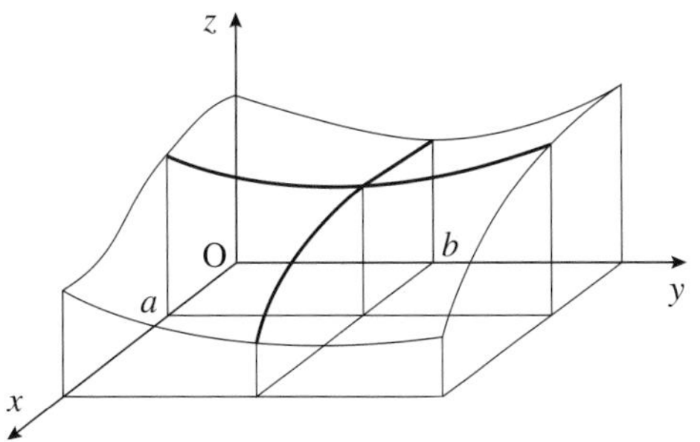

Figure 2.5

EXAMPLE 2.2

Draw the sections of the surface $z = x^2 + 2y^2 + xy - 7x$ cut by the planes $x = 3$ and $y = 2$.

SOLUTION

$$y = 2 \quad \Rightarrow \quad z = x^2 + 8 + 2x - 7x = x^2 - 5x + 8$$

and

$$x = 3 \quad \Rightarrow \quad z = 9 + 2y^2 + 3y - 21 = 2y^2 + 3y - 12.$$

So the sections are the parabolas $z = x^2 - 5x + 8$ in the plane $y = 2$ and $z = 2y^2 + 3y - 12$ in the plane $x = 3$. These are shown in figure 2.6 together with a perspective sketch showing how they fit together, passing through the point $(3, 2, 2)$ on the surface.

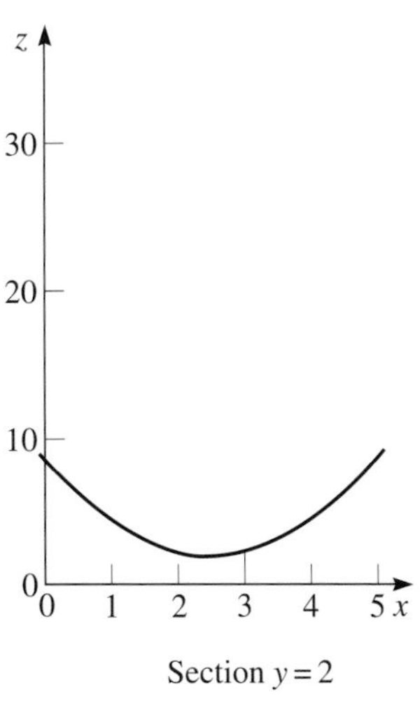

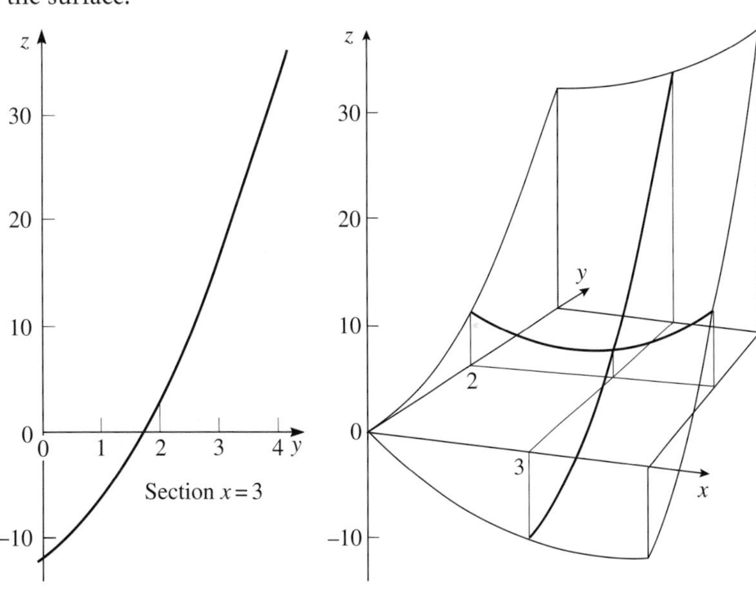

Figure 2.6

EXAMPLE 2.3

The surface $z = \frac{1}{10}(x^2 + 2y^2 + xy - 7x)$ represents a hillside, with the x and y axes due east and due north respectively. Footpaths running east–west and north–south cross at the point (3, 2, 0.2). Find the angle each path makes with the horizontal at this point.

SOLUTION

The surface is the same as in Example 2.2, except for the vertical scaling factor $\frac{1}{10}$.

The east–west footpath is the parabola $z = \dfrac{1}{10}(x^2 - 5x + 8)$ in the plane $y = 2$.

On this curve $\dfrac{dz}{dx} = \dfrac{1}{10}(2x - 5) = 0.1$ when $x = 3$, so the path slopes upwards to the east at an angle of arctan $0.1 \approx 6°$.

On the north–south path $z = \dfrac{1}{10}(2y^2 + 3y - 12)$ and so $\dfrac{dz}{dy} = \dfrac{1}{10}(4y + 3) = 1.1$ when $y = 2$, so the path slopes upwards to the north at an angle of arctan $1.1 \approx 48°$.

EXERCISE 2B

1 Using the information given in Question 1 of Exercise 2A, draw sections to show:

(i) how the length of day at latitude 50°N varies throughout the year
(ii) how the length of day at latitude 80°N varies throughout the year
(iii) how the length of day on October 15th varies with latitude.

2 Sketch the sections of the surface $z = x^2 - y^2$ for which:

(i) $x = 0, \pm 1, \pm 2$ **(ii)** $y = 0, \pm 1, \pm 2$.

3 The depth of water, z m, in a wave tank is given at time t seconds by the formula $z = \mathrm{h}(x, t) = 1.5 + 0.2\sin(0.5x - t)$, where x m is the distance from one end of the tank.

(i) Sketch on the same axes the sections $z = \mathrm{h}(x, 3)$ and $z = \mathrm{h}(x, 5)$ and explain what these show.
(ii) Sketch on the same axes the sections $z = \mathrm{h}(3, t)$ and $z = \mathrm{h}(5, t)$ and explain what these show.
(iii) How fast do the waves move along the tank?

4 **(i)** Find the equations of the sections of the surface $z = x^3 + y^2 - 4xy^2$ cut by the planes $x = 3$ and $y = 1$.
(ii) Sketch the graphs of these sections.
(iii) Find the gradient of each of these sections at the point (3, 1, 16).

5 Part of a desert surface can be modelled by the equation

$$z = 3 + 2\sin(0.4x - 0.3y),$$

where the x and y axes are due east and due north respectively. Give a general description of the surface. Tracks running east–west and north–south meet at the point where $x = 5$ and $y = 2$. Find the angle each track makes with the horizontal at this point.

6 Given that $f(x, y) = \dfrac{x^3}{y^2 + 1}$ find:

(i) $f(5, 3)$

(ii) the equations of the sections of the surface $z = f(x, y)$ cut by the planes $x = 5$ and $y = 3$

(iii) the gradients of these sections when $x = 5$ and $y = 3$.

7 Find the equations of the sections of the surface $z = (x - 2y)\ln(x^2 + 3y)$ cut by the planes $x = a$ and $y = b$. Find also the gradients of these sections when $x = a$ and $y = b$.

8 The diagram shows a framework ABCD made by joining the points A(10, 10, 2), B(−10, 10, −2), C(−10, −10, 2), D(10, −10, −2). Each side is divided into the same number of equal segments (six in this diagram) and corresponding points of division are joined by straight lines parallel to the planes $x = 0$ (such as EG) or $y = 0$ (such as FH).

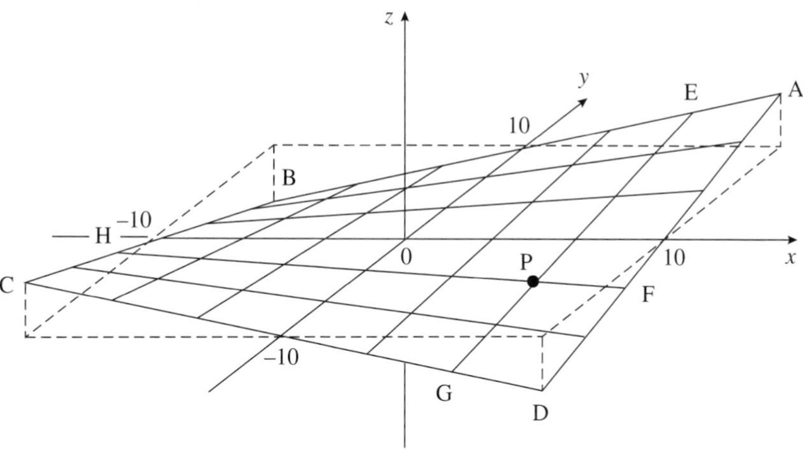

(i) Show that the co-ordinates of E and G are $\left(\lambda, 10, \dfrac{\lambda}{5}\right)$ and $\left(\lambda, -10, -\dfrac{\lambda}{5}\right)$ respectively, where $-10 \leqslant \lambda \leqslant 10$.

(ii) Find the co-ordinates of F and H, given that they lie on the plane $y = \mu$, where $-10 \leqslant \mu \leqslant 10$.

(iii) Show that the lines EG and FH intersect, at P say, and find the co-ordinates of P in terms of λ and μ.

(iv) Deduce that P lies on the surface $z = \frac{xy}{50}$.

(v) Show that the contours of this surface are hyperbolas. Are there any exceptions?

(vi) Show that the vertical sections in which the diagonal planes $y = \pm x$ cut this surface are parabolas. Investigate other vertical sections not parallel to the x or y axis.

(This surface is called a *hyperbolic paraboloid* because of the properties shown in parts **(v)** and **(vi)**. It is an example of a *ruled surface*, i.e. a surface generated by a family of straight lines; in this case there are two families of generators, the sections parallel to the $x = 0$ or $y = 0$ planes. Ruled surfaces can be constructed physically by using cables stretched across a framework as in the diagram above, to support the surface coating. This relatively simple and cheap method is used to form attractively shaped roofs.)

Partial differentiation

Example 2.3 showed that the gradient at the point (3, 2, 0.2) on the $y = 2$ section of the surface $z = \frac{1}{10}(x^2 + 2y^2 + xy - 7x)$ is 0.1. You can use the same method to find the gradient where $x = a$, on the section where the plane $y = b$ meets the surface $z = \mathrm{f}(x, y)$ by:

- putting $y = b$ into the equation to obtain $z = \mathrm{f}(x, b)$
- differentiating with respect to x
- putting $x = a$ into the result to find the gradient.

The same can be achieved more simply by:

- differentiating $z = \mathrm{f}(x, y)$ with respect to x, treating y as a constant
- putting $x = a$ and $y = b$ into the result.

The process of differentiating a function with respect to one variable while keeping the other variable(s) constant is called *partial differentiation*, and the expression for the gradient which this produces is called the *partial derivative*.

Various notations are used for the partial derivative of $z = \mathrm{f}(x, y)$ with respect to x. The first two are $\frac{\partial z}{\partial x}$ or $\frac{\partial \mathrm{f}}{\partial x}$. The symbol ∂, which should be distinguished from d or δ in handwriting, was introduced by Carl Jacobi (1804–51): it can be read as 'partial d' or 'curly d', and $\frac{\partial z}{\partial x}$ is read as 'partial dz by dx'. The next common notation for the same thing is $\mathrm{f}_x(x, y)$, which corresponds to Lagrange's $\mathrm{f}'(x)$ for the derivative of a function of one variable; this requires that the function involved should be named (f), but then has the advantage that it can show where the derivative is evaluated. In Example 2.3 the two gradients found can be written as '$\frac{\partial z}{\partial x}$ and $\frac{\partial z}{\partial y}$ evaluated at (3, 2)', but if you introduce $f(x, y) = \frac{1}{10}(x^2 + 2y^2 + xy - 7x)$ then you can use the simpler alternative '$f_x(3, 2)$ and $f_y(3, 2)$'. You may come across other notations too, such as $f'_x(x, y)$ or $f_1(x, y)$ but they are not used in this book.

EXAMPLE 2.4

Find $\frac{\partial z}{\partial x}$ and $\frac{\partial z}{\partial y}$ when:

(i) $z = \frac{1}{10}(x^2 + 2y^2 + xy - 7x)$ **(ii)** $z = x^3 e^{xy^2}$ **(iii)** $z = h\left(\frac{x^3}{y^2}\right)$

SOLUTION

(i) $\frac{\partial z}{\partial x} = \frac{1}{10}(2x + y - 7)$ $\frac{\partial z}{\partial y} = \frac{1}{10}(4y + x)$

(ii) The usual rules of differentiation (product rule, chain rule, etc.) still apply. Keeping y constant:

$$\frac{\partial z}{\partial x} = 3x^2 e^{xy^2} + x^3y^2e^{xy^2} = (3 + xy^2)x^2e^{xy^2}.$$

Keeping x constant:

$$\frac{\partial z}{\partial y} = x^3 \times 2xye^{xy^2} = 2x^4ye^{xy^2}.$$

(iii) Put $u = \frac{x^3}{y^2}$ so that $z = h(u)$. To differentiate partially with respect to x you use the chain rule, which now takes the form $\frac{\partial z}{\partial x} = \frac{dz}{du} \times \frac{\partial u}{\partial x}$.

$$\frac{\partial z}{\partial x} = h'(u) \times \frac{3x^2}{y^2} = h'\left(\frac{x^3}{y^2}\right) \times \frac{3x^2}{y^2}.$$

Similarly $\frac{\partial z}{\partial y} = h'(u) \times \left(-\frac{2x^3}{y^3}\right) = -h'\left(\frac{x^3}{y^2}\right) \times \frac{2x^3}{y^3}.$

EXERCISE 2C

1 Find $\frac{\partial z}{\partial x}$ and $\frac{\partial z}{\partial y}$.

(i) $z = \frac{x^2}{y^3}$ **(ii)** $z = \arctan\left(\frac{y}{x}\right)$

(iii) $z = x \cos y + y \cos x$ **(iv)** $z = xe^{\sqrt{xy}}$

2 If $f(x, y) = x^3 + 3xy^2 - \dfrac{y^4}{x}$ find $f_x(1, 3)$ and $f_y(-2, 5)$.

3 The temperature T (in °C) at a point in a room is linked by the function F to the distance x metres from a heater and the time t minutes after the heater has been switched on, so that $T = F(x, t)$. For each of the following statements give the appropriate units and say what the statement means in practical terms.

(i) $F_x(3, 10) = -0.3$ **(ii)** $F_t(3, 10) = 0.1$

4 The displacement of a vibrating guitar string 1 metre long from its rest position is given by $d(x, t) = 0.003 \sin(\pi x) \sin(2500t)$, where x m is the distance from one end of the string and t s is the time. Evaluate $d_x(0.4, 2)$ and $d_t(0.4, 2)$ and explain what each of these means in practical terms.

5 If $u = \dfrac{x+y}{1-xy}$, $v = \arctan x + \arctan y$, prove that $\dfrac{\partial u}{\partial x}\dfrac{\partial v}{\partial y} = \dfrac{\partial u}{\partial y}\dfrac{\partial v}{\partial x}$.

6 Van der Waal's equation $RT = \left(p + \dfrac{a}{V^2}\right)(V - b)$ connects the pressure p, volume V and temperature T of a quantity of gas of fixed mass, where a, b and R are constants.

Find $\dfrac{\partial T}{\partial p}$, $\dfrac{\partial p}{\partial V}$ and $\dfrac{\partial V}{\partial T}$. Hence show that $\left(\dfrac{\partial T}{\partial p}\right)\left(\dfrac{\partial p}{\partial V}\right)\left(\dfrac{\partial V}{\partial T}\right) = -1$.

7 The Cobb–Douglas production model states that $P = aK^bL^{1-b}$, where P is the total yearly production of an economy, K is the total capital investment, L is the total labour force, and a and b are constants with $0 < b < 1$.

Prove that $K\dfrac{\partial P}{\partial K} + L\dfrac{\partial P}{\partial L} = P$.

8 Prove that the relation $x\dfrac{\partial z}{\partial x} - y\dfrac{\partial z}{\partial y} = z$ is satisfied by every function of the form $z = xF(xy)$, where F is any function which can be differentiated.

9 **(i)** Prove that if $z = F\left(\dfrac{x}{y}\right)$ then $x\dfrac{\partial z}{\partial x} + y\dfrac{\partial z}{\partial y} = 0$. Check this with the function in Question 1 part **(ii)**.

(ii) Prove that if $z = y^n F\left(\dfrac{x}{y}\right)$ then $x\dfrac{\partial z}{\partial x} + y\dfrac{\partial z}{\partial y} = nz$.
Check this with the functions in Questions 2 and 7.

(This result is Euler's theorem on homogeneous functions, a *homogeneous function of degree n* being a function f such that $f(tx, ty) = t^n f(x, y)$.)

Differentiability

This section points out an important distinction between curves and surfaces.

Figure 2.7 shows a curve $y = \mathrm{f}(x)$ with its tangent at the point A. Another point Q on the tangent can be reached from A by means of an x-step AN followed by a y-step NQ. These steps are called *differentials* and are denoted by $\mathrm{d}x$ and $\mathrm{d}y$ respectively. Thus $\mathrm{d}x$ is an arbitrary (and not necessarily small) change in x and $\mathrm{d}y$ is the resulting change in y needed to reach a point on the *tangent* at A. Since the gradient of this tangent is $\mathrm{f}'(x)$, the connection between these differentials is $\mathrm{d}y = \mathrm{f}'(x)\,\mathrm{d}x$ (so that $\mathrm{d}y$ depends on the two variables x and $\mathrm{d}x$). From this it follows that $\frac{\mathrm{d}y}{\mathrm{d}x} = \mathrm{f}'(x)$, which explains the familiar but rather odd Leibniz notation for the derivative.

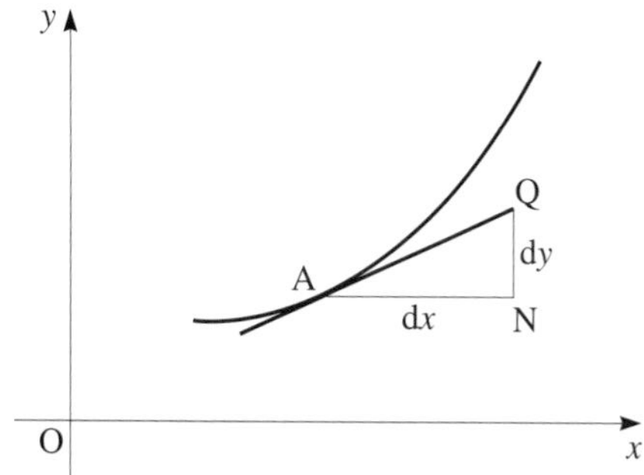

Figure 2.7

ACTIVITY 2.1

(i) If A is the point (2, 8) on the curve $y = x^3$, find $\mathrm{d}y$ when $\mathrm{d}x$ is

(a) 100 **(b)** -2 **(c)** 0.01.

Give the formula for $\mathrm{d}y$ in terms of $\mathrm{d}x$.

(ii) Give the formula for $\mathrm{d}y$ in terms of x and $\mathrm{d}x$ for the general point A on the curve $y = x^3$.

The tangent at A is the line which fits closest to the curve at A, and so can be used as the *linear approximation* to the curve near to A. This idea, which is the starting point for the discussion of Maclaurin approximations in Chapter 4 of *A2 Further Pure Mathematics* (*FP2*), can be written in the equivalent forms

$$\delta y \approx \frac{\mathrm{d}y}{\mathrm{d}x}\,\delta x \qquad \text{or} \qquad \delta y \approx \mathrm{f}'(x)\,\delta x \qquad \text{or} \qquad \mathrm{f}(x+h) \approx \mathrm{f}(x) + h\mathrm{f}'(x)$$

where δx $(= h)$ is a small change in x.

Notice that in moving from A to a neighbouring point P on the curve you use the *approximate* formula $\delta y \approx \mathrm{f}'(x)\,\delta x$, which applies only for small values of δx, whereas in moving from A to a point Q on the tangent you use the *exact* formula $\mathrm{d}y = \mathrm{f}'(x)\,\mathrm{d}x$, which is true for all values of $\mathrm{d}x$.

Figure 2.8 superimposes both changes, so that $\delta x = dx$, and shows that the error in the approximation is then $\delta y - dy$.

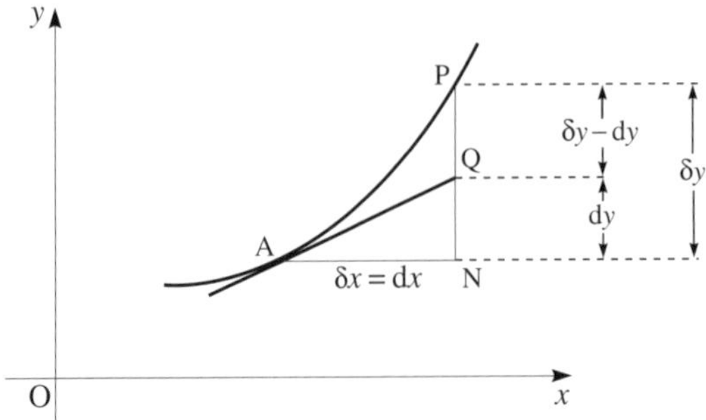

Figure 2.8

The same idea can be expressed in terms of limits instead of approximations:

$$\delta y = (f'(x) + \varepsilon)\,\delta x \qquad \text{or} \qquad f(x+h) = f(x) + h(f'(x) + \varepsilon)$$

where $\varepsilon \to 0$ as $\delta x \to 0$ or $h \to 0$.

You have met examples of functions which have no derivative for certain values of x. At the corresponding points on the graph of the function there is no tangent, and therefore no linear approximation. One simple example is $y = |x|$ at the origin (figure 2.9).

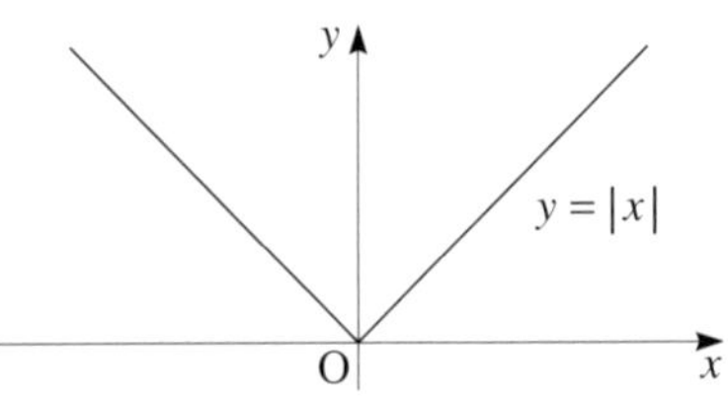

Figure 2.9

For a function of one variable, the properties:

(A) having a derivative when $x = a$
(B) having a tangent to the graph at $(a, f(a))$
(C) having a linear approximation in a neighbourhood of $x = a$

are all equivalent. In the case of a one variable function the statement that $f(x)$ is *differentiable* at $x = a$ tells you that the function has properties (A), (B) and (C).

With functions of two or more variables things are not so simple! Suppose that at the point A on the surface $z = f(x, y)$ you can find the partial derivatives $f_x(x, y)$ and $f_y(x, y)$. Then the sections through A in the x and y directions have tangents at A, and there is just one plane through A containing these two tangents. This plane gives satisfactory linear approximations to the surface in the x and y directions, but there is no guarantee that the surface stays close to the plane as you head in other directions.

For example, consider the surface $z = f(x, y)$ shown, together with its contours, in figure 2.10. It consists of the horizontal slab $z \leqslant 3$ from which are carved two V-shaped grooves parallel to the x and y axes defined by $z = |y|$ and $z = |x|$. Near the origin the surface is something like the adjacent portions of a slab of chocolate.

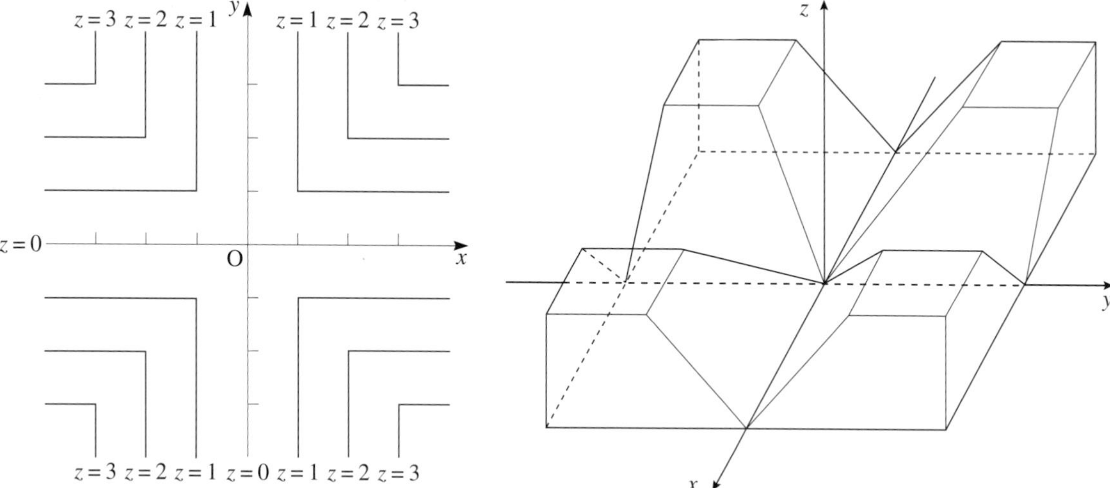

Figure 2.10

It is clear that the sections through the origin are just the x and y axes, so both partial derivatives are zero at the origin, and the plane $z = 0$ contains the tangents to these sections. But if you move on the surface heading in any other direction from the origin you have to ascend the face of a groove, moving away from the plane $z = 0$ by an amount proportional to the distance travelled. So the plane $z = 0$ cannot be regarded as a linear approximation to the surface at the origin. Nor can any other plane give a better approximation, since no other plane contains both the x and y axes. So this surface has *no* satisfactory approximating plane at the origin, even though both partial derivatives exist there. More formally, it is not possible to find constants p and q such that:

$$f(h, k) = f(0, 0) + h(p + \varepsilon_1) + k(q + \varepsilon_2)$$

where $\varepsilon_1 \to 0$ and $\varepsilon_2 \to 0$ as $\sqrt{h^2 + k^2} \to 0$.

Luckily this rather artificial example is not typical: for most points on most elementary surfaces the plane containing the tangents to the sections in the x and y directions can be used as a linear approximation to the entire surface in the neighbourhood of the point. When this happens you say that the function is *differentiable* at that point, and the plane is called the *tangent plane*. The example just given shows that for a function of two variables the following three properties are *not* equivalent:

(A′) having both partial derivatives when $x = a$ and $y = b$
(B′) having a tangent plane to the surface at $(a, b, f(a, b))$
(C′) having a linear approximation in the neighbourhood of $x = a$ and $y = b$.

ACTIVITY 2.2

Insert the correct symbol ($\Rightarrow$, $\Leftarrow$ or $\Leftrightarrow$) between these properties.

(i) (A′) (B′) **(ii)** (B′) (C′) **(iii)** (C′) (A′)

ACTIVITY 2.3

Use contours, sections and, if possible, a computer-generated perspective drawing to describe the surface $z = \sqrt[4]{x^2 y^2}$. In particular, find which (if any) of the properties (A′), (B′) and (C′) are true at the points:

(i) (0, 0, 0) **(ii)** (1, 0, 0) **(iii)** (1, 1, 1).

Tangent planes

A set of conditions sufficient to ensure that a function is differentiable (i.e. has a tangent plane) at a particular point will be given on page 70. Meanwhile you may assume that all the functions you meet in this book are differentiable at all relevant points, unless attention is drawn to the contrary. The practical task of finding the equation of the tangent plane at a point on a given surface is straightforward, as shown in Example 2.5.

EXAMPLE 2.5

Find the equation of the tangent plane at the point A(4, 3, 14) on the surface $z = x^2 + 2y^2 - 2xy + x$.

SOLUTION

Since $\dfrac{\partial z}{\partial x} = 2x - 2y + 1 = 3$ at A, the gradient of the section parallel to the x axis at A is 3. This means that, in moving along the tangent to this section at A, z increases by 3 when x increases by 1 and y remains constant. Therefore the vector $\begin{pmatrix} 1 \\ 0 \\ 3 \end{pmatrix}$ is in the direction of this tangent.

Similarly, since $\dfrac{\partial z}{\partial y} = 4y - 2x = 4$ at A, the vector $\begin{pmatrix} 0 \\ 1 \\ 4 \end{pmatrix}$ is in the direction of the tangent at A to the section parallel to the y axis (see figure 2.11).

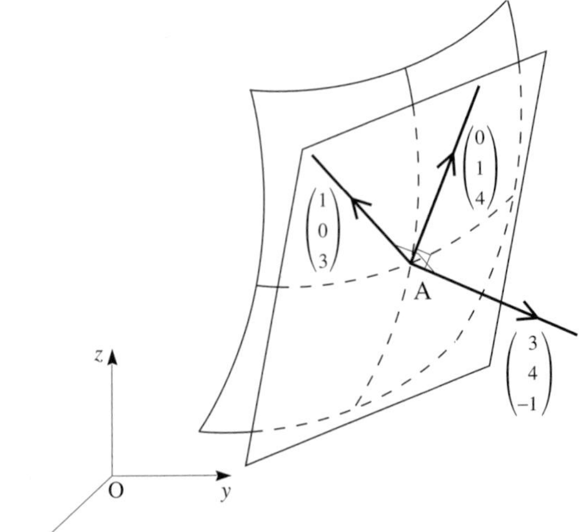

Figure 2.11

The tangent plane contains both these tangents, and so has normal vector:

$$\mathbf{n} = \begin{pmatrix} 0 \\ 1 \\ 4 \end{pmatrix} \times \begin{pmatrix} 1 \\ 0 \\ 3 \end{pmatrix} = \begin{pmatrix} 3 \\ 4 \\ -1 \end{pmatrix}.$$

The equation of the tangent plane is therefore:

$$3x + 4y - z = 3 \times 4 + 4 \times 3 - 14 = 10$$

or $\quad z = 3x + 4y - 10.$

The general procedure is similar. The equation of the tangent plane of the surface $z = \mathrm{f}(x, y)$ at the point $\mathrm{A}(a, b, c)$, where $c = \mathrm{f}(a, b)$, can be found as follows.

- Find the values of the partial derivatives at the point. Suppose that $\dfrac{\partial \mathrm{f}}{\partial x} = p$ and $\dfrac{\partial \mathrm{f}}{\partial y} = q$ when $x = a$ and $y = b$. Then the vectors $\begin{pmatrix} 1 \\ 0 \\ p \end{pmatrix}$ and $\begin{pmatrix} 0 \\ 1 \\ q \end{pmatrix}$ are in the directions of the tangents to the sections at A.
- A normal vector to the tangent plane is $\mathbf{n} = \begin{pmatrix} 0 \\ 1 \\ q \end{pmatrix} \times \begin{pmatrix} 1 \\ 0 \\ p \end{pmatrix} = \begin{pmatrix} p \\ q \\ -1 \end{pmatrix}.$
- The equation of the tangent plane is $(\mathbf{r} - \mathbf{a}) \,.\, \mathbf{n} = 0$, i.e.

$$\begin{pmatrix} x-a \\ y-b \\ z-c \end{pmatrix} . \begin{pmatrix} p \\ q \\ -1 \end{pmatrix} = 0 \qquad \text{or} \qquad z = p(x - a) + q(y - b) + c.$$

This equation can be put into another useful form. The differences $x - a$, $y - b$, $z - c$ are the changes in x, y, z needed to move from A to the general point (x, y, z) on the tangent plane at A. These local co-ordinates relative to A are called differentials (as on page 55) and denoted by $\mathrm{d}x$, $\mathrm{d}y$, $\mathrm{d}z$ respectively. Then it follows from the equation of the tangent plane given above that

$$\begin{pmatrix} dx \\ dy \\ dz \end{pmatrix} . \begin{pmatrix} \partial \mathrm{f} / \partial x \\ \partial \mathrm{f} / \partial y \\ -1 \end{pmatrix} = 0 \qquad \text{or} \qquad \mathrm{d}z = \frac{\partial \mathrm{f}}{\partial x}\mathrm{d}x + \frac{\partial \mathrm{f}}{\partial y}\mathrm{d}y$$

where the partial derivatives are evaluated at A. This is the result for a function of two variables corresponding to the formula $\mathrm{d}y = \mathrm{f}'(x)\,\mathrm{d}x$ given on page 55. It shows how the change $\mathrm{d}z$ needed to remain on the tangent plane is related to the changes $\mathrm{d}x$ and $\mathrm{d}y$. Notice that, in general, $\mathrm{d}z$ depends on the four variables x, y, $\mathrm{d}x$, $\mathrm{d}y$.

EXERCISE 2D

1 Find the equation of the normal line and of the tangent plane to the given surface at the given point.

(i) $z = 2x^2 - 3xy + 4y^2$, $(3, 1, 13)$ **(ii)** $z = \dfrac{x^3}{y^2}$, $(4, -8, 1)$

(iii) $z = \dfrac{20}{x^2 + y^2}$, $(2, 4, 1)$ **(iv)** $z = \mathrm{e}^x \cos y$, $(1, \pi, -\mathrm{e})$

2 A student who was asked to find the equation of the tangent plane to $z = x^2y^4$ at $(3, 1, 9)$ gave the answer $z = 2xy^4(x - 3) + 4x^2y^3(y - 1) + 9$.

(i) How can you tell at a glance that this is wrong?
(ii) What mistake did the student make?
(iii) What is the correct answer?

3 Given that $z = \dfrac{x^3 + y^3}{x - y}$, $x = 10$, $y = 8$, $\mathrm{d}x = 2$, $\mathrm{d}y = -3$, find $\mathrm{d}z$.

4 Given a particular function $z = \mathrm{f}(x, y)$ and particular values of x and y, is it always possible to find values of $\mathrm{d}x$ and $\mathrm{d}y$, not both zero, for which $\mathrm{d}z = 0$? Interpret your answer geometrically.

5 Find the co-ordinates of the point on $z = x^2 + 5xy + 2y^2$ where the tangent plane is parallel to $5x - 13y + z = 10$.

6 Show that the equation of the tangent plane to the surface $z = \dfrac{1}{xy}$ at the point $\left(h, k, \dfrac{1}{hk}\right)$ can be written in the form $kx + hy + h^2k^2z = 3hk$.

Prove that as h and k vary through positive values the tetrahedron formed by this plane and the planes $x = 0$, $y = 0$, $z = 0$ has constant volume.

7 Prove that the surfaces $z = x^2 + y^2 + 50$ and $z = 12x + 16y - x^2 - y^2$ touch, and find the equations of their common normal line and tangent plane.

8 The family of surfaces $S_1, S_2, S_3, \ldots$ is such that S_k has the equation

$z = k(x^2 + 3y^2)$ for $k = 1, 2, 3, \ldots$. The line $\begin{pmatrix} x \\ y \\ z \end{pmatrix} = \lambda \begin{pmatrix} a \\ b \\ c \end{pmatrix}$, where a, b, c are constant, meets S_k at the origin and at P_k, and the tangent plane to S_k at P_k is T_k.

(i) Find the equation of T_k.
(ii) Show that the planes $T_1, T_2, T_3, \ldots$ are all parallel.
(iii) Show that the distance of T_k from the origin is inversely proportional to k.

Directional derivatives

EXAMPLE 2.6

Find the angle of slope of a footpath leaving the point (3, 2, 0.2) on bearing 072°, for the hillside $z = \frac{1}{10}(x^2 + 2y^2 + xy - 7x)$ in Example 2.3.

SOLUTION

As in Example 2.3, $\frac{\partial z}{\partial x} = 0.1$ and $\frac{\partial z}{\partial y} = 1.1$ at (3, 2, 0.2).

Therefore the tangent plane at this point is $\mathrm{d}z = 0.1\mathrm{d}x + 1.1\mathrm{d}y$.

A horizontal line on a bearing of 072° makes an angle of 18° with the positive x axis, so the horizontal unit vector in this direction is $\begin{pmatrix} \cos 18° \\ \sin 18° \end{pmatrix}$.

To move a distance of 1 unit along this horizontal line you therefore need

$$\mathrm{d}x = \cos 18° \text{ and } \mathrm{d}y = \sin 18°$$

and to get back on to the tangent plane you need

$$\mathrm{d}z = 0.1 \times \cos 18° + 1.1 \times \sin 18° \approx 0.435$$

(see figure 2.12).

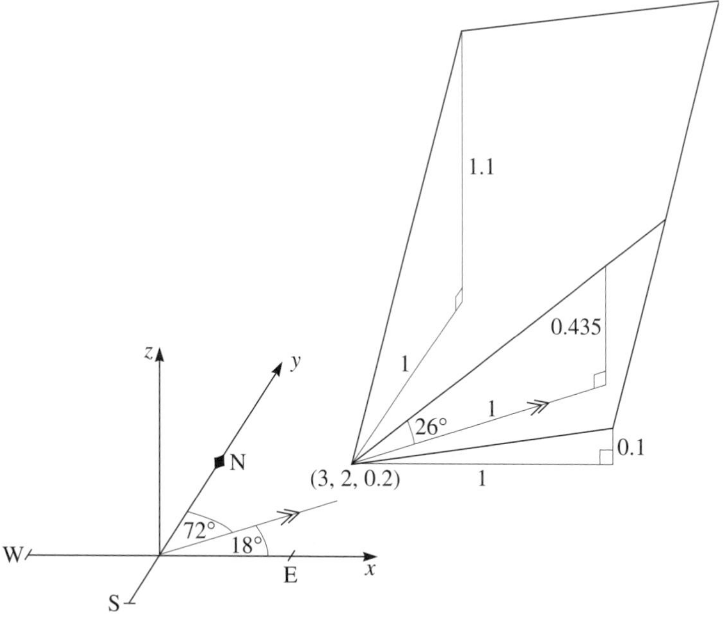

Figure 2.12

So a horizontal shift of 1 unit in the given direction produces a vertical shift of 0.435. The gradient of the footpath is 0.435, and its angle of slope is arctan 0.435 ≈ 26°.

The general procedure is similar. Suppose you want to find the gradient on the surface $z = \mathrm{f}(x, y)$ at the point $\mathrm{A}(a, b, c)$ in the direction defined by the horizontal unit vector $\hat{\mathbf{u}} = \begin{pmatrix} \cos\alpha \\ \sin\alpha \end{pmatrix}$. Putting $\mathrm{d}x = \cos\alpha$ and $\mathrm{d}y = \sin\alpha$ in the equation of the tangent at A gives $\mathrm{d}z = \frac{\partial \mathrm{f}}{\partial x}\cos\alpha + \frac{\partial \mathrm{f}}{\partial y}\sin\alpha$, where the partial derivatives are evaluated at A. Since this $\mathrm{d}z$ is the vertical change needed to get back to the tangent plane after a *unit* horizontal step, the required gradient is $\frac{\partial \mathrm{f}}{\partial x}\cos\alpha + \frac{\partial \mathrm{f}}{\partial y}\sin\alpha$. This scalar quantity is called the *directional derivative* in the direction of $\hat{\mathbf{u}}$.

The vector grad f

The directional derivative just found can be written as a scalar product.

$$\frac{\partial \mathrm{f}}{\partial x}\cos\alpha + \frac{\partial \mathrm{f}}{\partial y}\sin\alpha = \begin{pmatrix} \cos\alpha \\ \sin\alpha \end{pmatrix} . \begin{pmatrix} \partial \mathrm{f}/\partial x \\ \partial \mathrm{f}/\partial y \end{pmatrix} = \hat{\mathbf{u}} . \begin{pmatrix} \partial \mathrm{f}/\partial x \\ \partial \mathrm{f}/\partial y \end{pmatrix}.$$

The vector $\begin{pmatrix} \partial \mathrm{f}/\partial x \\ \partial \mathrm{f}/\partial y \end{pmatrix}$ is called **grad** f; alternative notations for this which you may meet are $\begin{pmatrix} \mathrm{f}_x \\ \mathrm{f}_y \end{pmatrix}$, $\begin{pmatrix} \partial z/\partial x \\ \partial z/\partial y \end{pmatrix}$, $\nabla \mathrm{f}$ or ∇z; as usual the partial derivatives are evaluated at the point in question.

Note

The symbol ∇ was introduced by Hamilton in 1843; he called it 'nabla' because it is shaped like a Hebrew musical instrument of that name; ∇ is also called 'del'.

It is natural to wonder how the *two*-dimensional vector **grad** f is related to the *three*-dimensional surface $z = \mathrm{f}(x, y)$ from which it arises. Suppose you are on the surface at A and want to walk along the contour line through A. Then you have to head in the direction of a unit vector $\hat{\mathbf{u}}$ which makes the directional derivative zero. But:

$$\hat{\mathbf{u}} . \mathbf{grad}\ \mathrm{f} = 0 \quad \Rightarrow \quad \hat{\mathbf{u}} \text{ is perpendicular to } \mathbf{grad}\ \mathrm{f}$$

(assuming for the moment that **grad** f $\neq 0$).

Therefore the direction along the contour through A is perpendicular to **grad** f, or, turning this around, **grad** f is a vector *normal* to the contour through A.

? What happens at a point where **grad** f = 0?

Now suppose that, instead of wanting to walk on the level, you want to walk in the steepest possible direction. Then you have to choose $\hat{\mathbf{u}}$ to maximise the directional derivative. But

$$\hat{\mathbf{u}} \cdot \mathbf{grad}\, \mathrm{f} = |\hat{\mathbf{u}}||\mathbf{grad}\, \mathrm{f}| \cos\theta$$

where θ is the angle between $\hat{\mathbf{u}}$ and **grad** f. Since $|\hat{\mathbf{u}}| = 1$ and $|\mathbf{grad}\, \mathrm{f}|$ is fixed, the directional derivative is maximised when $\cos\theta = 1$ (which is when $\hat{\mathbf{u}}$ is in the same direction as **grad** f, showing, not surprisingly, that the line of greatest slope is perpendicular to the contour), and the maximum gradient is $|\mathbf{grad}\, \mathrm{f}|$.

To summarise, if A(a, b, c) is a point on the surface $z = \mathrm{f}(x, y)$ and the contour with implicit equation $\mathrm{f}(x, y) = c$ is drawn in the x–y plane, then the vector **grad** f, drawn starting at the point A$'(a, b)$, is in the x–y plane, is normal to the contour, points in the direction of greatest slope, and has magnitude equal to the greatest gradient at A (see figure 2.13).

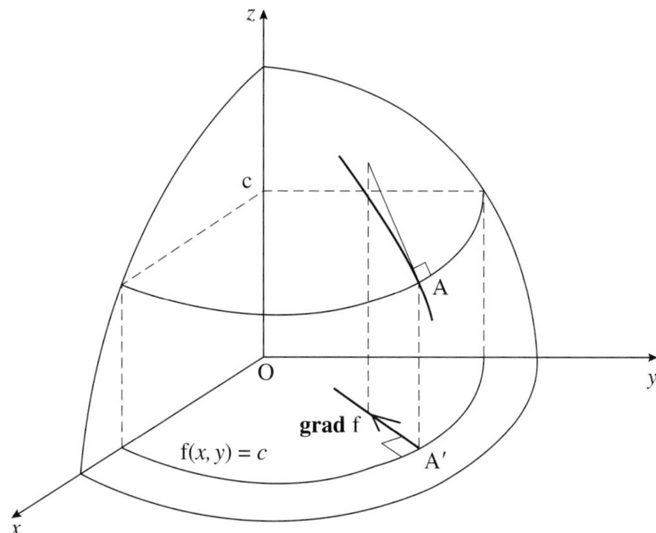

Figure 2.13

EXERCISE 2E

Where relevant in this exercise, take the x and y axes to be due east and due north respectively.

1 For the given expression $\mathrm{f}(x, y)$ find **grad** f and sketch the contour through (3, 2) with **grad** f at this point shown as a vector.

(i) xy **(ii)** $\dfrac{x}{y}$ **(iii)** $x^2 + 3y^2$ **(iv)** $\dfrac{x}{x^2 + y^2}$

2 Find the directional derivatives at the point (4, 3, 7) on the surface $z = x^2 - y^2$ in the directions of the eight principal points of the compass.

3 The point P(2, 1, 3.1) is on a hill represented by the surface $z = 4 - \frac{x^2}{5} - \frac{y^2}{10}$.

Find the gradient and angle of slope of the paths through P in the directions:

(i) north-east **(ii)** directly towards the top of the hill.

4 A rectangular metal plate bounded by the lines $x = 0$, $x = 20$, $y = 0$ and $y = 10$ is heated in such a way that its temperature T at the point (x, y) is given by

$$T = \frac{200}{4x^2 + y^2 + 1}.$$

(i) Where are the hottest and coolest points of the plate?

(ii) A small bug placed on the plate at (10, 5) moves in the direction in which the temperature decreases as rapidly as possible. Find this direction as a unit vector, and find the rate at which the temperature decreases.

(iii) Another type of small bug placed on the plate at (5, 7) finds the temperature to its liking, and moves in the direction which keeps the temperature constant. Find this direction as a unit vector.

5 Given that $f_x(a, b) = p$ and $f_y(a, b) = q$, find, in terms of p, q and θ, the gradient of the path on the surface $z = f(x, y)$ which passes through $(a, b, f(a, b))$ on the bearing of $\theta°$.

Stationary points

A point on the surface $z = f(x, y)$ at which the tangent plane is horizontal (i.e. parallel to the x–y plane) is called a *stationary point*. At a stationary point both $\frac{\partial z}{\partial x}$ and $\frac{\partial z}{\partial y}$ are zero, so the search for stationary points starts with solving the equations $\frac{\partial z}{\partial x} = 0$ and $\frac{\partial z}{\partial y} = 0$ simultaneously.

A stationary point may be the 'top of a hill' or the 'bottom of a hollow' or a 'col' (mountain pass) or something more complicated, as shown in the sketches and shaded contour maps of figure 2.14 (where light or dark shading shows high or low ground respectively).

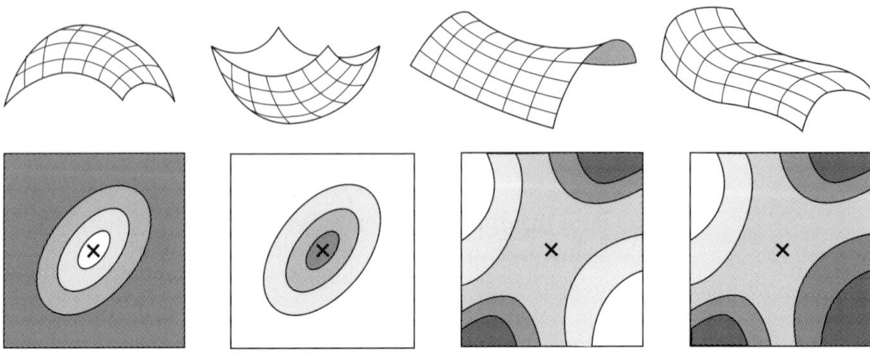

Figure 2.14 Maximum point Minimum point Two types of saddle point

More formally, a stationary point $(a, b, f(a, b))$ is:

- a *local maximum point* if $f(a + h, b + k) < f(a, b)$ for all sufficiently small h and k (not both zero)
- a *local minimum point* if $f(a + h, b + k) > f(a, b)$ for all sufficiently small h and k (not both zero)
- a *saddle point* if $f(a + h, b + k)$ is less than $f(a, b)$ for some h and k but greater than $f(a, b)$ for others.

There are other possibilities too, such as a point on a ridge (see Question 9 of Exercise 2F).

ACTIVITY 2.4

By considering contours and/or sections find what sort of stationary point the origin is on these surfaces.

(i) $z = x^2 + y^2$ **(ii)** $z = x^2 - y^2$ **(iii)** $z = -x^2 - y^2$ **(iv)** $z = xy$

There are tests involving second partial derivatives for distinguishing the types of stationary point but (as with the second derivative test for a function of one variable) they sometimes fail, and can be complicated to use. It is often simpler to use the definitions directly, as follows.

EXAMPLE 2.7

Investigate the stationary points of $z = x^3 + 6xy - 3y^2$.

SOLUTION

Since $\dfrac{\partial z}{\partial x} = 3x^2 + 6y$ and $\dfrac{\partial z}{\partial y} = 6x - 6y$ you solve the simultaneous equations

$$3x^2 + 6y = 0 \text{ and } 6x - 6y = 0$$

giving $y = x$ and $3x^2 + 6x = 0$, so $x = 0$ or -2.

This gives stationary points $(0, 0, 0)$ and $(-2, -2, 4)$.

At $(0, 0, 0)$ the $x = 0$ section is $z = -3y^2$, which might suggest that this is a maximum point. But the $y = 0$ section is $z = x^3$, so $z > 0$ for $x > 0$ and $z < 0$ for $x < 0$. Therefore by moving on the surface in the plane $y = 0$ it is possible either to ascend from the origin or to descend. These show that $(0, 0, 0)$ is a saddle point.

It is easy to show that both the sections $x = -2$ and $y = -2$ have maximum points at $(-2, -2, 4)$, but you still have to deal with sections in other directions. To do this you examine the value of z at the general point in the neighbourhood of the stationary point by putting $x = -2 + h$ and $y = -2 + k$.

Then $z = (-2+h)^3 + 6(-2+h)(-2+k) - 3(-2+k)^2$

$= -8 + 12h - 6h^2 + h^3 + 24 - 12k - 12h + 6hk - 12 + 12k - 3k^2$

$= 4 - 6h^2 + h^3 + 6hk - 3k^2$

$= 4 - 3(h-k)^2 - h^2(3-h)$

< 4 provided that $h < 3$.

Notice that the terms in h and k cancel, as they must at a stationary point.

Therefore $(-2, -2, 4)$ is a maximum point.

The surface is shown in figure 2.15.

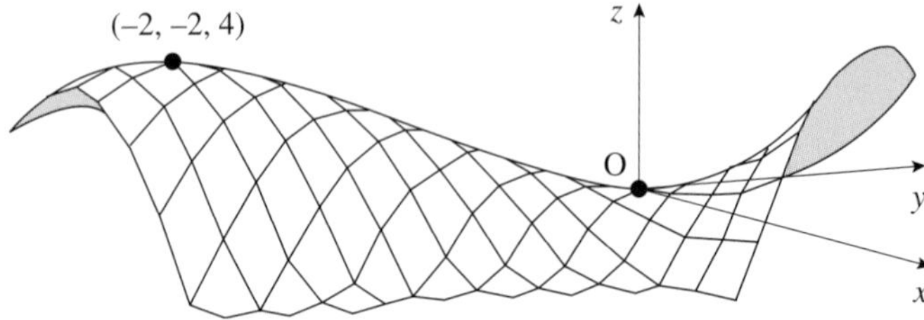

Figure 2.15

EXERCISE 2F

1 Show that $(1, 2, -7)$ is a stationary point of $z = x^2 + 2y^2 - xy - 7y$.

Show that if $x = 1 + h$ and $y = 2 + k$ then $z = -7 + (h - \frac{1}{2}k)^2 + \frac{7}{4}k^2$.

What can you deduce about the nature of the stationary point?

2 Find the co-ordinates of the stationary point of $z = x^2 - 4xy - y^2 + 20y - 15$ and determine, stating reasons, whether this is a maximum, minimum or saddle point.

3 Find both of the stationary points of $z = x^2 + y^3 - 12xy$ and determine their nature.

4 Investigate the stationary points of these surfaces.

(i) $z = (x + y)(xy + 1)$

(ii) $z = x^2 + y + \dfrac{2}{x} + \dfrac{4}{y}$

(iii) $z = xy + \ln|x| + 2y^2$

5 Show that $f(x, y) = (x^2 + y^2)^2 - 4(x^2 + 2y^2) + 15$ has a stationary value at the origin and find all other points (x, y) at which $f(x, y)$ is stationary.

By considering small displacements from the origin, $x = ht$ and $y = kt$, where h and k are constants, or otherwise, determine the nature of the stationary value at the origin.

[MEI]

6 Show that $z = Ax^2 + Bxy + Cy^2$ has a stationary point at the origin. Find conditions involving the constants A, B, C which ensure that this is:

(i) a maximum point
(ii) a minimum point
(iii) a saddle point.

7 (i) Prove that of all the cuboids with a given volume the one with the smallest surface area is the cube.

(ii) The base of a closed cuboidal cardboard carton with a given volume has an extra thickness of cardboard added for strength. Ignoring all other overlaps, find the shape of carton which minimises the amount of cardboard used.

8 Find and classify all the stationary points of $z = 2\cos x - y^2$. (This is the surface described in Example 2.1)

9 Investigate the stationary points of $z = e^x(1 - \cos y)$.

10 Prove that the surface $z = \dfrac{1}{x^2y}$ has no stationary points.

Find the points on this surface which are closest to the origin, and show that the distance of these points from the origin is $2^{3/4}$.

(**Hint:** Let the distance from the origin of the point (x, y, z) on this surface be L, find L^2 in terms of y and z and minimise L^2, treating y and z as independent variables.)

11 The diagram shows the cross-section of a proposed water channel. The section is to be an isosceles trapezium with area 20 m^2 and with width w m, depth d m and sides inclined at angle θ to the horizontal, as shown.

Show that $w = \dfrac{20}{d} - d\cot\theta$.

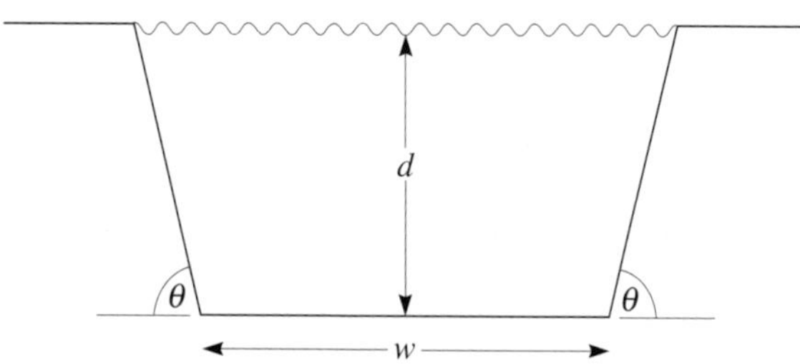

It is known that the average flow velocity of water through the channel is inversely proportional to the wetted perimeter p of the channel (i.e. the perimeter of the trapezium, excluding the top). Therefore the flow is maximised when p is minimised. Find the values of θ, d and w which achieve this.

12 The diagram shows the points (1, 2), (2, 5), (4, 4), (5, 6) and the line $y = mx + c$. The broken lines show the vertical deviations of the given points from the line. The *least squares line of best fit* is the line which minimises the sum of the square of these deviations, called Q. The squares of the deviations are used so that the positive or negative contributions from points on different sides of the line do not cancel.

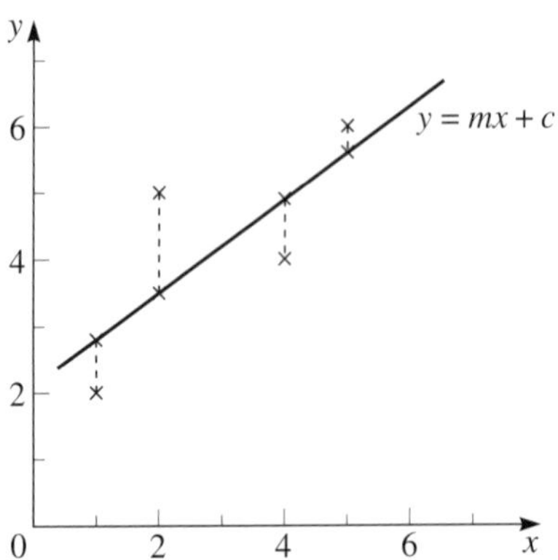

(i) Show that the y co-ordinates of the points on the line are $m + c$, $2m + c$, $4m + c$ and $5m + c$ respectively, and hence that:

$$Q = (m + c - 2)^2 + (2m + c - 5)^2 + (4m + c - 4)^2 + (5m + c - 6)^2.$$

(ii) Show that:

$$\frac{\partial Q}{\partial m} = 2(m + c - 2) + 4(2m + c - 5) + 8(4m + c - 4) + 10(5m + c - 6).$$

Deduce that $\dfrac{\partial Q}{\partial m} = 0 \quad \Leftrightarrow \quad 23m + 6c - 29 = 0.$

(iii) Show that $\dfrac{\partial Q}{\partial c} = 0 \quad \Leftrightarrow \quad 12m + 4c - 17 = 0.$

Deduce from this equation that the line of best fit passes through the point (3, 4.25), which is the centroid of the four original points.

(iv) Solve the equations in parts **(ii)** and **(iii)** simultaneously to find the values of m and c which minimise Q, and draw a diagram showing this line, the four original points and their centroid.

(v) By considering the form of the surface for which the equation is given in part **(i)**, explain how you can be sure that the stationary point is a minimum point.

13 This question generalises Question 12.
Suppose there are now n given points (x_i, y_i), $i = 1, 2, \ldots, n$, and that you want to find the values of m and c which minimise the sum of the squares of the vertical deviations of these points from the line $y = mx + c$, i.e. you want to minimise $Q = \sum(mx_i + c - y_i)^2$ (where in this question all the summation is from $i = 1$ to n).

(i) Describe the form of the surface $Q = \sum(mx_i + c - y_i)^2$, and explain why this shows that it has one stationary point, and that this is a minimum.

(ii) Show that at the minimum point $m\sum x_i^2 + c\sum x_i - \sum x_i y_i = 0$ and $m\sum x_i + nc - \sum y_i = 0$.

(iii) Deduce that the line of best fit passes through the centroid $(\bar{x}, \bar{y})$, where

$$\bar{x} = \frac{\sum x_i}{n},\ \bar{y} = \frac{\sum y_i}{n}, \text{ and has gradient } \frac{\sum x_i y_i - n\bar{x}\bar{y}}{\sum x_i^2 - n\bar{x}^2}.$$

Check that the line found in Question 12 agrees with this.

(In statistics this least squares line of best fit is called the *regression line of y on x*.)

Functions of more than two variables

The behaviour of a function of more than two variables is not easy to visualise. If $w = g(x, y, z)$ it may help to think of w as some physical quantity which varies with the position of the point (x, y, z) (for example, in astrophysics, the density within a star). Quantities which vary with position and time are represented by functions of four variables x, y, z, t, as when a meteorologist deals with the changing distribution of atmospheric pressure, or a designer of microwave ovens is concerned with the temperature distribution in a joint of meat as it cooks.

Here you will concentrate on a function of three variables, but using methods which can be applied just as well to more than three. The main result is the natural extension of the two-variable case, $\delta w \approx \frac{\partial w}{\partial x}\delta x + \frac{\partial w}{\partial y}\delta y + \frac{\partial w}{\partial z}\delta z$.

The proof of this, which follows, also gives information about the error in this approximation. The argument is a bit complicated but you should at least try to grasp the main steps, which have been emphasised by the italics.

Let $w = g(x, y, z)$, and let δw be the change in w caused by changes $\delta x, \delta y, \delta z$ in x, y, z. Then:

$$\begin{aligned}\delta w &= g(x+\delta x, y+\delta y, z+\delta z) - g(x, y, z)\\ &= \{g(x+\delta x, y+\delta y, z+\delta z) - g(x, y+\delta y, z+\delta z)\}\\ &\qquad + \{g(x, y+\delta y, z+\delta z) - g(x, y, z+\delta z)\}\\ &\qquad\qquad + \{g(x, y, z+\delta z) - g(x, y, z)\}\end{aligned}$$

Two pairs of extra terms, which cancel, have been inserted.

This manipulation has expressed δw as the sum of three differences (in braces {}) in each of which *only one variable changes*. Assuming that *all three partial derivatives exist* in the neighbourhood of $P(x, y, z)$ you can deal with these differences as on page 56:

$g(x+\delta x, y+\delta y, z+\delta z) - g(x, y+\delta y, z+\delta z) = (g_x(x, y+\delta y, z+\delta z)+\varepsilon_1)\delta x$
where $\varepsilon_1 \to 0$ as $\delta x \to 0$
$g(x, y+\delta y, z+\delta z) - g(x, y, z+\delta z) = (g_y(x, y, z+\delta z)+\varepsilon_2)\delta y$
where $\varepsilon_2 \to 0$ as $\delta y \to 0$
$g(x, y, z+\delta z) - g(x, y, z) = (g_z(x, y, z)+\varepsilon_3)\delta z$
where $\varepsilon_3 \to 0$ as $\delta z \to 0$.

Notice that g_x and g_y are evaluated at $(x, y+\delta y, z+\delta z)$ and $(x, y, z+\delta z)$ respectively, not at (x, y, z). If you make the further assumption that g_x *and* g_y *are continuous* at (x, y, z) then:

$g_x(x, y+\delta y, z+\delta z) = g_x(x, y, z) + \eta_1$, where $\eta_1 \to 0$ as δy and $\delta z \to 0$

$g_y(x, y, z+\delta z) = g_y(x, y, z) + \eta_2$, where $\eta_2 \to 0$ as $\delta z \to 0$.

Putting all this together gives:

$$\delta w = (g_x(x, y, z)+\varepsilon_1+\eta_1)\delta x + (g_y(x, y, z)+\varepsilon_2+\eta_2)\delta y + (g_z(x, y, z)+\varepsilon_3)\delta z.$$

Since all the partial derivatives are now evaluated at (x, y, z) you can revert to writing them as $\frac{\partial w}{\partial x}, \frac{\partial w}{\partial y}$ and $\frac{\partial w}{\partial z}$. Also you can tidy up all the terms which tend to zero: for if $\delta s = \sqrt{(\delta x)^2+(\delta y)^2+(\delta z)^2}$ each of $\delta x, \delta y, \delta z$ must tend to zero as $\delta s \to 0$. Therefore the error terms $(\varepsilon_1+\eta_1)\delta x + (\varepsilon_2+\eta_2)\delta y + \varepsilon_3\delta z$ can be replaced by $\varepsilon\delta s$, where $\varepsilon \to 0$ as $\delta s \to 0$ (see the activity below). This gives the final version:

$$\delta w = \frac{\partial w}{\partial x}\delta x + \frac{\partial w}{\partial y}\delta y + \frac{\partial w}{\partial z}\delta z + \varepsilon\delta s, \text{ where } \varepsilon \to 0 \text{ as } \delta s \to 0.$$

ACTIVITY 2.5 Justify the steps in the following argument.

Let $\varepsilon = \dfrac{(\varepsilon_1+\eta_1)\delta x+(\varepsilon_2+\eta_2)\delta y+\varepsilon_3\delta z}{\delta s}$.

Then $$|\varepsilon| \leqslant |\varepsilon_1+\eta_1|\left|\frac{\delta x}{\delta s}\right| + |\varepsilon_2+\eta_2|\left|\frac{\delta y}{\delta s}\right| + |\varepsilon_3|\left|\frac{\delta z}{\delta s}\right|$$
$$< |\varepsilon_1+\eta_1| + |\varepsilon_2+\eta_2| + |\varepsilon_3|$$

so $\varepsilon \to 0$ as $\delta s \to 0$.

Notes

1 The conditions used here (all partial derivatives exist near P and all but one of these are continuous at P) are sufficient to ensure differentiability at P (see page 57).

2 If dx, dy and dz are independent differentials then the *total differential* of w is defined to be:

$$dw = \frac{\partial w}{\partial x}dx + \frac{\partial w}{\partial y}dy + \frac{\partial w}{\partial z}dz$$

and it has been proved that if the function is differentiable and $dx = \delta x$, $dy = \delta y$, $dz = \delta z$ then $\delta w \approx dw$ when δs is small.

EXAMPLE 2.8

Check this last statement numerically in the case where $w = \frac{xy^2}{\sqrt{z}}$, $x = 10$, $y = 3$, $z = 36$, $\delta x = 0.01$, $\delta y = 0.02$ and $\delta z = 0.03$.

SOLUTION

$$\delta w = \frac{10.01 \times 3.02^2}{\sqrt{36.03}} - \frac{10 \times 3^2}{\sqrt{36}} = 0.209531.$$

Evaluating the partial derivatives at (10, 3, 36):

$$\frac{\partial w}{\partial x} = \frac{y^2}{\sqrt{z}} = \frac{3}{2}, \quad \frac{\partial w}{\partial y} = \frac{2xy}{\sqrt{z}} = 10, \quad \frac{\partial w}{\partial z} = -\frac{1}{2}xy^2z^{-3/2} = -\frac{5}{24}.$$

Therefore $dw = \frac{3}{2} \times 0.01 + 10 \times 0.02 - \frac{5}{24} \times 0.03 = 0.208\,75$.

So dw gives δw with an error of less than 0.4%.

Approximations and errors

The approximation $\delta w \approx \frac{\partial w}{\partial x}\delta x + \frac{\partial w}{\partial y}\delta y + \frac{\partial w}{\partial z}\delta z$ or its equivalent for two or more than three variables can be used to estimate the effect of errors in a calculation. The availability of powerful calculating aids has reduced the practical need for this, but it still gives a useful way of analysing which errors have the greatest impact.

EXAMPLE 2.9

A surveyor calculates the area Δ of a triangular plot by measuring two sides a and b and the included angle C, and then using the formula $\Delta = \frac{1}{2}ab \sin C$.

Estimate the percentage error in Δ caused by errors of 1.5% in each of a and b, and an error of 1° in C when:

(i) $a = 50$ m, $b = 70$ m, $C = 75°$ **(ii)** $a = 50$ m, $b = 70$ m, $C = 15°$.

SOLUTION

$$\Delta = \tfrac{1}{2}ab \sin C \Rightarrow \delta\Delta \approx \frac{\partial \Delta}{\partial a}\delta a + \frac{\partial \Delta}{\partial b}\delta b + \frac{\partial \Delta}{\partial C}\delta C$$
$$= \tfrac{1}{2}b \sin C\, \delta a + \tfrac{1}{2}a \sin C\, \delta b + \tfrac{1}{2}ab \cos C\, \delta C.$$

Dividing by Δ ($=\frac{1}{2}ab\sin C$) to get the fractional error gives:

$$\frac{\delta\Delta}{\Delta} \approx \frac{\delta a}{a} + \frac{\delta b}{b} + \cot C\,\delta C.$$

The percentage error is $100 \times$ the fractional error, so this shows that the percentage error in Δ is $1.5 + 1.5 + \cot C\,\delta C \times 100$, since the errors in a and b are each 1.5%. (Notice that the actual values of a and b do not appear in this.) Since we have used $\cos C$ as the derivative of $\sin C$ the angle C is here measured in radians, and so $\delta C = \frac{\pi}{180} \approx 0.0175$. Therefore the percentage error in Δ is approximately $3 + 1.75 \cot C$. For the given values this gives:

(i) $3 + 1.75 \cot 75° \approx 3.47$ **(ii)** $3 + 1.75 \cot 15° \approx 9.53$.

Since $\cot C$ is large when C is small this shows that the surveyor needs to be particularly careful to measure C accurately when the corner of the plot being used is very sharp – it would be better to use another corner!

ACTIVITY 2.6

Estimate the actual errors in the calculated value of Δ for the values given in parts **(i)** and **(ii)** in Example 2.9.

EXERCISE 2G

1 Given that $w = kx^p y^q z^r$, where k, p, q, r are positive constants, prove that an error of $\pm 1\%$ in each of x, y, z gives a maximum error of approximately $(p + q + r)\%$ in w. What is the corresponding result if q and r are negative?

2 The temperature T at a point (x, y, z) in a rectangular cartesian co-ordinate system is given by $T = 10(9x^2 + 10y^2 + 6z^2)^{1/2}$.

Find the temperature at the point (2.00, 1.00, 3.00) and use partial differentiation to find an approximation to the difference in temperature δT between this point and the nearby point (2.03, 0.94, 3.15).

[MEI]

3 A cuboid has volume V and surface area S. Show:

(i) by using partial differentiation

(ii) by a geometrical argument

that if the length of each side increases by the small amount ε then $\delta V \approx \frac{1}{2}S\varepsilon$.

What is the corresponding result for a sphere?

4 In a standard physics experiment the value of g (the acceleration due to gravity) is found by measuring the time of swing T of a compound pendulum and using the formula $g = \frac{4\pi^2}{T^2}$. In this formula the length ℓ is given by $\ell = s + \frac{k^2}{s}$, where s and k are lengths measured from the pendulum.

If the measurements of s and k are accurate to within 1% find the approximate maximum percentage error in ℓ.

If the measurement of T is accurate to within 0.5% find the approximate maximum percentage error in the computed value of g.

5 The following two methods are suggested for calculating the volume V of a right circular cone.

(A) Measure the base radius r and the semi-vertical angle α.
(B) Measure the base radius r and the generator length ℓ.

(i) Find the appropriate formula for V for each method.

(ii) Find an approximate formula for $\dfrac{\delta V}{V}$ in terms of the measured quantities and their errors for each method.

(iii) Explain why method **(A)** is particularly suitable when $\alpha \approx \dfrac{\pi}{4}$ and method **(B)** is particularly suitable when $\alpha \approx \arcsin\sqrt{\tfrac{2}{3}}$.

6 The length of the side a of an obtuse-angled triangle is to be calculated using the cosine rule: $a^2 = b^2 + c^2 - 2bc\cos A$, where A is the obtuse angle.

(i) Find $\dfrac{\partial(a^2)}{\partial b}$, $\dfrac{\partial(a^2)}{\partial c}$ and $\dfrac{\partial(a^2)}{\partial A}$.

(ii) Write down an equation involving the increment in a^2 relating to increments δb in b, δc in c and δA in A.

(iii) Calculate an approximation for the maximum error in a, using a method involving partial differentiation, when the measurements are given as $b = 25 \pm 1.0$ cm, $c = 30 \pm 1.5$ cm, $A = 120 \pm 2°$.

(iv) The area Δ of the triangle is calculated using the formula $\Delta = \tfrac{1}{2}bc\sin A$. Use methods of partial differentiation to estimate the maximum percentage error in Δ with the measurements given in part **(iii)**.

[MEI]

7 The side b of a triangle is found from measurements of the side a and the angles B and C. There may be an error not exceeding h (in either direction) in the measurements of a, and an error not exceeding α in either or both of B and C, where h and α are small. Show that, if $B + C < \dfrac{\pi}{2}$, the greatest error in b is approximately $b\left(\dfrac{h}{a} + \alpha\cot B\right)$. Find the greatest error when $B + C > \dfrac{\pi}{2}$, and explain the difference in the two cases.

The vector grad g

EXAMPLE 2.10

The temperature T at the point (x, y, z) inside a solid is given by

$$T = x^2 + 3xy + 2z^2.$$

(i) Find the average temperature gradient from A(2, 1, 3) to B(4, 2, 1).

(ii) Find the actual temperature gradient at A in the direction towards B.

SOLUTION

(i) Since $T = 28$ at (2, 1, 3) and $T = 42$ at (4, 2, 1), the change in T from A to B is 14. The distance $\text{AB} = \sqrt{2^2 + 1^2 + (-2)^2} = 3$, and so the average temperature gradient is $\frac{14}{3}$.

(ii) Since $\mathbf{AB} = \begin{pmatrix} 2 \\ 1 \\ -2 \end{pmatrix}$ and $|\mathbf{AB}| = 3$, the vector of length δs in the direction from A to B is $\delta r = \begin{pmatrix} 2\delta s/3 \\ \delta s/3 \\ -2\delta s/3 \end{pmatrix}$.

At A the partial derivatives of T are $\dfrac{\partial T}{\partial x} = 2x + 3y = 7$, $\dfrac{\partial T}{\partial y} = 3x = 6$, $\dfrac{\partial T}{\partial z} = 4z = 12$.

Putting all this into $\delta T = \dfrac{\partial T}{\partial x}\delta x + \dfrac{\partial T}{\partial y}\delta y + \dfrac{\partial T}{\partial z}\delta z + \varepsilon\delta s$ gives:

$$\delta T = 7 \times \frac{2\delta s}{3} + 6 \times \frac{\delta s}{3} + 12 \times \left(-\frac{2\delta s}{3}\right) + \varepsilon\delta s = \left(-\frac{4}{3} + \varepsilon\right)\delta s$$

where $\varepsilon \to 0$ as $\delta s \to 0$.

The limit of $\dfrac{\delta T}{\delta s}$ as $\delta s \to 0$ is $-\frac{4}{3}$, which is the required temperature gradient.

The argument in part **(ii)** of this solution is typical of the general case.

Let $w = g(x, y, z)$ and let $\delta \mathbf{r} = \begin{pmatrix} \delta x \\ \delta y \\ \delta z \end{pmatrix}$ be a vector of length $|\delta \mathbf{r}| = \delta s$ in a given fixed direction. Then:

$$\delta w = \frac{\partial w}{\partial x}\delta x + \frac{\partial w}{\partial y}\delta y + \frac{\partial w}{\partial z}\delta z + \varepsilon \delta s$$

$$\Rightarrow \frac{\delta w}{\delta s} = \frac{\partial w}{\partial x}\frac{\delta x}{\delta s} + \frac{\partial w}{\partial y}\frac{\delta y}{\delta s} + \frac{\partial w}{\partial z}\frac{\delta z}{\delta s} + \varepsilon \qquad ①$$

where $\varepsilon \to 0$ as $\delta s \to 0$.

But $\frac{\delta x}{\delta s}$, $\frac{\delta y}{\delta s}$ and $\frac{\delta z}{\delta s}$ are the components of the *unit* vector in the given direction, $\hat{\mathbf{u}}$ say.

If the vector **grad** $w = \begin{pmatrix} \partial w / \partial x \\ \partial w / \partial y \\ \partial w / \partial z \end{pmatrix}$ is introduced you can write ① as:

$$\frac{\delta w}{\delta s} = \hat{\mathbf{u}} \,.\, \mathbf{grad}\ w + \varepsilon.$$

Taking the limit as $\delta s \to 0$ gives the *directional derivative* in the direction of $\hat{\mathbf{u}}$:

$$\frac{dw}{ds} = \hat{\mathbf{u}} \,.\, \mathbf{grad}\ w.$$

This corresponds directly with the form of the directional derivative for a function of two variables given on page 62. The only difference is a small change of notation: there **grad** f was used (rather than **grad** z), and here **grad** w is used (rather than **grad** g). To emphasise the common form of the result whatever the number of independent variables, and because it will be more convenient in the next section, from now on we shall refer to the directional derivative in the form $\hat{\mathbf{u}} \,.\, \mathbf{grad}\ g$, where $\mathbf{grad}\ g = \begin{pmatrix} \partial g / \partial x \\ \partial g / \partial y \\ \partial g / \partial z \end{pmatrix}$.

As before, **grad** g may also be written as ∇g.

The greatest possible value of the directional derivative is $|\mathbf{grad}\ g|$; this occurs when $\hat{\mathbf{u}}$ is in the direction of **grad** g. Therefore you can interpret **grad** g as the vector of which the magnitude and direction give the greatest rate of change of w and the direction in which this occurs.

EXAMPLE 2.11

The density w inside a gas cloud is given by $w = \dfrac{88}{\sqrt{x^2 + y^2 + 2z^2}}$. The point A has co-ordinates (8, 5, 4). Find, at A:

(i) the density

(ii) the greatest rate of change of density with distance, and the direction in which this occurs

(iii) the rate of change of density with distance in the direction from A to the origin O.

SOLUTION

(i) For brevity, let $R = \sqrt{x^2 + y^2 + 2z^2}$; then $w = \dfrac{88}{R}$.

At A, $R = \sqrt{64 + 25 + 32} = 11$, and so $w = 8$.

(ii) $\dfrac{\partial w}{\partial x} = -88x(x^2 + y^2 + 2z^2)^{-3/2} = \dfrac{88x}{R^3}$.

Similarly $\dfrac{\partial w}{\partial y} = -\dfrac{88y}{R^3}$ and $\dfrac{\partial w}{\partial z} = -\dfrac{176z}{R^3}$.

Therefore, at A: $\dfrac{\partial w}{\partial x} = -\dfrac{64}{121}$, $\dfrac{\partial w}{\partial y} = -\dfrac{40}{121}$, $\dfrac{\partial w}{\partial z} = -\dfrac{64}{121}$.

So **grad** $w = \begin{pmatrix} -\frac{64}{121} \\ -\frac{40}{121} \\ -\frac{64}{121} \end{pmatrix}$ and $|\mathbf{grad}\ w| = \dfrac{\sqrt{64^2 + 40^2 + 64^2}}{121} = \dfrac{\sqrt{9792}}{121} \approx 0.818.$

Therefore the greatest rate of change of w is 0.818, occurring in the direction of $\begin{pmatrix} -\frac{64}{121} \\ -\frac{40}{121} \\ -\frac{64}{121} \end{pmatrix}$ or, more simply, $\begin{pmatrix} -8 \\ -5 \\ -8 \end{pmatrix}$.

(iii) $\overrightarrow{AO} = \begin{pmatrix} -8 \\ -5 \\ -4 \end{pmatrix}$ and $|AO| = \sqrt{64 + 25 + 16} = \sqrt{105}$, so the unit vector in the direction from A to O is $\hat{\mathbf{u}} = \dfrac{1}{\sqrt{105}}\begin{pmatrix} -8 \\ -5 \\ -4 \end{pmatrix}$.

The rate of change of density in this direction is:

$$\hat{\mathbf{u}} \,.\, \mathbf{grad}\ w = \frac{1}{\sqrt{105}} \times \frac{1}{121}(8 \times 64 + 5 \times 40 + 4 \times 64) = \frac{968}{121\sqrt{105}} \approx 0.781.$$

EXERCISE 2H

1 Find the directional derivative of $g(x, y, z)$ at the point P in the direction of $\mathbf{u}$.

(i) $g(x, y, z) = x^2 - 9y^2 + 4z^2$, $P = (2, 1, 0)$, $\mathbf{u} = \mathbf{i} + \mathbf{j} + \mathbf{k}$

(ii) $g(x, y, z) = \dfrac{xy}{z}$, $P = (3, 1, -1)$, $\mathbf{u} = \mathbf{i} - 2\mathbf{j} + 2\mathbf{k}$

(iii) $g(x, y, z) = e^x \cos y$, $P = (\ln 3, \pi, 7)$, $\mathbf{u} = 3\mathbf{i} + 4\mathbf{k}$

2 Find a function $g(x, y, z)$ for which:

(i) $\mathbf{grad}\ g = (y + z)\mathbf{i} + (z + x)\mathbf{j} + (x + y)\mathbf{k}$

(ii) $\mathbf{grad}\ g = \dfrac{x\mathbf{i} + y\mathbf{j} + z\mathbf{k}}{x^2 + y^2 + z^2}$.

3 Let $\mathbf{r} = x\mathbf{i} + y\mathbf{j} + z\mathbf{k}$. Prove that:

(i) $w = |\mathbf{r}| \quad \Rightarrow \quad \textbf{grad}\ w = \hat{\mathbf{r}}$

(ii) $w = |\mathbf{r}|^n \quad \Rightarrow \quad \textbf{grad}\ w = n|\mathbf{r}|^{n-1}\hat{\mathbf{r}}$.

4 In what directions at a point P does the directional derivative equal $\frac{1}{2}|\textbf{grad}\ \mathrm{g}|$?

5 The concentration S of sugar in a liquid is given by $S = x^3 + y^2(4 + z^2)$. A sweet-toothed bug is placed in the liquid at (2, 3, 1) and swims in the direction in which the concentration increases fastest.

(i) Find the unit vector in this direction.

(ii) If x, y, z are measured in centimetres and the bug swims in this direction at 0.5 cm s^{-1}, at what rate does the concentration increase?

6 A space probe is moving along a spiral so that at time t its position vector $\mathbf{r}$ is given by $\mathbf{r} = \cos t\mathbf{i} + \sin t\mathbf{j} + t\mathbf{k}$. It passes a gaseous star centred at (–6, 0, 0) for which the distribution of temperature T is given by $T = \dfrac{1000}{(x+6)^2 + y^2 + z^2}$.

(i) Find, in terms of t, the unit vector in the direction of motion of the probe.

(ii) Hence find the directional derivative of T in terms of t.

(iii) Show that there are three points along its path at which the temperature experienced by the probe has a stationary value.

(iv) Find, correct to three significant figures, the global maximum temperature experienced by the probe.

The surface g(x, y, z) = k

If $w = \mathrm{g}(x, y, z)$ and k is a constant then the set of points (x, y, z) for which $w = k$ forms a surface with implicit equation $\mathrm{g}(x, y, z) = k$. Such a surface is the three-dimensional equivalent of a contour or level curve $\mathrm{f}(x, y) = c$ of a function of two variables. It is sometimes called a *contour surface* or *level surface* (though in this case 'level' does not mean 'horizontal' or even 'plane'). For example, if $w = x^2 + y^2 + z^2$ then each level surface is a sphere centred at the origin, with equation $x^2 + y^2 + z^2 = k$ (for $k \geqslant 0$).

Suppose that A(a, b, c) is a point of the surface $w = k$, and that $\hat{\mathbf{u}}$ is any unit vector tangential to this surface at A. Since w remains constant in the surface, the directional derivative in the direction of $\hat{\mathbf{u}}$ is zero. Therefore $\hat{\mathbf{u}} \cdot \textbf{grad}\ \mathrm{g} = 0$, and so **grad** g is perpendicular to $\hat{\mathbf{u}}$. Thus **grad** g is perpendicular to all vectors in the tangent plane at A; in other words, **grad** g is a normal vector for the tangent plane at A. This makes it very easy to find the equations of the normal line and tangent plane at A:

- the normal line is the line $\mathbf{r} = \mathbf{a} + \lambda\ \textbf{grad}\ \mathrm{g}$
- the tangent plane is the plane $(\mathbf{r} - \mathbf{a}) \cdot \textbf{grad}\ \mathrm{g} = 0$.

EXAMPLE 2.12

Show that A(4, 2, 3) is on the surface $2x^2 - 3yz + 4z^2 = 50$, and find the equations of the normal line and the tangent plane at A.

SOLUTION

Let $g(x, y, z) = 2x^2 - 3yz + 4z^2$. Then:

$$\begin{aligned} g(4, 2, 3) &= 2 \times 4^2 - 3 \times 2 \times 3 + 4 \times 3^2 \\ &= 32 - 18 + 36 \\ &= 50 \end{aligned}$$

so A is on the surface.

At A, $\dfrac{\partial g}{\partial x} = 4x = 16$, $\dfrac{\partial g}{\partial y} = -3z = -9$, $\dfrac{\partial g}{\partial z} = -3y + 8z = 18$ so

$$\mathbf{grad}\ g = \begin{pmatrix} 16 \\ -9 \\ 18 \end{pmatrix}.$$

The normal line at A is $\begin{pmatrix} x \\ y \\ z \end{pmatrix} = \begin{pmatrix} 4 \\ 2 \\ 3 \end{pmatrix} + \lambda \begin{pmatrix} 16 \\ -9 \\ 18 \end{pmatrix}$.

The tangent plane at A is $\begin{pmatrix} x-4 \\ y-2 \\ z-3 \end{pmatrix} . \begin{pmatrix} 16 \\ -9 \\ 18 \end{pmatrix} = 0$

$$\begin{aligned} &\Leftrightarrow 16(x - 4) - 9(y - 2) + 18(z - 3) = 0 \\ &\Leftrightarrow \qquad 16x - 9y + 18z = 100. \end{aligned}$$

The equation of the tangent plane can be expressed in another way, using the differentials dx, dy, dz for the steps $x - a$, $y - b$, $z - c$ needed to move from A to the general point (x, y, z) on the tangent plane at A, so that $\mathbf{dr} = \begin{pmatrix} dx \\ dy \\ dz \end{pmatrix}$.

Then the tangent plane is $\mathbf{dr} . \mathbf{grad}\ g = 0$.

The similar version given on page 59 is a special case of this, since the surface $z = f(x, y)$ can be thought of as the level surface $g(x, y, z) = 0$, where $g(x, y, z) = f(x, y) - z$. So

$$\mathbf{grad}\ g = \begin{pmatrix} \partial f / \partial x \\ \partial f / \partial y \\ -1 \end{pmatrix}.$$

Historical note

The ideas of level surface and gradient vector have many applications in physics, in particular in connection with the idea of *potential*, a scalar quantity which is a function of position. The theory of gravitational potential started with Newton and was developed in the 18th century by Euler, Clairaut, Lagrange, Laplace and Monge (who emphasised the geometrical aspects). George Green (1793–1841, a self-educated son of a miller) used the notion of the potential function in the mathematical treatment of electricity and magnetism, and the experiments of Michael Faraday (1791–1867, a self-educated son of a blacksmith) led to the concept of *lines of force* (normal to *equipotential surfaces*).

James Clerk Maxwell (1831–71) expressed these ideas in mathematical form in 1864, and from his equations predicted the existence of electromagnetic waves. These were first actually produced in 1887 by Heinrich Hertz (1857–94), whose experiments led to the present vastly important technology of radio transmission.

EXERCISE 2I

1 Find the equation of the tangent plane to the ellipsoid $3x^2 + 5y^2 + z^2 = 39$ at the point $(1, -2, 4)$.

2 Find the equations of the normal line and tangent plane to the surface $x^2 - \dfrac{y}{z^2} = 10$ at:

(i) $(3, -1, 1)$ **(ii)** $(-4, 24, -2)$.

3 Find the co-ordinates of the point(s) on the surface $3x^2 - 2y^2 - z^2 = 4$ at which the tangent plane is parallel to $18x - 14y - 3z = 0$.

4 Prove that the equation of the tangent plane at the point (x_1, y_1, z_1) on the ellipsoid $\dfrac{x^2}{a^2} + \dfrac{y^2}{b^2} + \dfrac{z^2}{c^2} = 1$ can be written in the form $\dfrac{xx_1}{a^2} + \dfrac{yy_1}{b^2} + \dfrac{zz_1}{c^2} = 1$.

5 (i) Show that $x^2 + y^2 + z^2 + 2ax + 2by + 2cz + d = 0$ is the cartesian equation of a sphere provided that $d < a^2 + b^2 + c^2$, and say what the equation represents when:

(a) $d = a^2 + b^2 + c^2$ **(b)** $d > a^2 + b^2 + c^2$.

(ii) In the case of a sphere, prove that the normal line at every point of the sphere passes through the centre.

6 Prove that the sum of the squares of the intercepts on the x, y and z axes of every tangent plane to the surface $x^{2/3} + y^{2/3} + z^{2/3} = a^{2/3}$ is a constant.

7 Find the acute angle at which the surface $xy^2 + xz^2 = 10$ cuts the surface $z^3 - x - x^2y = 2$ at the point $(2, 1, 2)$. Find also the direction of the curve of intersection at this point.

8 **(i)** Given that $g(x, y, z) = 3x^2 - 2xy + 2y^2 + z^2 + 4z - 31$, find $\frac{\partial g}{\partial x}$, $\frac{\partial g}{\partial y}$ and $\frac{\partial g}{\partial z}$.

A surface S has equation $3x^2 - 2xy + 2y^2 + z^2 + 4z - 31 = 0$.

(ii) Find the equation of the normal line to S at the point P(2, 1, 3).

(iii) This normal line meets the surface again at the point Q. Find the co-ordinates of Q.

(iv) Find the two values of k for which $x + z = k$ is a tangent plane to the surface S.

[MEI]

9 **The hyperboloid of one sheet**

(i) Given that $g(x, y, z) = \frac{x^2}{a^2} + \frac{y^2}{b^2} - \frac{z^2}{c^2}$, show that all the horizontal contours of the surface $g(x, y, z) = 1$ are ellipses, and that all the vertical sections parallel to the planes $x = 0$ or $y = 0$ are hyperbolas. Sketch the surface, which is called a *hyperboloid of one sheet*.

(ii) Show that the equation $g(x, y, z) = 1$ can be written as

$\left(\frac{y}{b} - \frac{z}{c}\right)\left(\frac{y}{b} + \frac{z}{c}\right) = \left(1 - \frac{x}{a}\right)\left(1 + \frac{x}{a}\right)$. By putting $\dfrac{\frac{y}{b} - \frac{z}{c}}{1 - \frac{x}{a}} = u$ show that the

hyperboloid contains the line of intersection of the two planes

$$\frac{y}{b} - \frac{z}{c} = u\left(1 - \frac{x}{a}\right) \text{ and } u\left(\frac{y}{b} + \frac{z}{c}\right) = 1 + \frac{x}{a}.$$

(As u varies this gives a family of lines (called *generators*) which lie entirely in the surface, and so this is another example of a *ruled surface* (see Question 8 in Exercise 2B).)

(iii) Show similarly that the surface contains a second family of generators, namely the lines of intersection of the pairs of planes

$$\frac{y}{b} + \frac{z}{c} = v\left(1 - \frac{x}{a}\right) \text{ and } v\left(\frac{y}{b} - \frac{z}{c}\right) = 1 + \frac{x}{a}.$$

(iv) Show that the generator in part **(ii)** has direction vector

$\mathbf{d} = \begin{pmatrix} 2u/bc \\ (1-u^2)/ca \\ (1+u^2)/ab \end{pmatrix}$ and find, in a similar form, a direction vector $\mathbf{e}$ for the

generator in part **(iii)**.

(v) Find $\mathbf{d} \times \mathbf{e}$, and show that this is parallel to $\begin{pmatrix} (uv-1)/a \\ (u+v)/b \\ (u-v)/c \end{pmatrix}$. Why is this vector

normal to the surface at the point where these generators cross?

☆ **(vi)** By comparing the normal vector in part **(v)** with **grad** g, obtain parametric equations $x = a\dfrac{uv-1}{uv+1}$, $y = b\dfrac{u+v}{uv+1}$, $z = c\dfrac{v-u}{uv+1}$ for this hyperboloid.

(*Hyperbolic cog wheels* make use of this to transmit rotation about one given axis into rotation about another given axis by having two hyperboloids of one sheet which mesh along their generators, as in the diagram.)

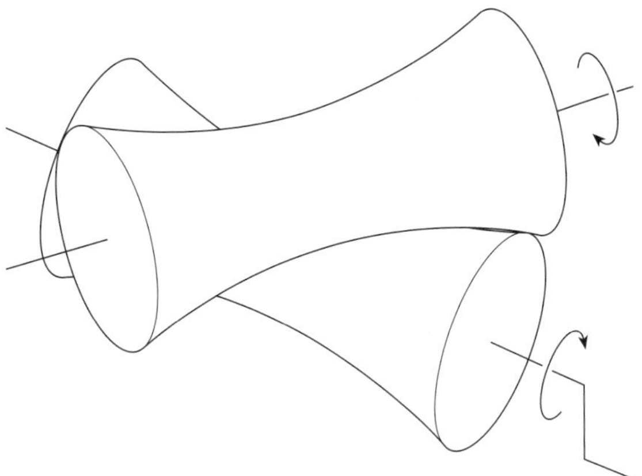

INVESTIGATION

e *The multivariable chain rule*

Figure 2.16 shows part of the surface $z = f(x, y)$. Suppose that, instead of being independent, the variables x and y are given in terms of a variable u by $x = p(u)$, $y = q(u)$. Then as u varies the point $P'(x, y, 0)$ moves along the curve $\mathscr{C}'$ in the $z = 0$ plane with parametric equations $x = p(u)$, $y = q(u)$, and the point $P(x, y, z)$ moves along the three-dimensional curve $\mathscr{C}$ in which the verticals through $\mathscr{C}'$ meet the surface. (Imagine a pastry cutter in the shape of $\mathscr{C}'$ cutting the surface in $\mathscr{C}$.) Thus z depends only on u, so you can write $z = F(u)$, where $F(u) = f(p(u), q(u))$.

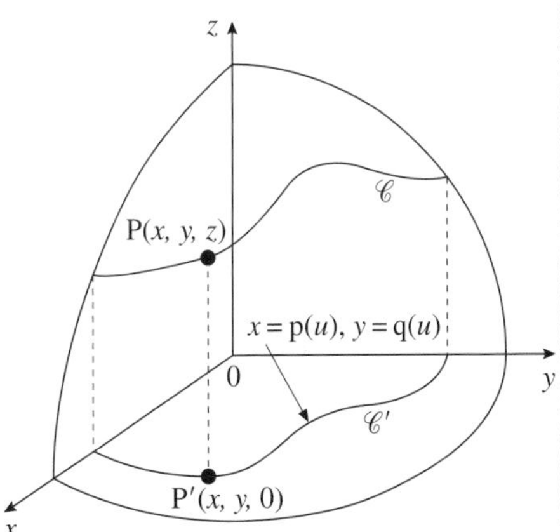

(i) Find $F(u)$ and $F'(u)$ when:

(a) $f(x, y) = x^2 - y^2$, $x = u^3 + 1$, $y = u^3 - 1$

(b) $f(x, y) = (x + y)e^y$, $x = \dfrac{1}{u}$, $y = \ln u$

(c) $f(x, y) = \arctan\left(\frac{x}{y}\right), x = 2u, y = 1 - u^2.$

(ii) It is not necessary to find $F(u)$ explicitly in order to find $F'(u)$. Suppose that changing u by δu causes changes δx and δy in x and y, which in turn cause z to change by δz. Starting with $\delta z = \frac{\partial z}{\partial x}\delta x + \frac{\partial z}{\partial y}\delta y + \varepsilon\delta s$ (as on page 70), prove that $\frac{dz}{du} = \frac{\partial z}{\partial x}\frac{dx}{du} + \frac{\partial z}{\partial y}\frac{dy}{du}$; this is the multivariable chain rule.

(iii) Use the chain rule to obtain $F'(u)$ again for the functions in part **(i)**.

(iv) The annual wheat production in a certain location, W units, depends on the mean annual temperature, T°C, and the mean annual rainfall, R cm. Agricultural experiments have shown that W decreases by 4.8 units for each 1 °C rise in temperature, and increases by 1.2 units for each 1 cm increase in rainfall. Climatologists judge that, due to global warming, T is increasing by 0.07 °C per year and R is decreasing by 0.16 cm per year. Estimate the change in W from this year to next. How is your calculation related to the multivariable chain rule?

(v) Suppose now that w depends on three variables, x, y, z, each of which depends on two variables, u and v. So $w = f(x, y, z) = F(u, v)$ where $x = p(u, v)$, $y = q(u, v)$, $z = r(u, v)$. Investigate the chain rules for $\frac{\partial w}{\partial u}$ and $\frac{\partial w}{\partial v}$, and show that they can be written in the form **grad** F = **M grad** f,

where $\mathbf{M} = \begin{pmatrix} \frac{\partial x}{\partial u} & \frac{\partial y}{\partial u} & \frac{\partial z}{\partial u} \\ \frac{\partial x}{\partial v} & \frac{\partial y}{\partial v} & \frac{\partial z}{\partial v} \end{pmatrix}$.

EXERCISE 2J

1 A surface has equation $z = x^2y - 2xy - y^2 - 3y + 8$.

(i) Find $\frac{\partial z}{\partial x}$ and $\frac{\partial z}{\partial y}$.

(ii) Find the co-ordinates of the three stationary points on the surface.

(iii) Find the equation of the tangent plane to the surface at the point (0, 1, 4).

(iv) The normal line at the point (2, 0, 8) meets the surface again at the point P. Find the co-ordinates of P.

[MEI]

2 **(i)** Given that $g(x, y, z) = 3x^2 + y^2 + 2z^2 - xy + 2xz - 9$, find $\frac{\partial g}{\partial x}$, $\frac{\partial g}{\partial y}$ and $\frac{\partial g}{\partial z}$.

A surface has equation $3x^2 + y^2 - 2z^2 - xy + 2xz - 9 = 0$.

(ii) Find the equation of the normal line to the surface at the point P(1, −1, −2).

(iii) This normal line meets the surface again at the point Q. Find the co-ordinates of Q, and show that the normal line at P is also the normal line at Q.

(iv) Find the co-ordinates of the two points on the surface where the tangent plane is parallel to the plane $x = 0$.

[MEI]

3 A surface S has equation $z = 2x^2 - 4xy^2 + y - 1$.

(i) Find $\dfrac{\partial z}{\partial x}$ and $\dfrac{\partial z}{\partial y}$.

(ii) Find the co-ordinates of the stationary point on the surface.

A$(0, 0, -1)$ and B$(1, \frac{1}{2}, \frac{1}{2})$ are two points on the surface S.

(iii) Find, in the form $ax + by + cz + d = 0$, the equation of the tangent plane at A and the equation of the tangent plane at B.

(iv) Show that the line AB is a tangent to the surface at the point B.

(v) Find the acute angle between the line AB and the tangent plane at A.

[MEI]

4 A surface has equation $z = 4x^2y - xy^2 - 8x^2 + 4x + 4$.

(i) Find $\dfrac{\partial z}{\partial x}$ and $\dfrac{\partial z}{\partial y}$.

(ii) Find the co-ordinates of the four stationary points on the surface.

(iii) Find the equation of the tangent plane to the surface at the point $(2, 3, 10)$.

(iv) Starting from $x = 2$, $y = 3$, $z = 10$, the values of x and y are both increased by the same small percentage, $h\%$. Show that z increases by approximately $(\frac{17}{5}h)\%$.

[MEI]

5 The temperature θ at the point (x, y, z) inside a combustion chamber is modelled by $\theta = 10xyz^2e^{x-2y}$.

(i) Find $\dfrac{\partial \theta}{\partial x}$, $\dfrac{\partial \theta}{\partial y}$ and $\dfrac{\partial \theta}{\partial z}$.

The point P$(4, 2, 1)$ lies on the surface $\theta = 80$.

(ii) Starting from P, the values of x, y and z are increased by small amounts δx, δy and δz respectively. Find an approximate expression for $\delta\theta$, the corresponding increase in temperature.

(iii) Find the equation of the normal line to the surface $\theta = 80$ at the point P, in the form $\mathbf{r} = \mathbf{a} + t\hat{\mathbf{n}}$, where $\hat{\mathbf{n}}$ is a unit vector.

(iv) The point Q lies on this normal line, at a small distance h from P. Show that the difference in temperature at the points P and Q is approximately $100\sqrt{5}h$.

(v) Show that there is no point on the surface $\theta = 80$ where the normal line is parallel to the z axis.

[MEI]

KEY POINTS

1 Contours $z = c$ and vertical sections $x = a$ or $y = b$ can be used to give information about the surface $z = \mathrm{f}(x, y)$.

2 The *partial derivative* $\frac{\partial z}{\partial x}\left(=\frac{\partial \mathrm{f}}{\partial x}=\mathrm{f}_x(x, y)\right)$ is found by differentiating with respect to x, keeping y constant; this gives the gradient of a vertical section parallel to the x axis. Similarly $\frac{\partial z}{\partial y}\left(=\frac{\partial \mathrm{f}}{\partial y}=\mathrm{f}_y(x, y)\right)$ gives the gradient of a vertical section parallel to the y axis.

3 If the surface $z = \mathrm{f}(x, y)$ has a tangent plane at the point (a, b, c) then its equation is $z - c = \frac{\partial \mathrm{f}}{\partial x}(x - a) + \frac{\partial \mathrm{f}}{\partial y}(y - b)$, where $\frac{\partial \mathrm{f}}{\partial x}$ and $\frac{\partial \mathrm{f}}{\partial y}$ are evaluated at the point (a, b, c).

4 The vector **grad** $\mathrm{f} = \begin{pmatrix} \partial \mathrm{f}/\partial x \\ \partial \mathrm{f}/\partial y \end{pmatrix}$ evaluated at the point A on the surface $z = \mathrm{f}(x, y)$ is normal to the contour through A.

5 The *directional derivative* $\hat{\mathbf{u}}\,.\,$**grad** f is the gradient of the surface in the direction of the unit vector $\hat{\mathbf{u}}$.

6 The stationary points on $z = \mathrm{f}(x, y)$ are found by solving **grad** f = **0**, i.e. solving $\frac{\partial z}{\partial x} = 0$ and $\frac{\partial z}{\partial y} = 0$ simultaneously. The nature of the stationary point (maximum, minimum or saddle point) can be found by comparing $\mathrm{f}(a + h, b + k)$ with $\mathrm{f}(a, b)$.

7 The approximation $\delta w \approx \frac{\partial w}{\partial x}\delta x + \frac{\partial w}{\partial y}\delta y + \frac{\partial w}{\partial z}\delta z$ or its equivalent for two or more than three variables can be used to estimate the effect of errors in a calculation.

8 The vector **grad** $\mathrm{g} = \begin{pmatrix} \partial \mathrm{g}/\partial x \\ \partial \mathrm{g}/\partial y \\ \partial \mathrm{g}/\partial z \end{pmatrix}$ gives the magnitude and direction of the greatest rate of change of $w = \mathrm{g}(x, y, z)$. The directional derivative in the direction of the unit vector $\hat{\mathbf{u}}$ is $\hat{\mathbf{u}}\,.\,$**grad** g.

9 For the point A with position vector **a** on the surface $\mathrm{g}(x, y, z) = k$ the normal line is $\mathbf{r} = \mathbf{a} + \lambda$ **grad** g and the tangent plane is $(\mathbf{r} - \mathbf{a})\,.\,$**grad** g = 0, where **grad** g is evaluated at point A.

3 Differential geometry

There is nothing in the world except empty, curved space. Matter, charge, electromagnetism and other fields are only manifestations of the curvature of space.

John Archibald Wheeler

Envelopes

ACTIVITY 3.1

(a) Stick a pin into a piece of paper. Place one edge of a ruler against the pin and draw a short, straight line, using the other edge of the ruler, as in figure 3.1**(a)**. Do this repeatedly, turning the ruler slightly around the pin each time. (A firmly held pen or pencil will do instead of a pin.)

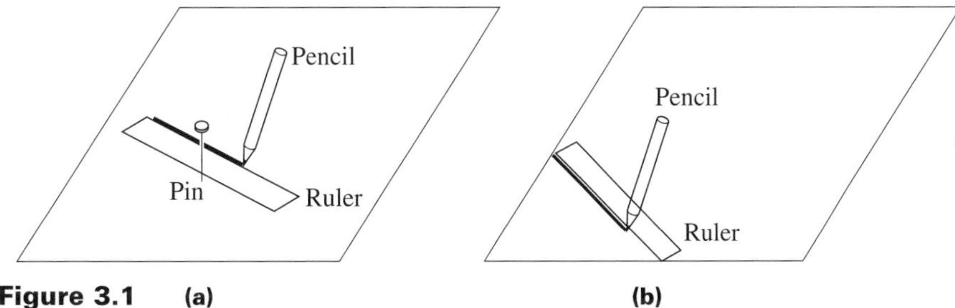

Figure 3.1 **(a)** **(b)**

(b) Place a short straight edge (e.g. a 15 cm ruler or the edge of a set square) so that its ends are on two perpendicular edges of a piece of paper. Rule a straight line, as in figure 3.1**(b)**. Do this repeatedly, moving the straight edge slightly each time but keeping its ends on these edges of the paper.

Although all you have done in Activity 3.1 is draw a set of straight lines, if these are close enough together your eye will also see the curve (not actually drawn) which all the lines touch. In **(a)** this curve is the circle with centre at the pin and radius the width of the ruler. In **(b)** it is not obvious what curve is produced: it will be identified later.

From plotting points on a graph or using a graphic calculator, you are used to thinking of a curve as a set of points, or as the path of a moving point. This activity shows that a curve can also be produced by a set of lines, or by a moving line. The set of lines is said to form a *family*, and the curve which every member of the family touches is called the *envelope* of the family. (To *envelop* means to 'wrap around'.)

The family may consist of curves rather than straight lines, and the envelope may be more than one curve, or only part of a curve.

EXAMPLE 3.1

Describe the envelope of the family of circles:

$$(x - 3\cos\theta)^2 + (y - 3\sin\theta)^2 = 1.$$

SOLUTION

The given circle has radius 1, and its centre $(3\cos\theta, 3\sin\theta)$ lies on the circle with centre O and radius 3 (see figure 3.2**(a)**). It is clear from figure 3.2**(b)** that the envelope consists of the two circles with centre O and radii 2 and 4.

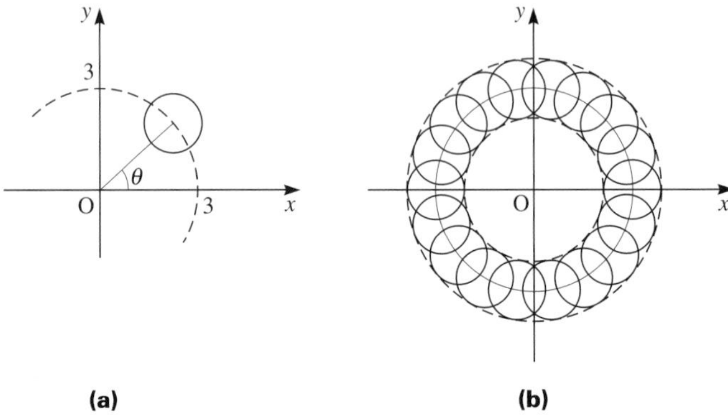

Figure 3.2

In this example the family of curves can be written in the form $f(x, y, \theta) = 0$, where $f(x, y, \theta) = (x - 3\cos\theta)^2 + (y - 3\sin\theta)^2 - 1$ is a function of the two co-ordinates x, y and the parameter θ which defines the particular member of the family.

The first step in finding the envelope of a family of curves is to write the equation of the curve similarly, in the form $f(x, y, p) = 0$, where p is a parameter. Thus in part **(a)** of Activity 3.1, if the width of the ruler is 2.5 cm and the angle ϕ is as in figure 3.3, then the equation of the line is:

$$x\cos\phi + y\sin\phi = 2.5$$

and so the family is $f(x, y, \phi) = x\cos\phi + y\sin\phi - 2.5 = 0$.

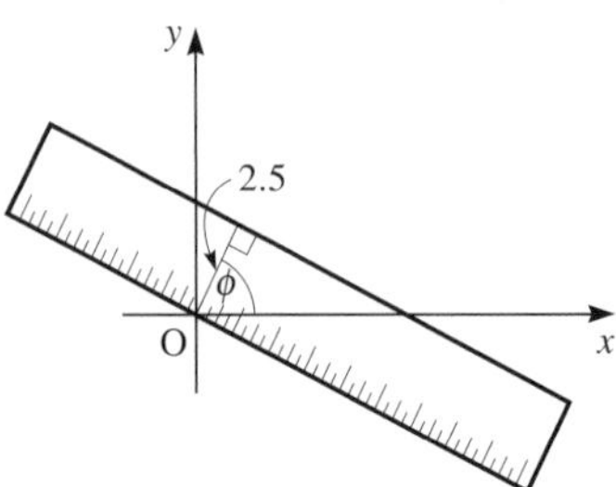

Figure 3.3

ACTIVITY 3.2 In part **(b)** of Activity 3.1, take the length of the straight edge to be 15 cm and the edges of the page as co-ordinate axes. Find the equation of the family:

(i) as $f_1(x, y, \theta) = 0$, where the parameter θ is the angle between the line and the x axis

(ii) as $f_2(x, y, L) = 0$, where the parameter L is the distance from the origin to the point where the line meets the x axis.

Figure 3.4 shows some members of the family $f(x, y, p) = 0$ and its envelope. The neighbouring members with equations $f(x, y, p) = 0$ and $f(x, y, p + \delta p) = 0$ meet at A, and touch the envelope at P and Q respectively.

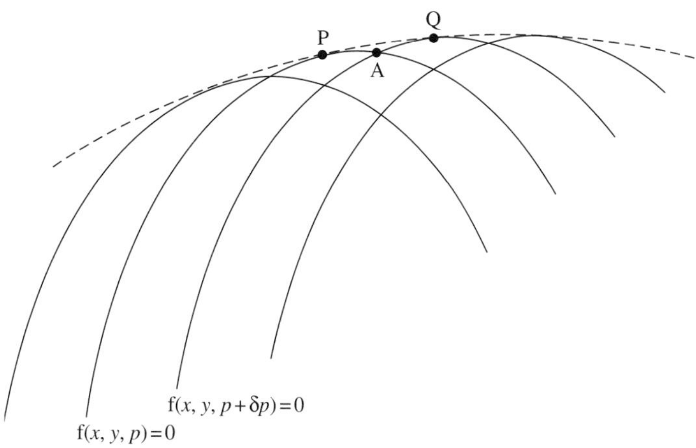

Figure 3.4

The diagram suggests that if these members of the family are close together then A is close to P, or more precisely that P is the limiting position of A as $\delta p \to 0$. This is true for families of 'reasonably smooth' curves (including all those in the following exercise), but it is beyond the scope of this book to define this exactly* and then prove it. So in what follows you will have to be content to *assume* this basic fact.

The co-ordinates of A satisfy both $f(x, y, p) = 0$ and $f(x, y, p + \delta p) = 0$, and so they also satisfy:

$$f(x, y, p + \delta p) - f(x, y, p) = 0$$

and therefore $\dfrac{f(x, y, p+\delta p) - f(x, y, p)}{\delta p} = 0.$

* A good discussion of all this is given in '*What is an envelope?*' by J. W. Bruce and P. J. Giblin in *The Mathematical Gazette*, October 1981, pages 186–192.

Therefore the co-ordinates of P (the limiting position of A as $\delta p \to 0$) satisfy:

$$\lim_{\delta p \to 0} \frac{f(x, y, p+\delta p) - f(x, y, p)}{\delta p} = 0$$

i.e. $$\frac{\partial}{\partial p} f(x, y, p) = 0.$$

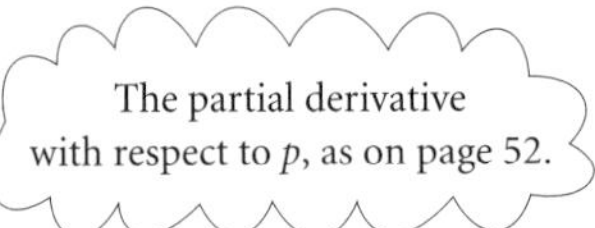

The partial derivative
with respect to *p*, as on page 52.

So the co-ordinates of P satisfy both $f(x, y, p) = 0$ and $\dfrac{\partial}{\partial p} f(x, y, p) = 0$.

The equation of the envelope is found by elimination from these two equations. Sometimes it is easy to eliminate p to give the cartesian equation of the envelope; in other cases it is better to give parametric equations expressing x and y in terms of p.

EXAMPLE 3.2

Find the envelope of a line of fixed length a moving with its end points on the co-ordinate axes (as in part **(b)** of Activity 3.1).

SOLUTION

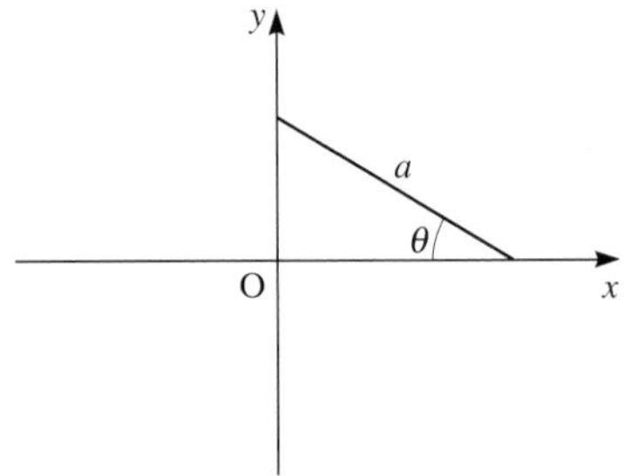

Figure 3.5

With the notation as in figure 3.5, the equation of the family is

$$f(x, y, \theta) = x \sec\theta + y \operatorname{cosec}\theta - a = 0.$$

$$\frac{\partial f}{\partial \theta} = x \sec\theta \tan\theta - y \operatorname{cosec}\theta \cot\theta = 0$$

$$\Rightarrow \quad x \sec\theta \tan\theta = y \operatorname{cosec}\theta \cot\theta$$

$$\Rightarrow \quad \frac{x \sin\theta}{\cos^2\theta} = \frac{y \cos\theta}{\sin^2\theta}$$

$$\Rightarrow \quad \frac{x}{\cos^3\theta} = \frac{y}{\sin^3\theta}$$

so that if $x = \lambda \cos^3\theta$ then $y = \lambda \sin^3\theta$.

Substituting these in $f(x, y, \theta) = 0$ gives:

$$\lambda \cos^2\theta + \lambda \sin^2\theta - a = 0$$

so that $\lambda = a$ and the parametric equations are $x = a \cos^3\theta$, $y = a \sin^3\theta$.

Since $\cos^2\theta + \sin^2\theta = 1$ you can eliminate θ to obtain the cartesian equation:

$$x^{2/3} + y^{2/3} = a^{2/3}.$$

The complete envelope (allowing the line to move in each quadrant) is a four-pointed star shape called an *astroid*, as in figure 3.6.

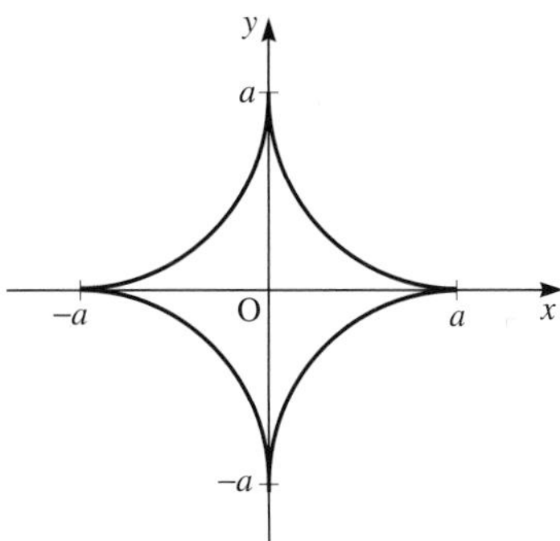

Figure 3.6

Figure 3.7 shows the plan of a door found (in pairs) in many buses. SRQ is the top of the door. The point Q moves in the groove OX at the top of the door frame and the point R is joined to the fixed point O by a horizontal link OR which is free to rotate at O and R. (There is a similar groove and link at the bottom of the door.) The lengths OR, SR and RQ are all equal. When the door is shut QRS lies along OX, with S at O.

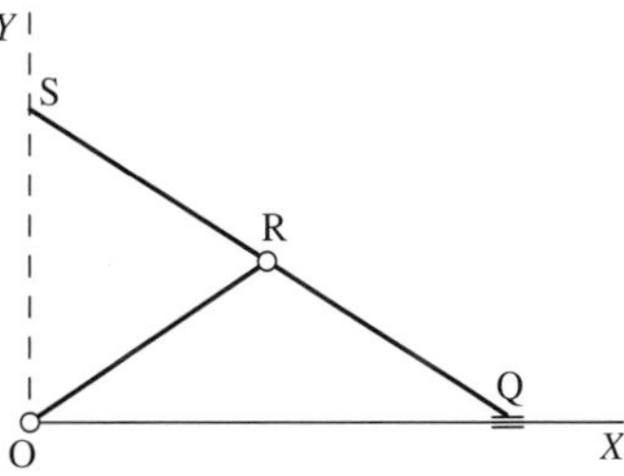

Figure 3.7

Explain why the locus of S as the door opens is the straight line OY perpendicular to OX. Deduce that the door sweeps out one quarter of an astroid as it opens.

EXAMPLE 3.3

Find the envelope of the family of circles which pass through the origin and have their centres on the rectangular hyperbola $xy = c^2$.

SOLUTION

Let the centre be at $\left(ct, \frac{c}{t}\right)$. Then the equation of the circle is:

$$(x - ct)^2 + \left(y - \frac{c}{t}\right)^2 = (ct)^2 + \left(\frac{c}{t}\right)^2$$

$$\Leftrightarrow \quad x^2 - 2xct + y^2 - \frac{2yc}{t} = 0$$

so that the equation of the family of circles is:

$$f(x, y, t) = 2xct^2 - (x^2 + y^2)t + 2yc = 0.$$

Multiplying throughout by t and rearranging.

$$\frac{\partial f}{\partial t} = 4xct - (x^2 + y^2) = 0$$

$\Rightarrow \quad t = \dfrac{x^2 + y^2}{4cx}$ unless $x = 0$, in which case $y = 0$ also.

Substituting for t in $f(x, y, t) = 0$ gives the equation of the envelope:

$$2cx\frac{(x^2 + y^2)^2}{16c^2x^2} - \frac{(x^2 + y^2)^2}{4cx} + 2cy = 0$$

$$\Leftrightarrow \quad (x^2 + y^2)^2 = 16c^2xy$$

(which includes the exceptional point (0, 0) noted above).

The hyperbola, circles and envelope are shown in figure 3.8.

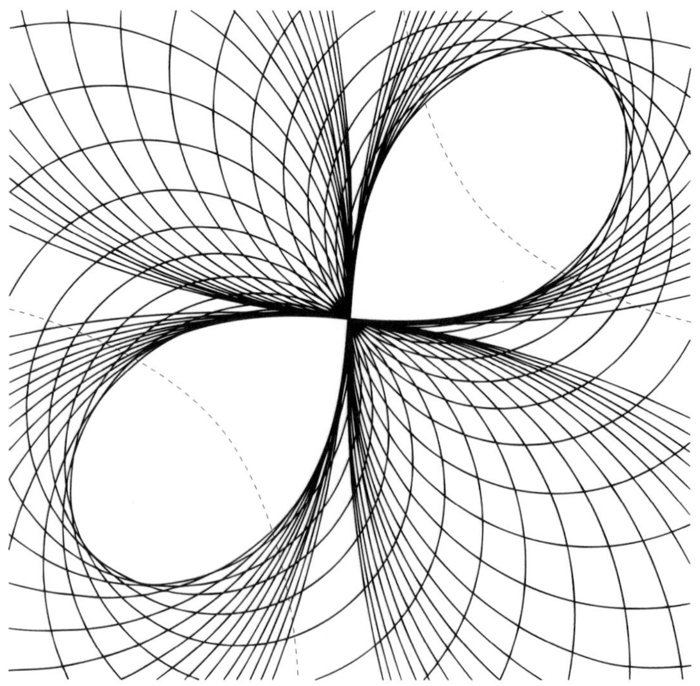

Figure 3.8

Note

The envelope can be identified by changing to polar co-ordinates.

$$(x^2 + y^2)^2 = 16c^2xy \Leftrightarrow r^4 = 16c^2r^2 \cos\theta \sin\theta$$
$$\Leftrightarrow r^2 = 8c^2 \sin 2\theta.$$

This envelope is Bernoulli's lemniscate (see *A2 Further Pure Mathematics* (*FP2*), page 29), but turned so that the line $\theta = \frac{\pi}{4}$ is an axis of symmetry. To see this note that $\sin 2\theta = \cos\left(2\theta - \frac{\pi}{2}\right) = \cos 2\left(\theta - \frac{\pi}{4}\right)$.

EXERCISE 3A

Throughout this exercise a is a constant.

1 Sketch the family of circles which have centres on $y = \frac{1}{2}x$ and touch the x axis. Show geometrically that the envelope is a pair of straight lines. Find these lines:

(i) by using $\tan(2\alpha)$, where $\tan\alpha = \frac{1}{2}$

(ii) by using the equation of the circle with centre $(2p, p)$ and radius p.

2 Find the envelope of the family of lines $y = px + \dfrac{a}{p}$.

3 Use the standard method to obtain the equations of the envelope in Example 3.1.

4 Find the envelope of the normals of the parabola $y^2 = 4ax$.

5 The diagram shows a common 'curve stitching' activity. The points which are joined are at equal steps along the lines XA and XB, and XA = XB.

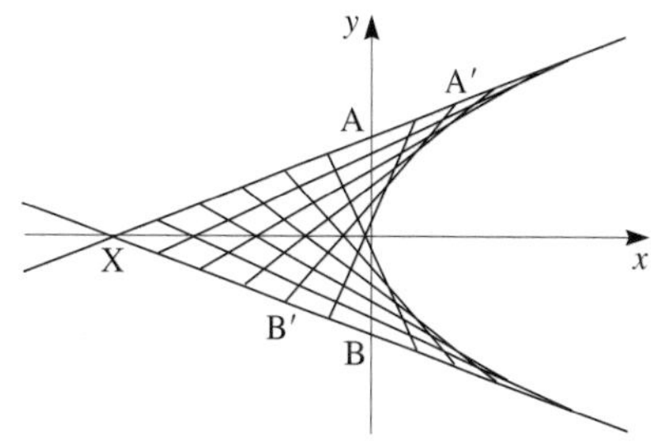

(i) Taking AB as the y axis and the perpendicular from X to AB as the x axis, show that the equations of XA and XB can be written as $y = hx + k$ and $y = -hx - k$, where h and k are constants.

(ii) Show that the co-ordinates of corresponding points which are joined, such as A′, B′, can be taken as $(p, hp + k)$, $(-p, hp - k)$, where p is a parameter. Find the equation of the line joining these points.

(iii) Deduce that the envelope is a parabola. What happens if the steps on each line continue on AX produced and BX produced?

6 **(i)** A family of curves is defined by $Ap^2 + Bp + C = 0$, where A, B and C are functions of x and y (so $A = A(x, y)$, etc.). Prove that the envelope is $B^2 = 4AC$.

(ii) Find the envelope of the family $A\cos\theta + B\sin\theta = C$, where A, B and C are functions of x and y.

7 A particle is thrown from the origin O in the plane of horizontal (x) and vertical (y) axes with initial speed u so that its initial direction of motion makes an angle θ with Ox. After time t its position (x, y) is given by: $x = ut\cos\theta$, $y = ut\sin\theta - \frac{1}{2}gt^2$. [See page 126 of *Mechanics 1*.]

(i) Show that its trajectory (flight path) is the parabola

$y = x\tan\theta - \dfrac{gx^2}{2u^2}\sec^2\theta$ where g is the acceleration due to gravity, and

that this can be written as $y = xp - \dfrac{gx^2}{2u^2}(1 + p^2)$ where $p = \tan\theta$.

(ii) Show that the envelope of the trajectories obtained as θ varies (with u and g fixed) is also a parabola. Find the co-ordinates of the focus and vertex of this envelope.

8 Find the envelope of the family of circles which have as their diameters the chords of the circle $x^2 + y^2 = 1$ parallel to the y axis.

9 Show that the envelope of the family of circles which pass through the origin and have centres on the circle $x^2 + y^2 - 2x = 0$ is the cardioid with polar equation $r = 2(1 + \cos\theta)$.

10 Show that the envelope of the family of ellipses $\dfrac{x^2}{u^2} + \dfrac{y^2}{v^2} = 1$, where $u^2 + v^2 = a^2$, is a square.

11 **The nephroid**

(i) Draw a circle (called the *base circle*) and one of its diameters. Then draw the family of circles which have centres on the base circle and touch this diameter. The curved envelope you obtain is called a *nephroid* (meaning 'kidney-shaped'.) What else is part of the envelope?

(ii) Take the base circle with centre at the origin of co-ordinates, O, and radius $2a$, and take the x axis as the diameter. Find the equation of the circle with centre R$(2a\cos\theta, 2a\sin\theta)$ touching the x axis. Hence find the parametric equations of this nephroid.

(iii) Show that these parametric equations can be written as:

$$x = 3a\cos\theta - a\cos 3\theta$$
$$y = 3a\sin\theta - a\sin 3\theta.$$

(iv) Now consider the circle with centre O and radius $4a$ as one cross-section of a mirror which is part of a circular cylinder (with its axis perpendicular to the plane of the diagram).

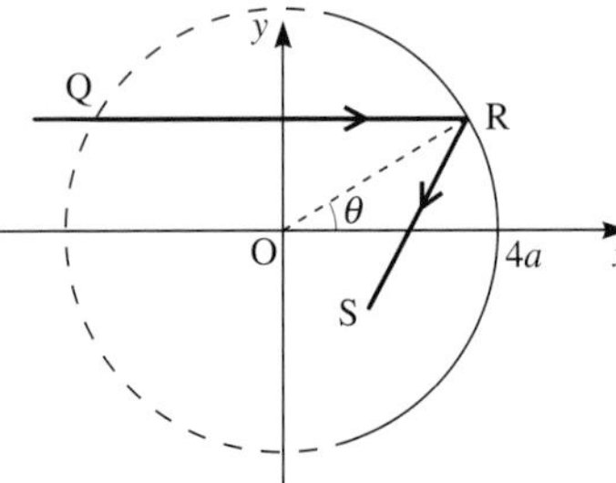

QR is a ray of light parallel to the x axis which is reflected along RS. Show that the envelope of RS for parallel rays QR is the same nephroid. Deduce the focal length of the mirror for small θ.

(An envelope of reflected rays is called a *caustic curve*. This particular caustic can be seen sometimes on the surface of a mug of tea held in sunlight.)

Arc length

One practical way to find the length of a curve between two of its points (for example to find the distance along the road between two towns, from a map) is to mark several intermediate points along the arc, join them successively with straight lines to form a polygonal line, and measure the total length of this open polygon to give an approximation to the length of the arc. If you start with a polygon P_1 and construct a new polygon P_2 by inserting extra points along the arc then P_2 will fit better than P_1, and the length of P_2 will be greater than the length of P_1 (see figure 3.9).

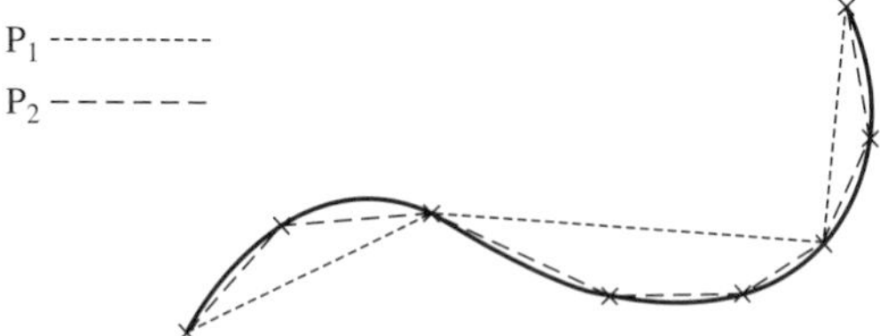

Figure 3.9

In this way, you can form more and more polygons with successively greater lengths. But since the shortest route between two points is the straight line joining them, the length of any such polygon does not exceed the length of the curve. So you would expect that the lengths of successive approximations would be bounded above (by the length of the curve), and that by putting the intermediate points sufficiently close together you could get an approximation as close as you like to the arc length.

For most curves that occur in practice this approach works, and leads to the calculus method of finding arc length, which is given below. But, contrary to intuition, there are some curves for which there is *no* upper bound to the length of the inscribed polygon between two fixed points. One example is Von Koch's 'snowflake' which is described in *AS Pure Mathematics*, page 189; another is given in Question 11 of Exercise 3B. Essentially what happens with these exceptional curves is that they wiggle so much that no chord, however short, is a good approximation. To rule out this possibility only curves for which the arc length PQ is nearly the same as the length of the chord PQ whenever the two points P and Q on the curve are close together are considered here. To be more precise, the *assumption* is made that:

$$\frac{\text{arc PQ}}{\text{chord PQ}} \to 1 \text{ as P} \to \text{Q}.$$

The positive sense along a curve

If the co-ordinates of a point P on a curve are given in terms of a parameter p then the sense in which P moves along the curve as p increases is called the *positive sense*. The same applies if you are using x or y instead of p as the independent variable. The positive sense on a curve depends on the particular way in which the cartesian equation or parametric equations are expressed. For example, the equations:

(a) $y = -x^3$ **(b)** $x = -\sqrt[3]{y}$ **(c)** $x = p, y = -p^3$ **(d)** $x = -q, y = q^3$

all give the same curve, using independent variables x, y, p, q respectively. In **(a)** and **(c)** the positive sense is from left to right across the page, but in **(b)** and **(d)** the opposite sense is positive (see figure 3.10).

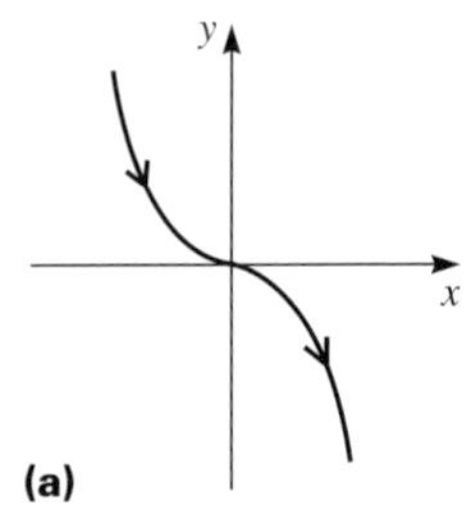

y
x
(b)

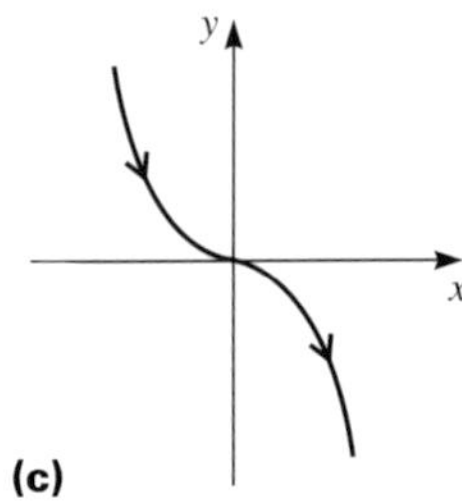

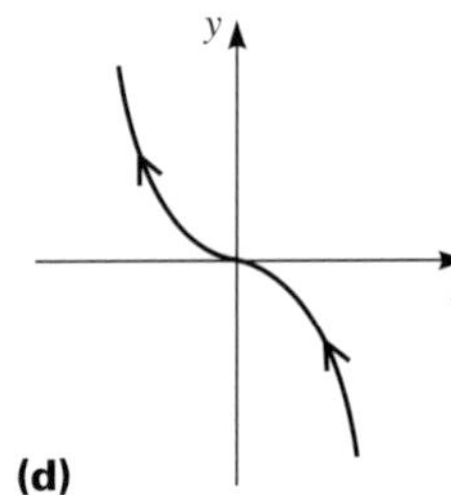

Figure 3.10

ACTIVITY 3.3 Draw diagrams to show the positive sense when the unit circle is expressed as:

(i) $x = \cos\theta, y = \sin\theta$ **(ii)** $x = \sin\phi, y = \cos\phi$ **(iii)** $y = \pm\sqrt{1-x^2}$.

Arc length with cartesian co-ordinates

To see how to find the length of an arc, look at part of a general curve, as shown in figure 3.11. There C is a fixed point on the curve, P is the point with parameter p, and s is the arc length from C to P, where s is positive if and only if the motion from C to P is in the positive sense along the curve.

Let P and Q have co-ordinates (x, y) and $(x + \delta x, y + \delta y)$, corresponding to parametric values p and $p + \delta p$ respectively, and let arc PQ $= \delta s$.

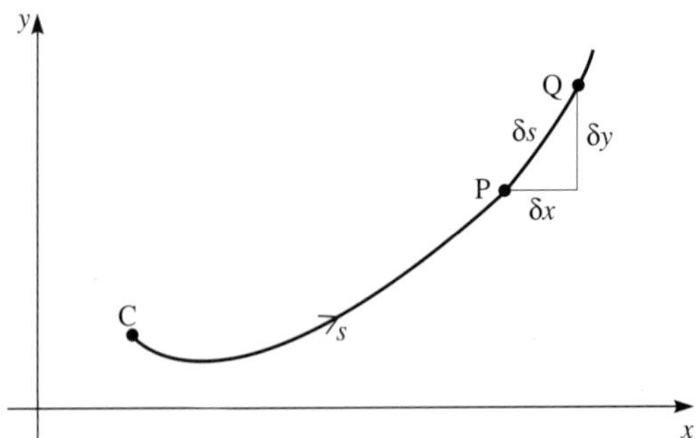

Figure 3.11

The chord length PQ is $|\mathbf{PQ}| = \sqrt{(\delta x)^2 + (\delta y)^2}$.

Therefore $\dfrac{\delta s}{\delta p} = \dfrac{\delta s}{|\mathbf{PQ}|} \times \dfrac{|\mathbf{PQ}|}{\delta p}$

$$= \frac{\delta s}{|\mathbf{PQ}|} \times \sqrt{\left(\frac{\delta x}{\delta p}\right)^2 + \left(\frac{\delta y}{\delta p}\right)^2}.$$

As $\delta p \to 0$, $\dfrac{\delta s}{\delta p}, \dfrac{\delta x}{\delta p}, \dfrac{\delta y}{\delta p}$ tend to $\dfrac{\mathrm{d}s}{\mathrm{d}p}, \dfrac{\mathrm{d}x}{\mathrm{d}p}, \dfrac{\mathrm{d}y}{\mathrm{d}p}$ respectively, and by the assumption stated above $\dfrac{\delta s}{|\mathbf{PQ}|} \to 1$. So taking limits as $\delta p \to 0$ gives the basic result:

$$\frac{\mathrm{d}s}{\mathrm{d}p} = \sqrt{\left(\frac{\mathrm{d}x}{\mathrm{d}p}\right)^2 + \left(\frac{\mathrm{d}y}{\mathrm{d}p}\right)^2}.$$

From this s can be found by integrating with respect to p.

If the independent variable is x (i.e. the equation of the curve is given in the form $y = \mathrm{f}(x)$), then you put $p = x$ in the basic result. Then:

$$\frac{\mathrm{d}x}{\mathrm{d}p} = \frac{\mathrm{d}x}{\mathrm{d}x} = 1 \quad \text{and} \quad \frac{\mathrm{d}y}{\mathrm{d}p} = \frac{\mathrm{d}y}{\mathrm{d}x}$$

so that

$$\frac{\mathrm{d}s}{\mathrm{d}x} = \sqrt{1 + \left(\frac{\mathrm{d}y}{\mathrm{d}x}\right)^2}.$$

Similarly, when the independent variable is y:

$$\frac{\mathrm{d}s}{\mathrm{d}y} = \sqrt{\left(\frac{\mathrm{d}x}{\mathrm{d}y}\right)^2 + 1}.$$

All these are easy to remember from the right-angled 'triangle' (see figure 3.12) in which $(\delta s)^2 \approx (\delta x)^2 + (\delta y)^2$ by Pythagoras' theorem. The three results follow in the limit from dividing by $(\delta p)^2$, $(\delta x)^2$ or $(\delta y)^2$ as appropriate, and then taking the positive square root of each side. Notice that the *positive* root is needed in each case, since by definition s increases with the independent variable.

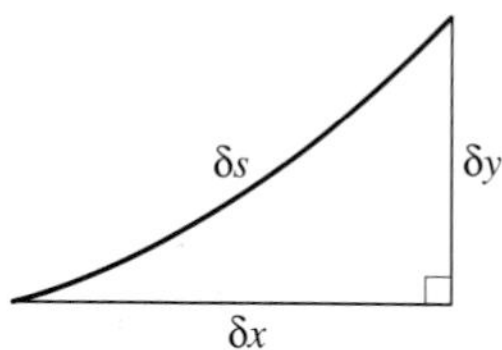

Figure 3.12

EXAMPLE 3.4

Find the length of the astroid $x = a\cos^3\theta$, $y = a\sin^3\theta$.

SOLUTION

$$\frac{dx}{d\theta} = -3a\cos^2\theta\sin\theta \qquad \frac{dy}{d\theta} = 3a\sin^2\theta\cos\theta$$

$$\Rightarrow \quad \frac{ds}{d\theta} = \sqrt{9a^2\cos^4\theta\sin^2\theta + 9a^2\sin^4\theta\cos^2\theta}$$

$$= 3a\sqrt{\cos^2\theta\sin^2\theta(\cos^2\theta + \sin^2\theta)} \qquad ①$$

$$= 3a\cos\theta\sin\theta.$$

The values of θ at the four cusps of the curve are as shown in figure 3.13, so the length of arc in the first quadrant is:

$$\int_0^{\pi/2} 3a\cos\theta\sin\theta\,d\theta = \left[\frac{3a}{2}\sin^2\theta\right]_0^{\pi/2} = \frac{3a}{2}$$

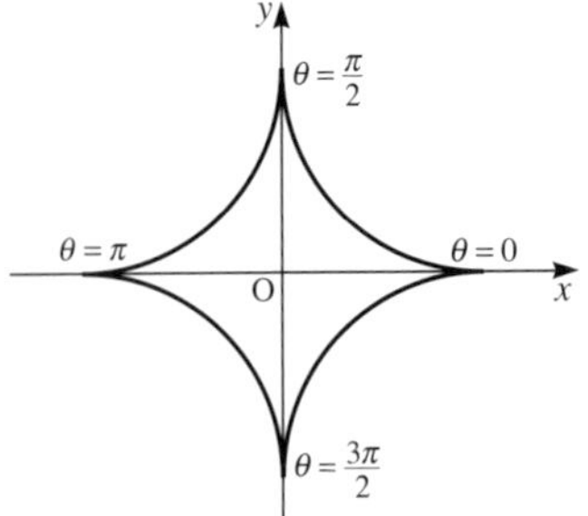

Figure 3.13

and the length of the complete astroid is

$$4 \times \frac{3a}{2} = 6a.$$

Note

If you try to find the whole length in a single integration you get $\int_0^{2\pi} 3a\cos\theta\sin\theta\,d\theta = \left[\frac{3a}{2}\sin^2\theta\right]_0^{2\pi} = 0$. This is because $\cos\theta\sin\theta < 0$ in the second and fourth quadrants, and the positive and negative contributions in the four quadrants have cancelled. When taking the square root at ① (and in similar cases) it is essential to check that you use an expression which is never negative throughout the range of integration.

Arc length with polar co-ordinates

The method of finding the length of a curve from its polar equation comes from differentiating the relations $x = r\cos\theta$, $y = r\sin\theta$ with respect to θ, remembering that r is a function of θ. Thus:

$$\frac{dx}{d\theta} = \frac{dr}{d\theta}\cos\theta - r\sin\theta \quad \text{and} \quad \frac{dy}{d\theta} = \frac{dr}{d\theta}\sin\theta + r\cos\theta$$

so that $$\left(\frac{dx}{d\theta}\right)^2 = \left(\frac{dr}{d\theta}\right)^2\cos^2\theta - 2r\frac{dr}{d\theta}\cos\theta\sin\theta + r^2\sin^2\theta$$

and $$\left(\frac{dy}{d\theta}\right)^2 = \left(\frac{dr}{d\theta}\right)^2\sin^2\theta + 2r\frac{dr}{d\theta}\cos\theta\sin\theta + r^2\cos^2\theta.$$

Adding these and using $\cos^2\theta + \sin^2\theta = 1$ gives:

$$\left(\frac{dx}{d\theta}\right)^2 + \left(\frac{dy}{d\theta}\right)^2 = \left(\frac{dr}{d\theta}\right)^2 + r^2$$

so that $\dfrac{ds}{d\theta} = \sqrt{\left(\dfrac{dr}{d\theta}\right)^2 + r^2}$

from which s is found by integrating with respect to θ.

? Figure 3.14 shows a curve through neighbouring points P and Q with polar co-ordinates (r, θ) and $(r + \delta r, \theta + \delta\theta)$. Identify in the diagram a right-angled 'triangle' with sides δs, δr and $r\delta\theta$, and explain how it can be used as a reminder of this result.

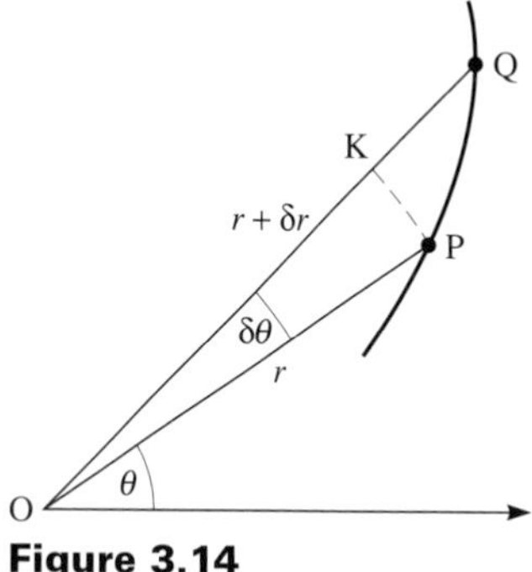

Figure 3.14

EXAMPLE 3.5

Find the length of the equiangular spiral $r = 3e^{\theta/3}$ from $\theta = 0$ to $\theta = \pi$.

SOLUTION

$$\frac{dr}{d\theta} = e^{\theta/3}$$

$$\Rightarrow \quad \frac{ds}{d\theta} = \sqrt{e^{2\theta/3} + 9e^{2\theta/3}} = \sqrt{10}\,e^{\theta/3}$$

$$\Rightarrow \quad s = \int_0^{\pi} \sqrt{10}\,e^{\theta/3}\,d\theta = \left[3\sqrt{10}\,e^{\theta/3}\right]_0^{\pi}$$

$$= 3\sqrt{10}(e^{\pi/3} - 1) \approx 17.5.$$

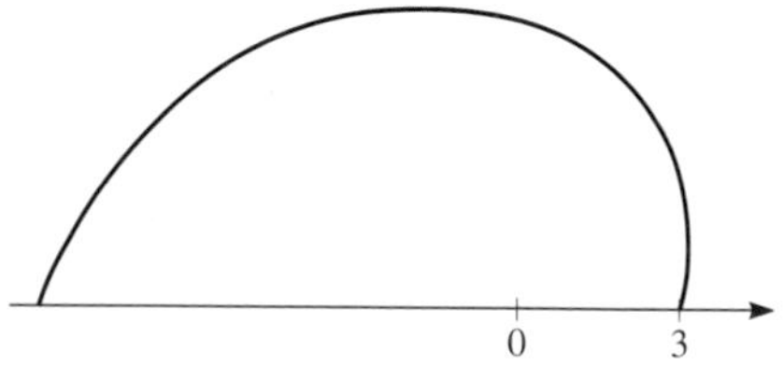

Figure 3.15

EXERCISE 3B

1 Find the length of the semi-cubical parabola $y^2 = x^3$ from (0, 0) to (4, 8).

(This curve was the first for which the length was found by calculus methods, by the Dutchman Heinrich van Heuraet, the Englishman William Neil and the Frenchman Pierre de Fermat independently, all between 1658 and 1660.)

2 Find the length of the curve $x = \dfrac{1}{1+p^2}$, $y = \dfrac{p}{1+p^2}$ from $p = 0$ to $p = 1$, and draw a sketch of the curve to explain your answer.

3 Find the length of the catenary $y = c\cosh\dfrac{x}{c}$ from $x = 0$ to $x = X$.

4 Show that $x = a\sinh^2 p$, $y = 2a\sinh p$ are parametric equations of the parabola $y^2 = 4ax$, and that the arc length from $p = 0$ to $p = P$ is $a\left(P + \frac{1}{2}\sinh 2P\right)$.

5 Prove that the length of one complete arch of the cycloid $x = a(\theta - \sin\theta)$, $y = a(1 - \cos\theta)$ is $8a$.
(This result was first given by Christopher Wren in 1659.)

6 Find the length of the nephroid $x = 3a\cos\theta - a\cos 3\theta$, $y = 3a\sin\theta - a\sin 3\theta$.

7 Prove that the length of the arc of the equiangular spiral $r = ae^{k\theta}$ from (r_1, θ_1) to (r_2, θ_2) is proportional to $(r_2 - r_1)$, and find the constant of proportionality in terms of k.

8 Find the length of the cardioid $r = a(1 + \cos\theta)$.

9 For the conic $\dfrac{\ell}{r} = 1 + e\cos\theta$ show that, if e is small, $s \approx \ell(\theta - e\sin\theta)$, where s is measured from where $\theta = 0$.

10 **(i)** For the ellipse $x = a\cos\theta$, $y = b\sin\theta$ prove that $\dfrac{ds}{d\theta} = a\sqrt{1 - e^2\cos^2\theta}$, where $b^2 = a^2(1 - e^2)$.

(ii) Prove that the perimeter of this ellipse is exactly the same as the length of one complete wave of the curve $y = ae\cos\dfrac{x}{b}$.

(iii) Prove that if e is small then the perimeter of this ellipse is approximately $2\pi a\left(1 - \frac{1}{4}e^2\right)$.

11 **A finite curve with infinite length**

Let $f(x) = x\cos\left(\dfrac{\pi}{2x^2}\right)$ for $x \neq 0$, $f(0) = 0$.

(i) Show that the curve $y = f(x)$ lies between the lines $y = \pm x$ and passes through the points $(1, 0), \left(\sqrt{\frac{1}{2}}, -\sqrt{\frac{1}{2}}\right), \left(\sqrt{\frac{1}{3}}, 0\right), \left(\sqrt{\frac{1}{4}}, -\sqrt{\frac{1}{4}}\right), \left(\sqrt{\frac{1}{5}}, 0\right), \left(\sqrt{\frac{1}{6}}, -\sqrt{\frac{1}{6}}\right), \left(\sqrt{\frac{1}{7}}, 0\right), \ldots$. Sketch the curve on a large scale for $0 \leqslant x \leqslant 1$ (or see what your graphic calculator makes of it).

(ii) Show that the length of the curve from $x = \dfrac{1}{\sqrt{2m+1}}$ to $x = \dfrac{1}{\sqrt{2m-1}}$ is greater than $\dfrac{2}{\sqrt{2m}} = \dfrac{\sqrt{2}}{\sqrt{m}}$.

(iii) Deduce that the length of the curve between $x = \dfrac{1}{\sqrt{2n+1}}$ and $x = 1$ is greater than $\sqrt{2}\left(\dfrac{1}{1} + \dfrac{1}{\sqrt{2}} + \dfrac{1}{\sqrt{3}} + \ldots + \dfrac{1}{\sqrt{n}}\right)$.

☆ **(iv)** By replacing each term of the sum by the smallest term, show that

$$\frac{1}{1}+\frac{1}{\sqrt{2}}+\frac{1}{\sqrt{3}}+\ldots+\frac{1}{\sqrt{n}} > \frac{n}{\sqrt{n}} = \sqrt{n}.$$

☆ **(v)** Deduce that this curve does not have a finite length between $x = 0$ and $x = 1$.

Solids of revolution

Figure 3.16 shows the region bounded by the curve $y = \mathrm{f}(x)$ and the lines $x = a$, $x = b$, $y = 0$. When this region is turned through one revolution about the x axis it sweeps out a solid called a *solid of revolution*. This has the x axis as an axis of symmetry, and every section perpendicular to the x axis is a circle (see figure 3.17). Similarly when the region between any curve and a line which does not cross the curve is rotated through 360° about that line, a solid of revolution is generated. Such solids, including anything turned on a lathe or a potter's wheel, are common in everyday life.

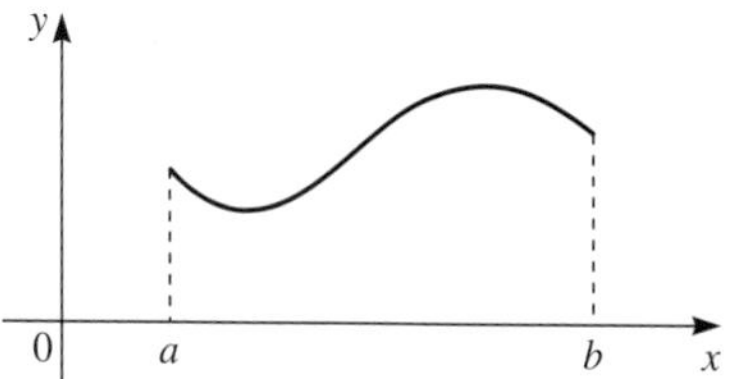

Figure 3.16

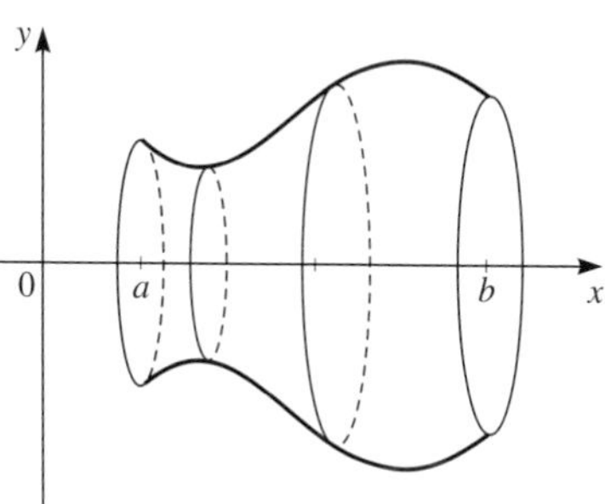

Figure 3.17

When a solid of revolution is formed by rotation about the x axis, the rectangular strip of height y and width δx generates a cylindrical disc of radius y and thickness δx whose volume is $\pi y^2\,\delta x$ (see figure 3.18).

The volume V of the solid of revolution is the limit as $\delta x \to 0$ of the sum of such discs, so that $V = \int_a^b \pi y^2 \mathrm{d}x$.

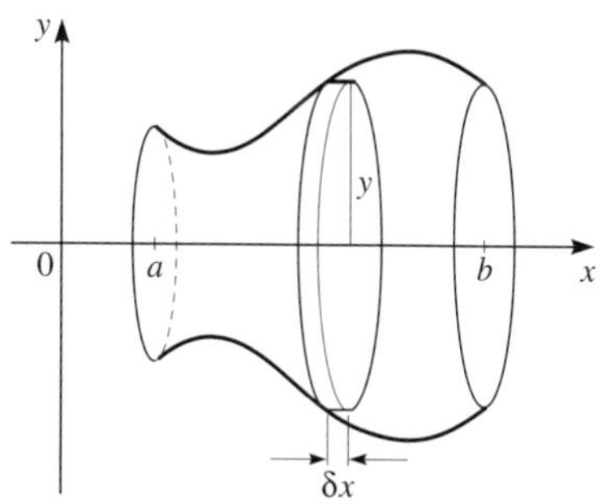

Figure 3.18

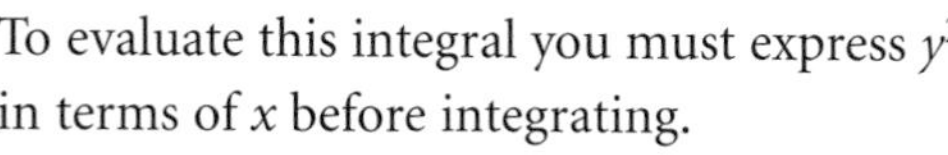

To evaluate this integral you must express y^2 in terms of x before integrating.

The curved surface area of a solid of revolution

First consider a simple case, the curved surface area of a right circular cone. If the cone has base radius r and slant height ℓ its curved surface, flattened out, is a sector of a circle with radius ℓ and arc length $2\pi r$, as in figure 3.19.

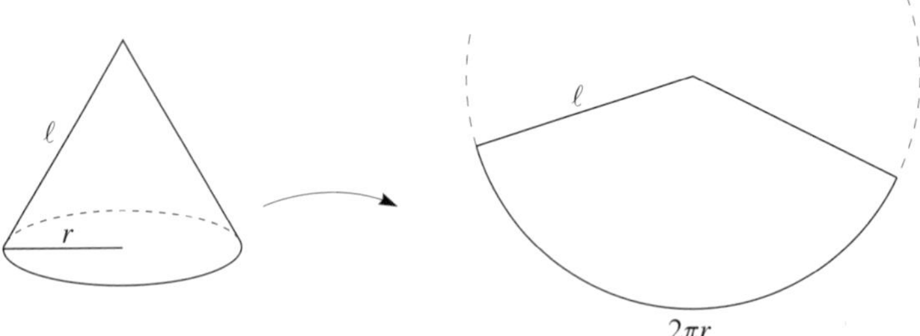

Figure 3.19

The angle at the centre of this sector is $\dfrac{2\pi r}{\ell}$ radians, and so the curved surface area of the cone is $\frac{1}{2}\ell^2 \times \dfrac{2\pi r}{\ell} = \pi r\ell$.

Now consider the solid of revolution formed by rotating about the x axis the line segment joining the points (x_1, y_1) and (x_2, y_2), where the distance between these points is δs. This solid, which is called a *frustum*, is the difference between two cones. Let the slant heights of these cones be ℓ_1 and ℓ_2 as shown in figure 3.20. Then $\delta s = \ell_2 - \ell_1$.

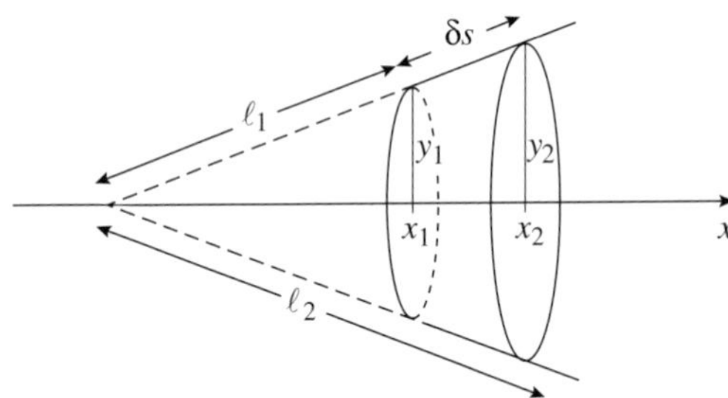

Figure 3.20

The curved surface area of the frustum, δS, is given by:

$$\delta S = \pi y_2\ell_2 - \pi y_1\ell_1 = \pi(y_2\ell_2 - y_1\ell_1).$$

But by similar triangles $\dfrac{\ell_1}{y_1} = \dfrac{\ell_2}{y_2}$ so that $y_2\ell_1 = y_1\ell_2$. Therefore:

$$\begin{aligned}\delta S &= \pi(y_2\ell_2 - y_2\ell_1 + y_1\ell_2 - y_1\ell_1)\\ &= \pi(y_2 + y_1)(\ell_2 - \ell_1)\\ &= 2\pi y\,\delta s\end{aligned}$$

Inserting extra terms which cancel.

where $y = \frac{1}{2}(y_1 + y_2)$, the average radius of the frustum.

It is now easy to see how to find the curved surface area of a solid of revolution: divide the arc AB which is rotated into elements of arc δs, each of which generates a surface with area approximately $2\pi y\, \delta s$. Then the total curved surface area is:

$$S = \lim_{\delta s \to 0} \sum_{A}^{B} 2\pi y\, \delta s = \int_{A}^{B} 2\pi y\, \mathrm{d}s.$$

The detailed evaluation of this integral depends on which independent variable is being used. If you are working in terms of x, with $x = a$ at A and $x = b$ at B, then:

$$S = \int_{a}^{b} 2\pi y \frac{\mathrm{d}s}{\mathrm{d}x}\, \mathrm{d}x$$

but if the independent variable is a parameter p, with $p = \alpha$ at A and $p = \beta$ at B, then:

$$S = \int_{\alpha}^{\beta} 2\pi y \frac{\mathrm{d}s}{\mathrm{d}p}\, \mathrm{d}p.$$

The corresponding results when the solid is generated by rotating about the y axis are:

$$S = \int_{c}^{d} 2\pi x \frac{\mathrm{d}s}{\mathrm{d}y}\, \mathrm{d}y$$

where $y = c$ at A and $y = d$ at B, and

$$S = \int_{\alpha}^{\beta} 2\pi x \frac{\mathrm{d}s}{\mathrm{d}p}\, \mathrm{d}p.$$

EXAMPLE 3.6

Find the curved surface area of the *paraboloid* formed by rotating the parabola $y^2 = 4ax$ about the x axis from $x = 0$ to $x = a$.

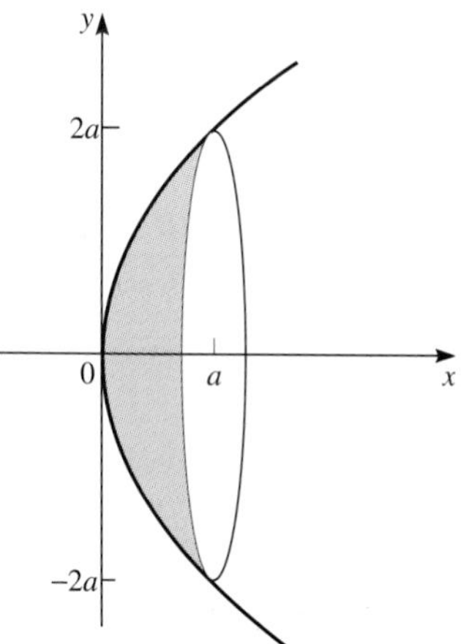

Figure 3.21

SOLUTION

$$y^2 = 4ax \quad \Rightarrow \quad 2y\frac{dy}{dx} = 4a \quad \Rightarrow \quad \frac{dy}{dx} = \frac{2a}{y} \quad \Rightarrow \quad \left(\frac{dy}{dx}\right)^2 = \frac{4a^2}{y^2} = \frac{a}{x}$$

so that:

$$\frac{ds}{dx} = \sqrt{1+\frac{a}{x}} = \frac{\sqrt{x+a}}{\sqrt{x}}$$

and :

$$y\frac{ds}{dx} = \sqrt{4ax}\,\frac{\sqrt{x+a}}{\sqrt{x}} = 2\sqrt{a}\sqrt{x+a}.$$

The required area is:

$$\begin{aligned} 4\pi\sqrt{a}\int_0^a \sqrt{x+a}\,dx &= \left[4\pi\sqrt{a}\times\tfrac{2}{3}(x+a)^{3/2}\right]_0^a \\ &= \tfrac{8}{3}\pi\sqrt{a}((2a)^{3/2} - a^{3/2}) \\ &= \tfrac{8}{3}\pi a^2(2^{3/2} - 1). \end{aligned}$$

EXAMPLE 3.7

Find the surface area of the solid generated by rotating the equiangular spiral $r = 3e^{\theta/3}$ from $\theta = 0$ to $\theta = \pi$ about the line $\theta = 0$.

You may use the result $\displaystyle\int e^{ax}\sin bx\,dx = \frac{e^{ax}(a\sin bx - b\cos bx)}{a^2+b^2}$.

SOLUTION

As in Example 3.5: $\displaystyle\frac{ds}{d\theta} = \sqrt{10}\,e^{\theta/3}$

and $y = r\sin\theta = 3e^{\theta/3}\sin\theta$ so the required area is:

$$\int_0^{\pi} 2\pi\times 3e^{\theta/3}\sin\theta\times\sqrt{10}\,e^{\theta/3}\,d\theta = 6\sqrt{10}\pi\int_0^{\pi} e^{2\theta/3}\sin\theta\,d\theta.$$

Using the result above for $\displaystyle\int e^{ax}\sin bx\,dx = \frac{e^{ax}(a\sin bx - b\cos bx)}{a^2+b^2}$

with $a = \frac{2}{3}$ and $b = 1$, the area is:

$$\begin{aligned} 6\sqrt{10}\pi\left[e^{2\theta/3}\frac{\frac{2}{3}\sin\theta - \cos\theta}{\frac{4}{9}+1}\right]_0^{\pi} &= \frac{54\sqrt{10}\pi}{13}(e^{2\pi/3}+1) \\ &\approx 376.4. \end{aligned}$$

EXERCISE 3C

1 Find the curved surface area of the solid generated by rotating the curve about the x axis. Leave your answers in terms of π.

(i) the line $4y = 3x$ from $x = 4$ to $x = 8$

(ii) the circle $x^2 + y^2 = a^2$ from $x = -a$ to $x = a$

(iii) the catenary $y = c\cosh\dfrac{x}{c}$ from $x = -a$ to $x = a$

(iv) the parabola $x = ap^2$, $y = 2ap$ from $p = 1$ to $p = 2$

(v) one arch of the cycloid $x = a(\theta - \sin\theta)$, $y = a(1 - \cos\theta)$

(vi) the astroid $x = a\cos^3 p$, $y = a\sin^3 p$

(vii) one loop of the lemniscate $r^2 = a^2\cos 2\theta$ $\left(\text{i.e. from } \theta = 0 \text{ to } \theta = \dfrac{\pi}{4}\right)$

(viii) the cardioid $r = a(1 + \cos\theta)$.

2 Show that the arc of the circle $(x + a\cos\alpha^2) + y^2 = a^2$ for which $x \geqslant 0$ subtends an angle 2α at the centre of the circle. Find the area of the curved surface generated when this arc is rotated about:

(i) the x axis **(ii)** the y axis.

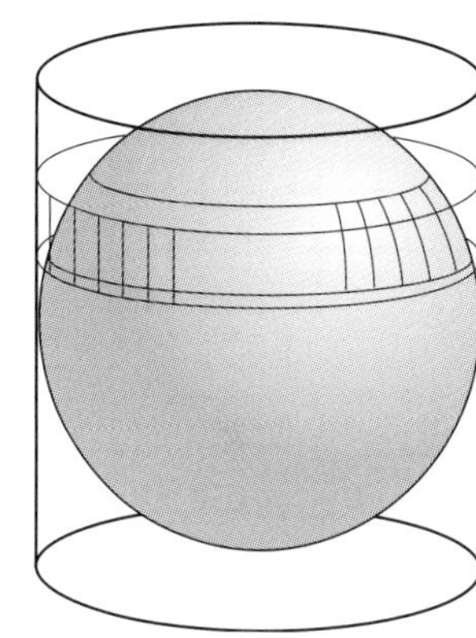

3 Archimedes' tombstone

The diagram shows a sphere circumscribed by a cylinder with a vertical axis which touches the sphere at its horizontal equator. Two horizontal planes cut both the sphere and the cylinder. Prove that the portions of the sphere and the cylinder between these planes have equal curved surface areas.

(Archimedes (287–212 BC) was so pleased to discover this that, at his request, a representation of a sphere circumscribed by a cylinder was carved on his tombstone in Sicily, where it was found and restored by the Roman author Cicero about a century later.)

4 Use the 'Archimedes' tombstone' theorem to find:

(i) the surface area of a sphere of radius a

(ii) the surface area of 'the tropics', i.e. the part of the Earth between the circles of latitude 23.47° N (the Tropic of Cancer) and 23.47° S (the Tropic of Capricorn). Take the Earth to be a sphere of radius 6370 km, and give your answer in km^2 to 3 significant figures.

5 A solid of revolution is generated by rotating the curve $y = \dfrac{1}{x}$ about the x axis from $x = 1$ to $x = k$, where $k > 1$.

(i) Prove that the volume V of this solid is $\pi\left(1 - \dfrac{1}{k}\right)$.

(ii) Prove that the curved surface area S is given by $S = \displaystyle\int_1^k \frac{2\pi}{x}\sqrt{1 + \frac{1}{x^4}}\,\mathrm{d}x$.

Noting that $1 + \dfrac{1}{x^4} > 1$, deduce that $S > 2\pi\ln k$.

(This gives a paradox. If an infinitely long hollow vessel of this shape were placed with its axis vertical then a volume π of paint poured into it would completely fill it, but no amount of paint however large would be enough to cover the surface!)

INVESTIGATION

The Pappus–Guldin theorems

These two theorems (for volumes (A) and for surface areas (B)) were first stated by Pappus of Alexandria in about 320, then rediscovered by Paul Guldin who published them in 1641. They use the idea of the centroid of a plane region or arc: see *Mechanics 3*, page 156.

(i) A solid of revolution with volume V is formed by rotating about the x axis a region of area A which does not cut the x axis. The distance of the centroid of the region from the x axis is $\bar{y}$ (see figure 3.22).

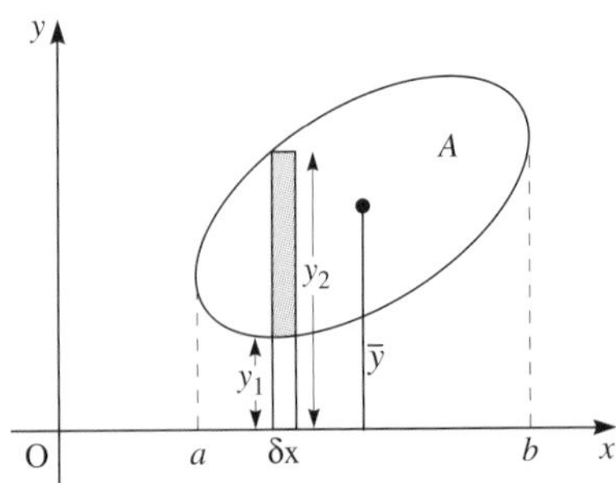

Figure 3.22

Show that $V = \int_a^b \pi\left(y_2^2 - y_1^2\right)\mathrm{d}x$ and

that $\bar{y}A = \int_a^b \frac{1}{2}\left(y_1 + y_2\right)\left(y_2 - y_1\right)\,\mathrm{d}x.$

(ii) Deduce that $V = 2\pi\bar{y}A$, and show that this means that

volume of solid of revolution
= area of region × distance moved by centroid. (A)

This is the Pappus–Guldin theorem for volumes.

(iii) An isosceles triangle ABC has AB = AC and BC = $2h$. The length of the perpendicular from A to BC is r. Use the theorem to find the volume of the solid obtained when the triangle is rotated about BC, and deduce the formula for the volume of a right circular cone.

(iv) A solid of revolution with surface area S is formed by rotating about the x axis an arc of length s_0 which does not cut the x axis.

The distance of the centroid of the arc from the x axis is $\bar{y}$ (see figure 3.23).

Explain why

$$\bar{y}s_0 = \lim_{\delta s \to 0} \sum y\ \delta s = \int_\alpha^\beta y \frac{\mathrm{d}s}{\mathrm{d}p}\ \mathrm{d}p,$$

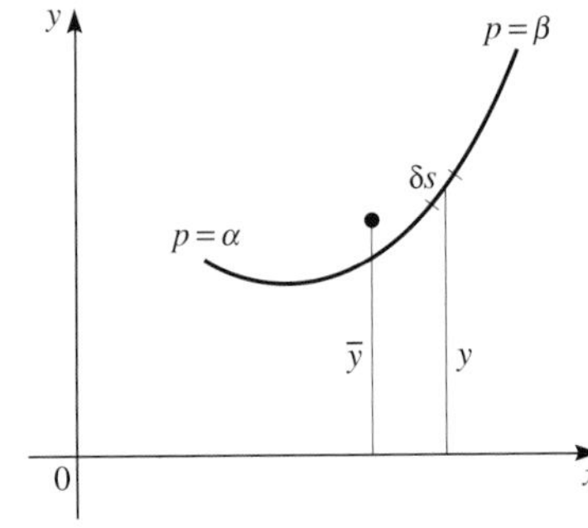

Figure 3.23

where α and β are the initial and final values of the parameter p in terms of which the curve is defined.

(v) Deduce that $S = 2\pi\bar{y}s_0$, and show that this means that

surface area of solid of revolution
= length of arc × distance moved by centroid. (B)

This is the Pappus–Guldin theorem for surface areas. The theorem still applies if the arc is a closed loop: in this case (x, y) makes a complete circuit of the loop as p varies from α to β.

(vi) Find the volume and surface area of the *torus* formed by rotating a circle of radius a about a line at a distance b $(> a)$ from its centre.

(vii) Use the theorems to find the position of the centroids of

(a) a semi-circular region **(b)** a semi-circular arc.

(viii) The rectangle in figure 3.24 is rotated about AB to form a solid. Use the Pappus–Guldin theorems to find the volume and surface area of this solid. Check your results by other methods.

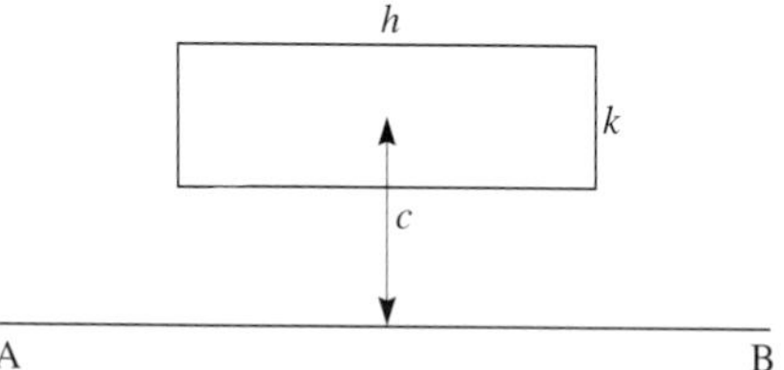

Figure 3.24

Intrinsic equations

With cartesian or polar co-ordinates the equation of a particular curve may take many forms according to the way the co-ordinate system is set up. For example, the equation of the same rectangular hyperbola is $x^2 - y^2 = a^2$ when referred to its axes of symmetry, but $xy = \frac{1}{2}a^2$ when referred to its asymptotes, and it is not immediately apparent that these two equations give the same curve.

ACTIVITY 3.4 Show that a unit circle could have polar equation

(i) $r = 1$ or

(ii) $r = 2\sin\theta$ or

(iii) $r^2 - 10\sqrt{2}r(\cos\theta + \sin\theta) + 99 = 0$, if its centre has polar co-ordinates

$$\left(10, \frac{\pi}{4}\right).$$

An alternative way to describe a curve is to find an equation connecting its arc length s with the angle ψ (the Greek letter psi) which its tangent makes with a fixed direction. It is still necessary to choose:

(A) the point of the curve where $s = 0$ and the direction where $\psi = 0$

(B) the sense along the curve in which s increases (as usual, ψ is measured in radians in the anticlockwise sense).

The effect of the choices in (A) is minor since they can only change s or ψ by a constant. The sign of s is more significant, particularly in connection with the work on curvature in the next section. The relation between s and ψ is called the *intrinsic equation* of the curve ('intrinsic' means 'belonging naturally to itself'), and when s and ψ are used in this way they are called *intrinsic co-ordinates.*

ACTIVITY 3.5

Show how to measure s and ψ so that the intrinsic equation of a circle of radius a is $s = a\psi$.

EXAMPLE 3.8

The curve in which a uniform flexible cord or chain hangs when held at its two ends is called a *catenary*. Find the intrinsic equation of the catenary, and show that its cartesian equation can take the form $y = c\cosh\frac{x}{c}$.

SOLUTION

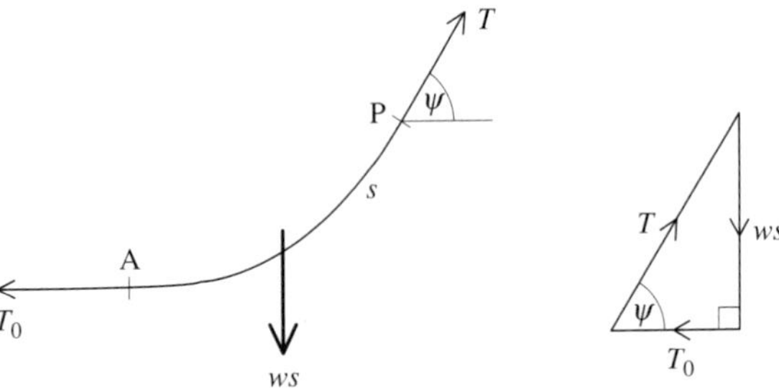

Figure 3.25

Let the cord have weight w per unit length. Consider the part of the cord from the lowest point A to another point P, where arc AP $= s$ and the tangent at P makes an angle ψ with the horizontal. There are three external forces acting on this portion: the horizontal tension T_0 at A, the tension T at P and the weight ws, as shown in figure 3.25.

Since the cord is in equilibrium the vectors representing these three forces form a closed triangle, from which:

$$ws = T_0 \tan \psi$$

or $\quad s = c \tan \psi$

where c is the constant $\frac{T_0}{w}$. This is the intrinsic equation.

To find the cartesian equation you use the fact that $\tan\psi = \frac{\mathrm{d}y}{\mathrm{d}x}$ (since ψ is measured from the horizontal), and so, from the intrinsic equation, $\frac{\mathrm{d}y}{\mathrm{d}x} = \frac{s}{c}$.

Therefore $\quad \dfrac{ds}{dx} = \sqrt{1+\left(\dfrac{dy}{dx}\right)^2} = \sqrt{1+\dfrac{s^2}{c^2}} = \dfrac{\sqrt{c^2+s^2}}{c}$

and $\quad \dfrac{dx}{ds} = \dfrac{c}{\sqrt{c^2+s^2}}$.

Integrating with respect to s gives: $x = c\,\text{arsinh}\,\dfrac{s}{c} + k$

where k is a constant. If we choose axes so that the y axis is the vertical through A then $s = 0$ when $x = 0$, and so $k = 0$.

Therefore $\dfrac{s}{c} = \sinh\dfrac{x}{c}$.

But $\dfrac{dy}{dx} = \dfrac{s}{c}$ and so $\dfrac{dy}{dx} = \sinh\dfrac{x}{c}$.

Integrating with respect to x gives

$y = c\cosh\dfrac{x}{c} + k'$, where k' is a constant.

If you now fix the origin at a distance c below A (as in figure 3.26) then $y = c$ when $x = 0$, and so $k' = 0$. With these co-ordinate axes the cartesian equation is $y = c\cosh\dfrac{x}{c}$.

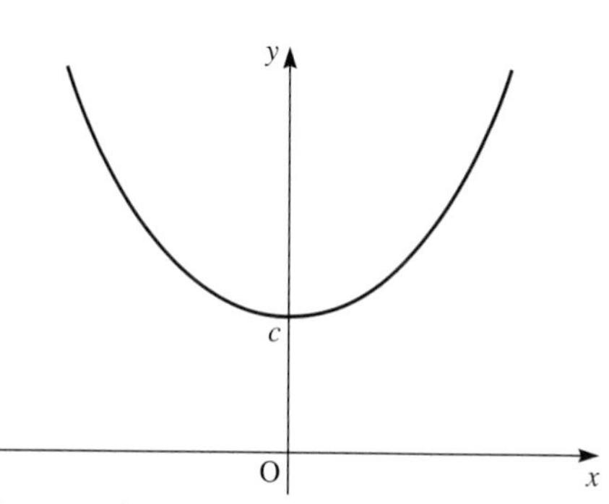

Figure 3.26

When dealing with links between intrinsic and cartesian co-ordinates always measure ψ from the direction of the positive x axis. Then $\tan\psi = \dfrac{dy}{dx}$ and from this two other useful results follow.

- $\dfrac{ds}{dx} = \sqrt{1+\left(\dfrac{dy}{dx}\right)^2} = \sqrt{1+\tan^2\psi} = \sec\psi$ so that $\dfrac{dx}{ds} = \cos\psi$.
- $\dfrac{dy}{ds} = \dfrac{dy}{dx} \times \dfrac{dx}{ds} = \tan\psi \times \cos\psi = \sin\psi$.

These results can be remembered easily by using the 'differential triangle' shown in figure 3.27.

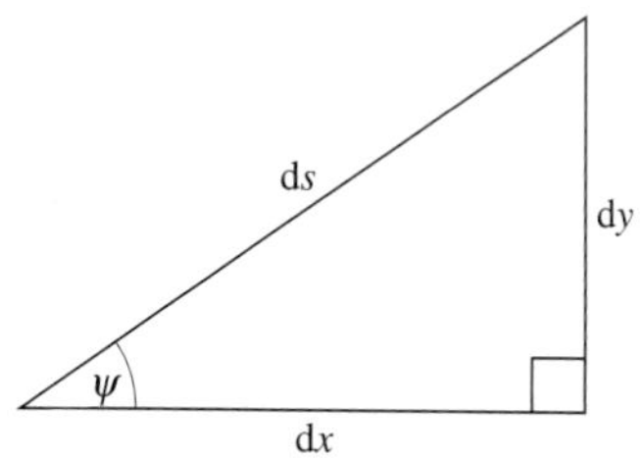

Figure 3.27

Example 3.9 illustrates a general method for finding cartesian or parametric equations of a curve from its intrinsic equation.

EXAMPLE 3.9

Find parametric and cartesian equations for the curve $s = \frac{3}{2} a \sin^2 \psi$, where $0 \leqslant \psi \leqslant \frac{\pi}{2}$.

SOLUTION

$$s = \frac{3}{2} a \sin^2 \psi \quad \Rightarrow \quad \frac{ds}{d\psi} = 3a \sin \psi \cos \psi$$

$$\Rightarrow \quad \frac{dx}{d\psi} = \frac{dx}{ds} \times \frac{ds}{d\psi} = \cos \psi \times 3a \sin \psi \cos \psi = 3a \cos^2 \psi \sin \psi$$

and $$\frac{dy}{d\psi} = \frac{dy}{ds} \times \frac{ds}{d\psi} = \sin \psi \times 3a \sin \psi \cos \psi = 3a \sin^2 \psi \cos \psi.$$

Integrating with respect to ψ gives:

$$x = -a \cos^3 \psi \text{ and } y = a \sin^3 \psi$$

provided that $x = -a$ and $y = 0$ when $\psi = 0$.

These are parametric equations for the astroid with cartesian equation $x^{2/3} + y^{2/3} = a^{2/3}$ (see page 88).

The quarter of the curve from $(-a, 0)$ to $(0, a)$ is described as ψ increases from 0 to $\frac{\pi}{2}$.

EXERCISE 3D

1 For the curve $y = \ln \sec x$ prove that $\frac{ds}{dx} = \sec x$ and that $\psi = x$. Hence find the intrinsic equation.

2 For the semi-cubical parabola $x = 3ap^2$, $y = 2ap^3$ prove that $\tan \psi = p$. Deduce that $\frac{ds}{d\psi} = 6a \tan \psi \sec^3 \psi$, and hence find the intrinsic equation.

3 For the nephroid $x = 3a \cos \theta - a \cos 3\theta$, $y = 3a \sin \theta - a \sin 3\theta$ (see Exercise 3A, Question 11) prove that $\psi = 2\theta$ and that the intrinsic equation is $s = 6a(1 - \cos \frac{1}{2}\psi)$.

4 The *cycloid* is the locus of a point P on the circumference of a circle of radius a as the circle rolls, without slipping, along the x axis. The diagram shows the circle after it has turned through angle θ; it then touches the x axis at A, and AB is a diameter.

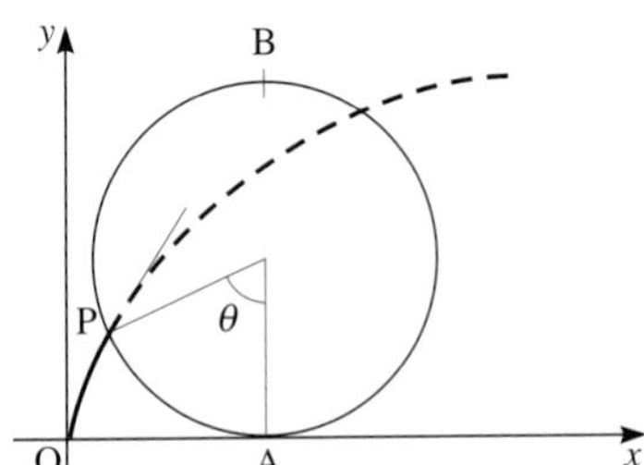

(i) Show from this diagram that the parametric equations are $x = a(\theta - \sin\theta)$, $y = a(1 - \cos\theta)$.

(ii) The tangent to the cycloid at P is in the direction of motion of P. Noting that A has zero velocity (since the circle does not slip), deduce that the tangent at P passes through B, and hence that $\psi = \frac{\pi}{2} - \frac{\theta}{2}$.

(iii) Prove that $\psi = \frac{\pi}{2} - \frac{\theta}{2}$ by a different method, using calculus.

(iv) Prove that if s is measured from O then the intrinsic equation of one arch is $s = 4a(1 - \sin\psi)$.

(v) Now turn the arch upside-down and put the origin at the minimum point. Prove that with s measured from this new origin the intrinsic equation is now $s = 4a\sin\psi$.

(vi) Find the parametric equations of the cycloid in this new position.

5 If the intrinsic equation of a curve is $s = a\psi$, prove that its cartesian equation must be $(x - h)^2 + (y - k)^2 = a^2$, where h and k are constants.

6 Given that $s = \ln\tan\frac{\psi}{2}$ and that $x = 0$ and $y = \frac{\pi}{2}$ when $\psi = \frac{\pi}{2}$, find x in terms of y.

7 Use the method of Example 3.9 to prove again that, with a suitable choice of origin $s = c\tan\psi \quad \Rightarrow \quad y = c\cosh\frac{x}{c}$.

8 If $s = ae^{k\psi}$ and $z = x + yj$, prove that $\frac{dz}{d\psi} = ake^{(k+j)\psi}$. Use this to find the polar equation, and deduce that the curve is an equiangular spiral.

Curvature

If a curve is bending sharply, then the direction of the tangent, measured by ψ, changes considerably in a short distance along the curve, but for a gentle bend there is a smaller change in ψ for the same change in s.

To put this more precisely (referring to figure 3.28), if the changes in ψ and s between the points P and Q on the curve are $\delta\psi$ and δs then the *average curvature* $\frac{\delta\psi}{\delta s}$ gives a measure of how much the curve curves between P and Q.

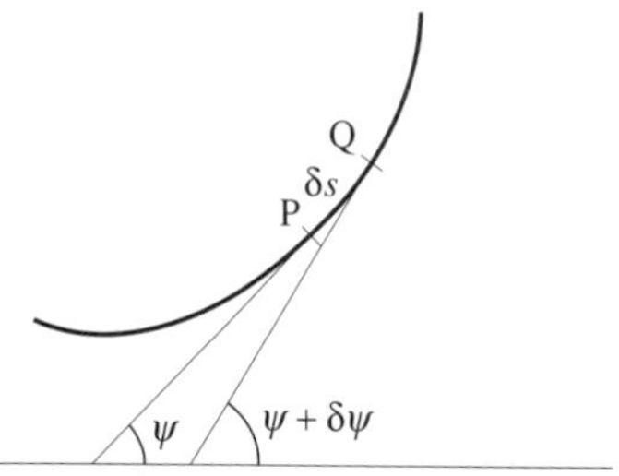

Figure 3.28

Taking the limit as Q → P leads to the following definition.

The *curvature* at a point P is the rate of change of ψ with respect to s at P.

Curvature is denoted by κ (the Greek letter kappa), and so:

$$\kappa = \frac{d\psi}{ds}.$$

If κ is positive then ψ increases with s, and the curve curves to the left of the positive tangent at P (as in figure 3.28) but if κ is negative then ψ decreases with s and the curve curves to the right. If P is a point of inflection then $\kappa = 0$, but the converse is not true, as will be shown in Example 3.11.

For a straight line ψ is constant, and so $\kappa = 0$ at every point.

For a circle of radius a described anticlockwise from its lowest point (see figure 3.29), the intrinsic equation $s = a\psi$ gives $\frac{ds}{d\psi} = a$, and so $\kappa = \frac{1}{a}$.

As you might expect, this shows that a circle has constant curvature, large when the radius is small and small when the radius is large.

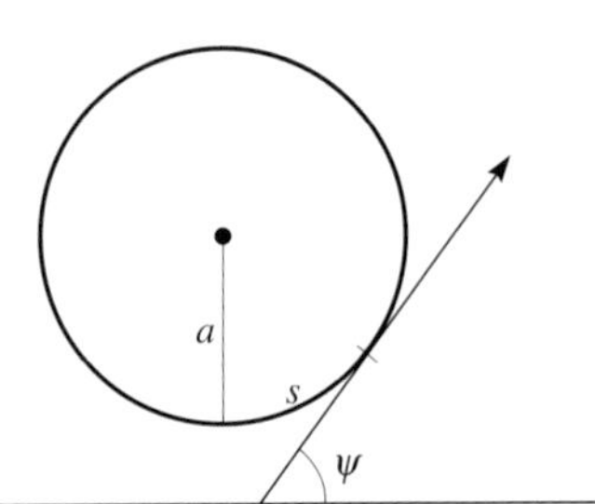

Figure 3.29

Finding curvature

If the intrinsic equation of a curve is known then finding the curvature is straightforward.

EXAMPLE 3.10

Find the curvature of the catenary $s = c\tan\psi$ when $\psi = \frac{\pi}{4}$ and find where the curvature is greatest.

SOLUTION

$$s = c\tan\psi \quad \Rightarrow \quad \frac{ds}{d\psi} = c\sec^2\psi$$

$$\Rightarrow \quad \kappa = \frac{d\psi}{ds} = \frac{1}{c}\cos^2\psi.$$

Using $\sec\psi = \frac{1}{\cos\psi}$.

$$\psi = \frac{\pi}{4} \quad \Rightarrow \quad \kappa = \frac{1}{2c}.$$

The greatest curvature is $\frac{1}{c}$ and this occurs when $\psi = 0$ (at the minimum point).

If the intrinsic equation is not available then it is not quite so simple to find the curvature. Suppose the curve is defined in terms of a parameter p. For brevity you can use a prime (′) to show differentiation with respect to p, so that x' stands for $\frac{dx}{dp}$, x'' for $\frac{d^2x}{dp^2}$ and so on.

You know that $s' = \sqrt{x'^2 + y'^2}$ and to find ψ' you differentiate $\tan\psi$ with respect to p:

$$\tan\psi = \frac{dy}{dx} = \frac{y'}{x'} \quad \Rightarrow \quad \sec^2\psi\psi' = \frac{x'y'' - y'x''}{x'^2}.$$

But $$\sec^2\psi = 1 + \tan^2\psi = 1 + \frac{y'^2}{x'^2} = \frac{x'^2 + y'^2}{x'^2}$$

and so $$\psi' = \frac{x'y'' - y'x''}{x'^2 + y'^2}.$$

Therefore $$\kappa = \frac{\psi'}{s'} = \frac{x'y'' - y'x''}{(x'^2 + y'^2)^{3/2}}.$$

ACTIVITY 3.6 Show that for the parabola $x = ap^2$, $y = 2ap$ this formula gives $\kappa = -\dfrac{1}{2a(1+p^2)^{3/2}}$ What is the geometrical significance of the negative sign?

The formula for curvature when y is given in terms of x can be deduced immediately by putting $p = x$. Then $x' = 1$, $x'' = 0$, $y' = \dfrac{dy}{dx}$ and $y'' = \dfrac{d^2y}{dx^2}$.

So $$\kappa = \frac{\dfrac{d^2y}{dx^2}}{\left\{1 + \left(\dfrac{dy}{dx}\right)^2\right\}^{3/2}}.$$

ACTIVITY 3.7 Find the formula for κ when x is given in terms of y.

Example 3.11 shows that the curvature can be zero even where there is no point of inflection.

EXAMPLE 3.11

Find the points of least and greatest curvature on the curve $y = x^4$.

SOLUTION

$$y = x^4 \quad \Rightarrow \quad \frac{dy}{dx} = 4x^3 \text{ and } \frac{d^2y}{dx^2} = 12x^2$$

$$\Rightarrow \quad \kappa = \frac{12x^2}{(1+16x^6)^{3/2}}.$$

To differentiate κ with respect to x would involve some heavy algebra, which can be avoided to some extent by substituting $u = x^2$ and $v = \dfrac{\kappa^2}{144}$.

Then $v = \dfrac{u^2}{(1+16u^3)^3}$ and so $\dfrac{dv}{du} = \dfrac{(1+16u^3)^3 \times 2u - u^2 \times 3(1+16u^3)^2 \times 48u^2}{(1+16u^3)^6}$.

$$\begin{aligned}\text{Therefore } \frac{dv}{du} = 0 \quad &\Leftrightarrow \quad 2u(1+16u^3 - 72u^3) = 0 \\ &\Leftrightarrow \quad u = 0 \text{ or } 1 - 56u^3 = 0 \\ &\Leftrightarrow \quad u = 0 \text{ or } u = \left(\tfrac{1}{56}\right)^{1/3} \\ &\Leftrightarrow \quad x = 0 \text{ or } x = \pm\left(\tfrac{1}{56}\right)^{1/6} \approx \pm 0.511.\end{aligned}$$

The expression for κ is never negative, so the least value of κ is 0, where $x = 0$ (which is at the minimum point of the curve, *not* at a point of inflection). The curvature is greatest when v is greatest, at $x = \pm\left(\tfrac{1}{56}\right)^{1/6}$ where $\kappa \approx 2.151$, as in figure 3.30.

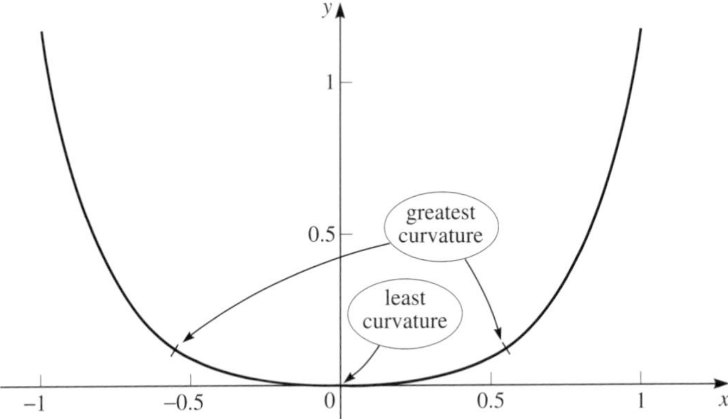

Figure 3.30

To find the curvature from a polar equation $r = f(\theta)$ it is always possible to treat θ as a parameter, with $x = f(\theta)\cos\theta$ and $y = f(\theta)\sin\theta$, though the working is likely to be complicated. An alternative approach, which is much simpler for some standard curves, is outlined in Question 15 of Exercise 3E.

EXERCISE 3E

1 Find the curvature of $y = x^3$ at the points $(1, 1)$ and $(-2, -8)$.

2 Find the curvature of $y = \ln x$ at $(1, 0)$.

3 Prove that the curvature of $y = \sin x$ varies from -1 to 1 during one cycle.

4 The intrinsic equation of an equiangular spiral is $s = ae^{k\psi}$. Prove that the curvature is inversely proportional to s.

5 Prove that if $|\psi|$ is small then $\kappa \approx \dfrac{d^2y}{dx^2}(1 - \tfrac{3}{2}\tan^2\psi)$. Find the greatest value of $|\psi|$ for which $\dfrac{d^2y}{dx^2}$ may be used instead of κ with an error of less than 10%.

6 Find the curvature of the astroid:

(i) using the intrinsic equation $s = \frac{3}{2}a\sin^2\psi$

(ii) using the parametric equations $x = a\cos^3 p$, $y = a\sin^3 p$.

Explain the connection between your two answers.

7 For the parabola $y^2 = 4ax$ prove that $\kappa = -\dfrac{\sin^3\psi}{2a}$.

8 For the rectangular hyperbola $xy = c^2$ prove that $\kappa = \dfrac{2c^2}{r^3}$, where $r^2 = x^2 + y^2$.

9 Find κ in terms of θ for the ellipse $x = a\cos\theta$, $y = b\sin\theta$. Check that your answer gives what you would expect when $a = b$.

10 For the catenary $y = c\cosh\dfrac{x}{c}$ prove that $\kappa = \dfrac{c}{y^2}$.

11 Find the greatest curvature on the curve $y = e^x$, and the co-ordinates of the point where this occurs.

12 If x and y are given in terms of the arc length s, and primes denote differentiation with respect to s, prove that:

(i) $\kappa = -\dfrac{x''}{y'} = \dfrac{y''}{x'}$ **(ii)** $\kappa^2 = (x'')^2 + (y'')^2$.

Hint: Start by differentiating $x' = \cos\psi$ with respect to s.

13 The cartesian co-ordinates of a point P are (x, y). A second pair of axes is obtained by rotating the original pair through the angle α about the origin O. Referring to these axes, the co-ordinates of P are (X, Y) as shown in the diagram.

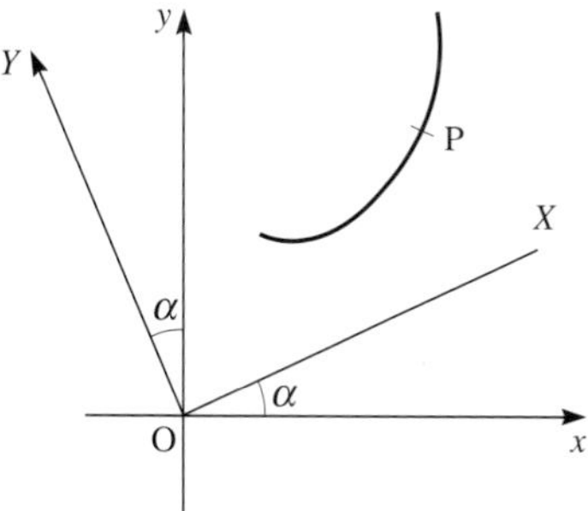

(i) Show that

$$\begin{pmatrix} X \\ Y \end{pmatrix} = \begin{pmatrix} \cos\alpha & \sin\alpha \\ -\sin\alpha & \cos\alpha \end{pmatrix}\begin{pmatrix} x \\ y \end{pmatrix}.$$

(ii) Now suppose that P is on a curve so that x and y (and therefore X and Y) are given in terms of a parameter p. Show that the same curvature at P is obtained whichever co-ordinate system is used in its calculation.

(iii) Show in a similar way that a shift of origin does not affect the value of the curvature at P.

(This confirms that curvature is an intrinsic property of the curve, independent of the choice of co-ordinate axes.)

14 By working in cartesian co-ordinates with θ as a parameter, show that the curvature of the spiral of Archimedes, $r = a\theta$, is $\dfrac{2+\theta^2}{a(1+\theta^2)^{3/2}}$.

15 **(i)** For a curve with polar equation $r = \mathrm{f}(\theta)$, the angle between the radius and the positive tangent is denoted by ϕ as shown in the diagram. Prove that $\psi = \phi + \theta$.

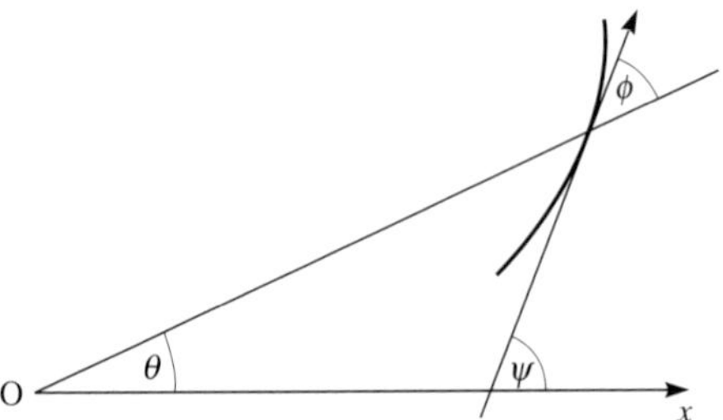

(ii) Deduce from $x = r\cos\theta$, $y = r\sin\theta$ that $\tan\psi = \dfrac{r't + r}{r' - rt}$, where $r' = \dfrac{\mathrm{d}r}{\mathrm{d}\theta}$ and $t = \tan\theta$. Hence show that $\tan\phi = \tan(\psi - \theta) = \dfrac{r}{r'} = r\dfrac{\mathrm{d}\theta}{\mathrm{d}r}$.

(iii) Explain how the 'elementary triangle' PKQ shown in the diagram can be used to remember the basic result that $\tan\phi = r\dfrac{\mathrm{d}\theta}{\mathrm{d}r}$.

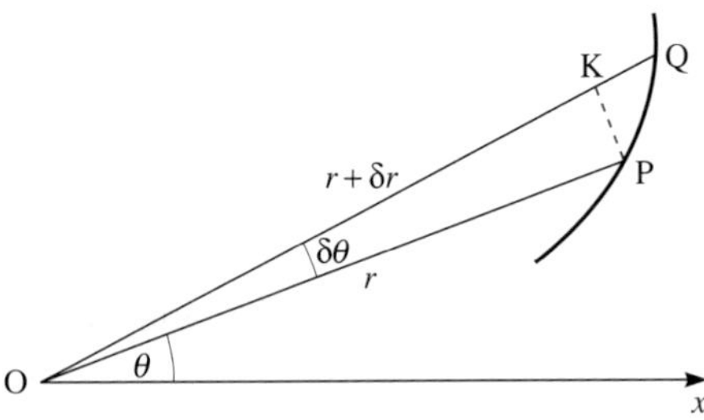

(iv) For the equiangular spiral $r = ae^{\theta\cot\alpha}$ where α is constant with $0 < \alpha < \pi$, prove that $\phi = \alpha$. Use $\dfrac{\mathrm{d}\psi}{\mathrm{d}\theta}$ and $\dfrac{\mathrm{d}s}{\mathrm{d}\theta}$ to show that $\kappa = \dfrac{\sin\alpha}{r}$.

(v) Prove that the curvature of the cardioid $r = a(1 + \cos\theta)$ is $\dfrac{3}{4a}\sec\dfrac{\theta}{2}$.

The circle of curvature

Figure 3.31 shows a curve with its tangent and normal at a point P, where the curvature is κ. Every circle through P with centre on the normal touches the curve at P. The member of this family of circles which fits the curve best at P is the one for which the curvature is also κ; this is called the *circle of curvature* at P.

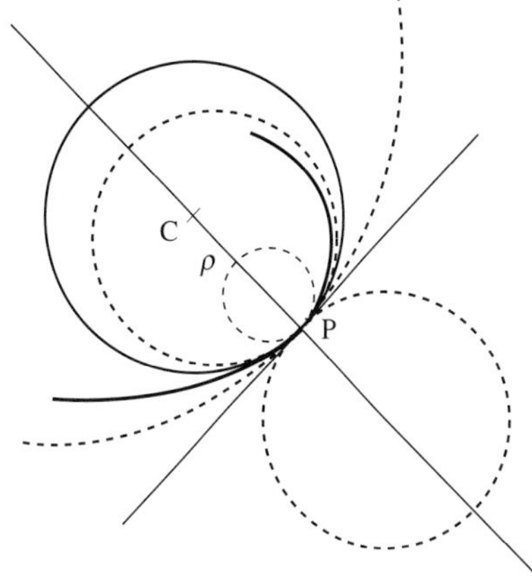

Figure 3.31

Its centre C is the *centre of curvature*, and its radius ρ (the Greek letter rho) is the *radius of curvature*. Since the curvature of a circle of radius ρ is $\frac{1}{\rho}$ it follows that $\frac{1}{\rho} = \kappa$, and therefore that $\rho = \frac{1}{\kappa} = \frac{\mathrm{d}s}{\mathrm{d}\psi}$.

The radius of curvature can be found directly from the parametric or cartesian equations:

$$\rho = \frac{\left(x'^2 + y'^2\right)^{3/2}}{x'y'' - y'x''} = \frac{\left\{1 + \left(\frac{dy}{dx}\right)^2\right\}^{3/2}}{\frac{\mathrm{d}^2y}{\mathrm{d}x^2}}.$$

If the curvature is negative then the definition $\rho = \frac{1}{\kappa}$ means that ρ is negative too. It may seem strange to talk of a circle with a negative radius, and some texts insist that the radius of curvature should be positive by defining $\rho = \left|\frac{1}{\kappa}\right|$, but in fact this turns out to be useful when interpreted correctly.

To show this two special unit vectors, $\hat{\mathbf{t}}$ and $\hat{\mathbf{n}}$ are introduced. The *positive tangent* at a point on a curve is the tangent in the direction of the positive sense at that point; the direction of the *positive normal* is $\frac{\pi}{2}$ ahead of this in the anticlockwise sense, so that the positive normal makes the angle $\psi + \frac{\pi}{2}$ with the positive x axis (see figure 3.32 overleaf). The unit vectors in the directions of the positive tangent and positive normal are $\hat{\mathbf{t}}$ and $\hat{\mathbf{n}}$ respectively. In components:

$$\hat{\mathbf{t}} = \begin{pmatrix} \cos\psi \\ \sin\psi \end{pmatrix} \quad \text{and} \quad \hat{\mathbf{n}} = \begin{pmatrix} -\sin\psi \\ \cos\psi \end{pmatrix}.$$

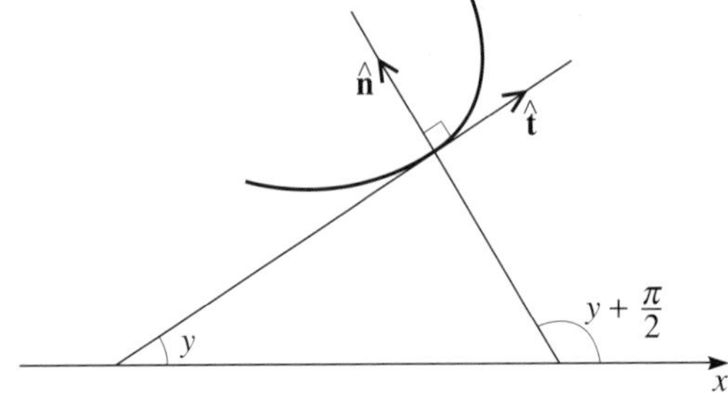

Figure 3.32

If $\kappa > 0$ then the curve bends to the left of the positive tangent and $\hat{\mathbf{n}}$ points towards the concave side of the curve. The centre of curvature C is a distance ρ from P along the positive normal, so that $\mathbf{PC} = \rho\hat{\mathbf{n}}$ (see figure 3.33).

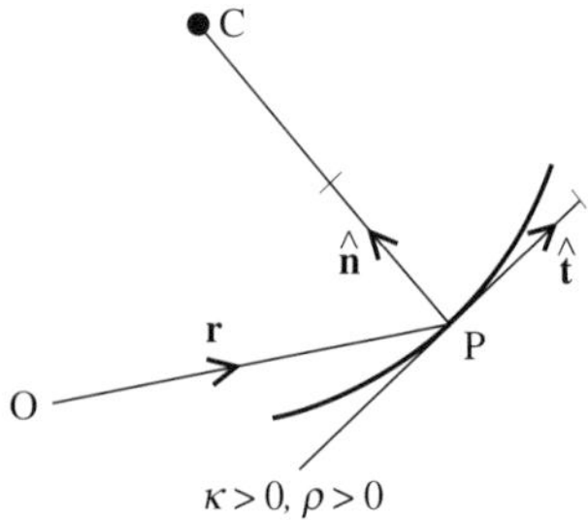

Figure 3.33

But if $\kappa < 0$ (in which case ρ is also negative) then $\hat{\mathbf{n}}$ points away from the concave side of the curve, and to get from P to C you go a distance $-\rho$ in the direction of $-\hat{\mathbf{n}}$ (see figure 3.34).

Therefore $\mathbf{PC} = (-\rho)(-\hat{\mathbf{n}}) = \rho\hat{\mathbf{n}}$ as before.

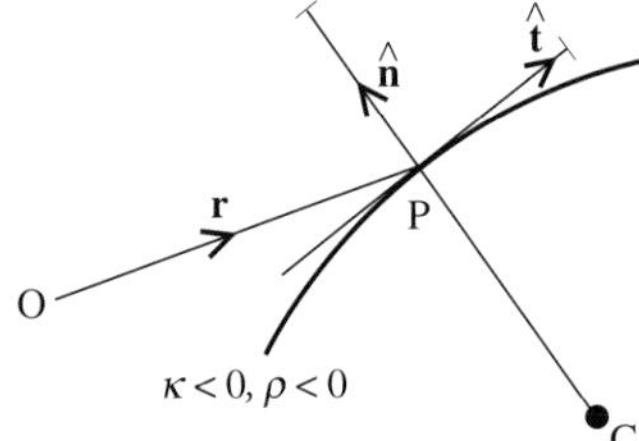

Figure 3.34

This shows that, whatever the sign of κ and ρ, the position vector $\mathbf{c}$ of the centre of curvature is given by $\mathbf{c} = \mathbf{r} + \rho\hat{\mathbf{n}}$.

The same result can be expressed in the co-ordinate form:

$$\xi = x - \rho \sin \psi$$

$$\eta = y + \rho \cos \psi$$

where (ξ, η) is the centre of curvature for the point (x, y). (The symbols ξ and η are the Greek letters xi and eta.)

EXAMPLE 3.12

Find $\hat{\mathbf{t}}$, $\hat{\mathbf{n}}$ and $\mathbf{c}$ for the point (4, 3) on the rectangular hyperbola $xy = 12$.

SOLUTION

Taking x as the independent variable, the positive sense along the curve is to the right.

$$y = \frac{12}{x} \quad \Rightarrow \quad \frac{dy}{dx} = -\frac{12}{x^2} = -\frac{3}{4} \text{ at } (4,3).$$

Therefore $\hat{\mathbf{t}} = \begin{pmatrix} \frac{4}{5} \\ -\frac{3}{5} \end{pmatrix}$ and $\hat{\mathbf{n}} = \begin{pmatrix} \frac{3}{5} \\ \frac{4}{5} \end{pmatrix}$.

$$\frac{d^2y}{dx^2} = \frac{24}{x^3} = \frac{3}{8} \text{ at } (4, 3) \quad \Rightarrow \rho = \frac{\left\{1 + \left(-\frac{3}{4}\right)^2\right\}^{3/2}}{\frac{3}{8}} = \frac{\left\{\frac{25}{16}\right\}^{3/2}}{\frac{3}{8}} = \frac{125}{24}$$

and so $\mathbf{c} = \begin{pmatrix} 4 \\ 3 \end{pmatrix} + \frac{125}{24}\begin{pmatrix} \frac{3}{5} \\ \frac{4}{5} \end{pmatrix} = \begin{pmatrix} 4 \\ 3 \end{pmatrix} + \begin{pmatrix} \frac{25}{8} \\ \frac{25}{6} \end{pmatrix} = \begin{pmatrix} 7\frac{1}{8} \\ 7\frac{1}{6} \end{pmatrix}$.

EXERCISE 3F

1 Find the co-ordinates of the centre of curvature of the curve $xy = 16$ at the point (4, 4).

2 Find the vectors $\hat{\mathbf{t}}$, $\hat{\mathbf{n}}$ and $\mathbf{c}$ when $x = \frac{\pi}{4}$ on the curve $y = \tan x$.

3 Prove that the co-ordinates of the centre of curvature are $\left(x - \frac{dy}{d\psi}, y + \frac{dx}{d\psi}\right)$.

Hence show that the centre of curvature at the point (X, Y) on $y = \ln \sec x$ is $(X - \tan X, Y + 1)$.

[**Hint**: See Exercise 3D, Question 1.]

4 For the equiangular spiral $r = ke^{\theta}$ show that $\psi = \theta + \frac{\pi}{4}$. Use the method of Question 3 to find the cartesian co-ordinates of the centre of curvature in terms of θ.

5 On a sketch, show the catenary $y = c\cosh\frac{x}{c}$ with the tangent and normal at a point P. Prove that if the normal meets the x axis at D then the centre of curvature C is the reflection of D in the tangent.

6 Let the equation of the circle of curvature at the point $P(3p^2, 2p^3)$ of the curve $27y^2 = 4x^3$ be $x^2 + y^2 + 2ax + 2by + c = 0$. Find the values of a, b and c by using the facts that the circle and the curve have triple point contact, i.e.

(i) both pass through P

(ii) both have the same gradient at P

(iii) both have the same value of $\frac{d^2y}{dx^2}$ at P.

7 Prove that the centre of curvature of the ellipse $\frac{x^2}{a^2} + \frac{y^2}{b^2} = 1$ at $(a \cos \theta, b \sin \theta)$ is $\left(\frac{a^2 - b^2}{a}\cos^3\theta, -\frac{a^2 - b^2}{b}\sin^3\theta\right)$. What can be said about the eccentricity of the ellipse if the centre of curvature at $(0, b)$ is:

(i) inside **(ii)** on **(iii)** outside

the ellipse?

The evolute of a curve

As the point P moves along a given curve, the centre of curvature C also moves. The locus of the centre of curvature is called the *evolute* of the curve.

EXAMPLE 3.13 Find the equation of the evolute of the parabola $y^2 = 4ax$.

SOLUTION

Use the parametric equations $x = ap^2$, $y = 2ap$.

Then $x' = 2ap$, $y' = 2a$, $x'' = 2a$, $y'' = 0$ so that:

$$\rho = \frac{\left\{(2ap)^2 + (2a)^2\right\}^{3/2}}{2ap \times 0 - 2a \times 2a} = -2a\left\{p^2 + 1\right\}^{3/2}$$

$$\tan\psi = \frac{1}{p} \text{ and } \hat{\mathbf{n}} = \begin{pmatrix} -1/\sqrt{p^2+1} \\ p/\sqrt{p^2+1} \end{pmatrix}.$$

Therefore $\mathbf{c} = \mathbf{r} + \rho\hat{\mathbf{n}}$

$$= \begin{pmatrix} ap^2 \\ 2ap \end{pmatrix} - 2a\{p^2+1\}^{3/2}\begin{pmatrix} -1/\sqrt{p^2+1} \\ p/\sqrt{p^2+1} \end{pmatrix}$$

$$= \begin{pmatrix} ap^2 \\ 2ap \end{pmatrix} - 2a(p^2+1)\begin{pmatrix} -1 \\ p \end{pmatrix}$$

$$= \begin{pmatrix} 2a + 3ap^2 \\ -2ap^3 \end{pmatrix}.$$

The parametric equations of the evolute are:

$$x = 2a + 3ap^2, \; y = -2ap^3$$

from which the cartesian equation is

$$27ay^2 = 4(x - 2a)^3.$$

The evolute is a semi-cubical parabola with its cusp at $(2a, 0)$, as shown in figure 3.35.

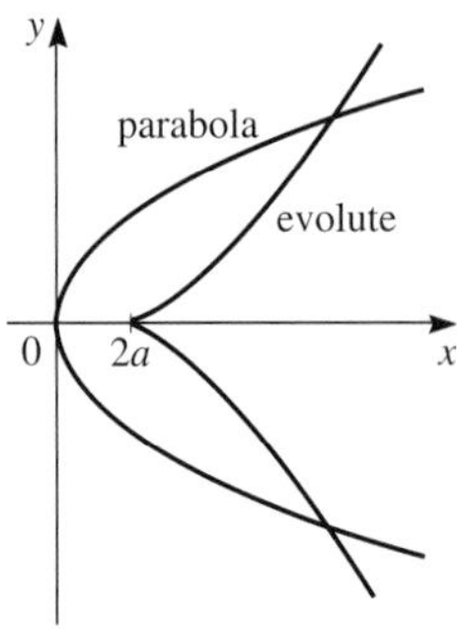

Figure 3.35

The evolute as the envelope of the normals

An alternative view of the evolute comes from differentiating the relation $\mathbf{c} = \mathbf{r} + \rho\hat{\mathbf{n}}$ with respect to the arc length s:

$$\frac{\mathrm{d}\mathbf{c}}{\mathrm{d}s} = \frac{\mathrm{d}\mathbf{r}}{\mathrm{d}s} + \frac{\mathrm{d}\rho}{\mathrm{d}s}\hat{\mathbf{n}} + \rho\frac{\mathrm{d}\hat{\mathbf{n}}}{\mathrm{d}s}.$$

The right-hand side simplifies considerably, since:

$$\frac{\mathrm{d}\mathbf{r}}{\mathrm{d}s} = \begin{pmatrix} \mathrm{d}x / \mathrm{d}s \\ \mathrm{d}y / \mathrm{d}s \end{pmatrix} = \begin{pmatrix} \cos\psi \\ \sin\psi \end{pmatrix} = \hat{\mathbf{t}}$$

and

$$\rho\frac{\mathrm{d}\hat{\mathbf{n}}}{\mathrm{d}s} = \frac{\mathrm{d}s}{\mathrm{d}\psi}\frac{\mathrm{d}\hat{\mathbf{n}}}{\mathrm{d}s} = \frac{\mathrm{d}\hat{\mathbf{n}}}{\mathrm{d}\psi} = \begin{pmatrix} -\cos\psi \\ -\sin\psi \end{pmatrix} = -\hat{\mathbf{t}}.$$

Therefore $\dfrac{\mathrm{d}\mathbf{c}}{\mathrm{d}s} = \dfrac{\mathrm{d}\rho}{\mathrm{d}s}\hat{\mathbf{n}}.$

In this equation the left-hand side is a vector in the direction of the tangent to the evolute at C, and the right-hand side is a vector in the direction of the normal PC. Therefore this normal touches the evolute at C, and so the evolute is the envelope of the normals. Finding this envelope is often the simplest way to find the evolute.

EXAMPLE 3.14

Use the envelope of the normals to find the evolute of the parabola $y^2 = 4ax$ again.

SOLUTION

As before: $x = ap^2$, $y = 2ap \Rightarrow \dfrac{\mathrm{d}y}{\mathrm{d}x} = \dfrac{1}{p}$

so the gradient of the normal is $-p$ and the equation of the normal is:

$$y - 2ap = -p(x - ap^2)$$

or $\mathrm{f}(x, y, p) = px + y - 2ap - ap^3 = 0.$

$$\frac{\partial \mathrm{f}}{\partial p} = x - 2a - 3ap^2 = 0 \qquad \Rightarrow \qquad x = 2a + 3ap^2.$$

Substituting this in $\mathrm{f}(x, y, p) = 0$ gives:

$$2ap + 3ap^3 + y - 2ap - ap^3 = 0 \qquad \Rightarrow \qquad y = -2ap^3$$

so you get the same parametric equations as on page 118, with much less effort (see figure 3.36).

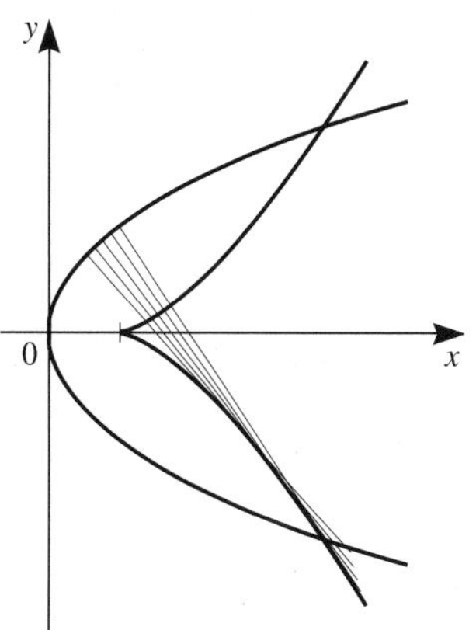

Figure 3.36

What happens to the evolute:

(i) when there is a cusp on the curve
(ii) when there is a point of inflection on the curve
(iii) when the curvature is greatest or least?

EXERCISE 3G

1 Find parametric equations for the evolute of the rectangular hyperbola

$$x = ct,\ y = \frac{c}{t}.$$

2 Show that the equation of the normal of the standard ellipse at $(a \cos \theta, b \sin \theta)$ can be written in the form

$$ax \sec \theta - by \operatorname{cosec} \theta - a^2 + b^2 = 0.$$

Use the envelope of the normals to find parametric equations for the evolute. (Compare this with Exercise 3F, Question 7.)

Show the ellipse and its evolute in a sketch, indicating how the centre of curvature moves round the evolute as θ increases from 0 to 2π.

3 For the nephroid $x = 3a \cos \theta - a \cos 3\theta$, $y = 3a \sin \theta - a \sin 3\theta$, use the fact that $\psi = 2\theta$ (see Exercise 3D, Question 3) to show that the evolute has parametric equations $x = \frac{1}{2}a(3 \cos \theta + \cos 3\theta)$, $y = \frac{1}{2}a(3 \sin \theta + \sin 3\theta)$.

Show that the evolute is another nephroid, half the size of the original and turned through a right angle. Draw a sketch of the original nephroid and its evolute.

4 Show that the equation of the normal to the astroid $x = a \cos^3 \theta$, $y = a \sin^3 \theta$ can be put into the form $x \cos \theta - y \sin \theta = a(\cos^2 \theta - \sin^2 \theta)$.

Find the co-ordinates of the points U and V at which this normal meets the lines $y = x$ and $y = -x$, and show that UV $= 2a$ for all θ.

Deduce that the evolute of the astroid is another astroid twice as large, and show both astroids in a sketch.

5 The equiangular spiral with polar equation $r = ak^\theta$ has the remarkable property that turning the curve about O is equivalent to enlarging it from the centre O: to see this, note that adding β to θ multiplies r by k^β.

Deduce from this that, for every point P on the curve, the angle between OP and the tangent at P is constant (hence the name *equiangular*). (See also Exercise 3E, Question 15**(iv)**.)

The diagram shows the normal PN meeting at N the line through O perpendicular to OP. The constant angle between OP and the tangent is α.

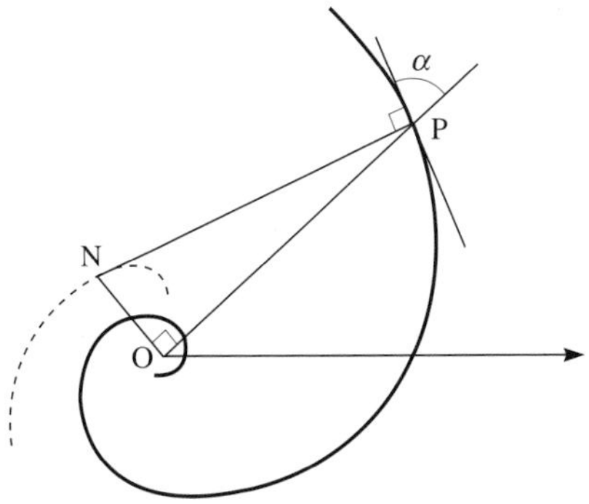

(i) Explain why the locus of N as P varies is a spiral (shown dashed) which is similar to, and therefore congruent to, the original spiral.

(ii) Show that PN touches this new spiral.

(iii) Deduce that the new spiral is the evolute of the original spiral, and that N is the centre of curvature at P.

(iv) Is it possible for a curve to be its own evolute?

6 Prove that the evolute of the cycloid $x = a(\theta - \sin\theta)$, $y = a(1 - \cos\theta)$ has parametric equations $x = a(\theta + \sin\theta)$, $y = -a(1 - \cos\theta)$.
Prove that the evolute is a congruent cycloid, and draw a sketch to show how the two cycloids are related.

7 A point P moves so that its position vector at time t is $\mathbf{r}$.

(i) By differentiating $\mathbf{r}$ with respect to t, prove that its velocity is $v\hat{\mathbf{t}}$, where $v = \dfrac{\mathrm{d}s}{\mathrm{d}t}$.

(ii) Prove that its acceleration is $\dfrac{\mathrm{d}v}{\mathrm{d}t}\hat{\mathbf{t}} + \dfrac{v^2}{\rho}\hat{\mathbf{n}}$.

(This splits the acceleration into *tangential* and *normal* components; these are the same as if P were moving round the circle of curvature.)

8 The envelope of the normals again

(i) Let the co-ordinates of a point (x, y) on a curve be given parametrically in terms of ψ, and let (ξ, η) be any point on the normal to the curve at (x, y). Show that $\eta - y + \cot\psi(\xi - x) = 0$.

(ii) Let $\mathrm{f}(\xi, \eta, \psi) = \eta - y + \cot\psi(\xi - x)$, so that $\mathrm{f}(\xi, \eta, \psi) = 0$ is the equation of the family of normals, with parameter ψ.

Show that $\dfrac{\partial \mathrm{f}}{\partial \psi}$ can be written in the form

$-\rho\sin\psi - \operatorname{cosec}^2\psi(\xi - x) - \cot\psi \times \rho\cos\psi$ and deduce that

$\mathrm{f} = 0$ and $\dfrac{\partial \mathrm{f}}{\partial \psi} = 0 \Rightarrow \xi - x = -\rho\sin\psi$ and $\eta - y = \rho\cos\psi$.

(iii) Deduce that the envelope of the normals has parametric equations:

$$\xi = x - \rho\sin\psi, \qquad \eta = y + \rho\cos\psi$$

or $\mathbf{c} = \mathbf{r} + \rho\hat{\mathbf{n}}$.

e Involutes

The equation $\frac{d\mathbf{c}}{ds} = \frac{d\rho}{ds}\hat{\mathbf{n}}$ on page 119 gives another interesting result. You have seen that $\frac{d\mathbf{r}}{ds} = \hat{\mathbf{t}}$, which means that differentiating the position vector of a point on a curve with respect to the arc length of the curve gives the tangential unit vector. Now suppose that the arc length of the evolute is σ (the Greek letter sigma), measured from a fixed point of the evolute in the positive sense along the evolute (i.e. the sense in which C moves as s increases). Then the result for the evolute corresponding to $\frac{d\mathbf{r}}{ds} = \hat{\mathbf{t}}$ for the original curve is $\frac{d\mathbf{c}}{d\sigma} = \hat{\mathbf{n}}$, since $\hat{\mathbf{n}}$ is the tangential unit vector for the evolute.

$$\begin{aligned}\text{So } \hat{\mathbf{n}} &= \frac{d\mathbf{c}}{d\sigma} \\ &= \frac{d\mathbf{c}}{ds} \times \frac{ds}{d\sigma} \\ &= \frac{d\rho}{ds}\hat{\mathbf{n}} \times \frac{ds}{d\sigma} \qquad \left(\text{since } \frac{d\mathbf{c}}{ds} = \frac{d\rho}{ds}\hat{\mathbf{n}}\right) \\ &= \frac{d\rho}{d\sigma}\hat{\mathbf{n}}.\end{aligned}$$

Therefore $\frac{d\rho}{d\sigma} = 1$, which means that ρ and σ differ by a constant.

So if C moves from C_1 to C_2 as P moves from P_1 to P_2 then arc $C_1C_2 = \sigma_2 - \sigma_1 = \rho_2 - \rho_1$ (see figure 3.37).

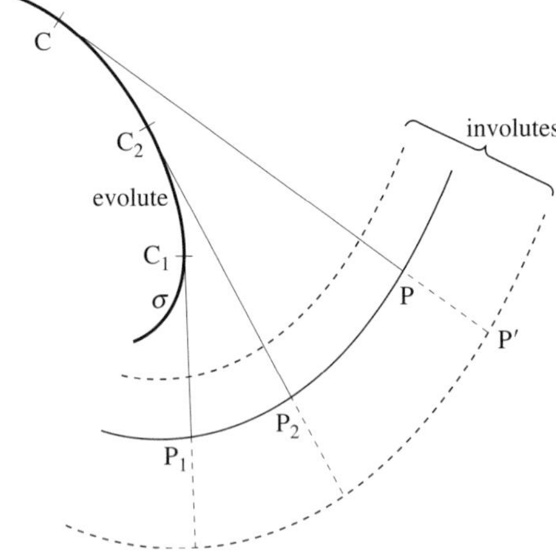

Figure 3.37

If a string $C_2C_1P_1$ is wrapped around the evolute and then unwound so that the free part is always kept straight, then the free end P traces out the original curve. Moreover, if P′ is another point on CP, or on CP produced, then the locus of P′ is another curve which has the same evolute. Each curve produced by a point P′ in this way (including the original curve) is called an *involute* of the evolute. Any two involutes can be regarded as 'parallel' curves, since each normal to one is also normal to the other, and the distance between the curves measured along the normal remains constant.

EXAMPLE 3.15

The evolute of the parabola $y^2 = 4ax$ meets the parabola at A and B. Find the length of the evolute from A to B.

SOLUTION

The centre of curvature at $(ap^2, 2ap)$ is $(2a + 3ap^2, -2ap^3)$ (as on pages 118 and 119), which is also on the parabola if and only if:

$$
\begin{aligned}
& (-2ap^3)^2 = 4a(2a + 3ap^2) \\
\Leftrightarrow \quad & 4a^2p^6 = 8a^2 + 12a^2p^2 \\
\Leftrightarrow \quad & p^6 = 2 + 3p^2 \\
\Leftrightarrow \quad & u^3 = 2 + 3u \text{ where } u = p^2 \\
\Leftrightarrow \quad & u = 2 \text{ by inspection} \\
\Leftrightarrow \quad & p = \pm\sqrt{2}.
\end{aligned}
$$

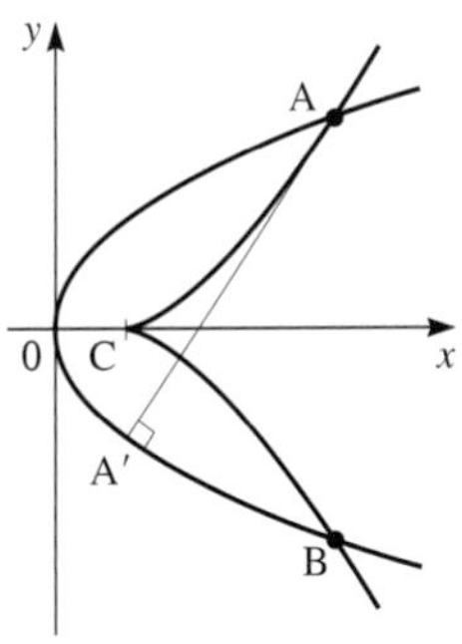

Figure 3.38

The value $p = -\sqrt{2}$ gives the point $A'(2a, -2\sqrt{2}a)$ on the parabola with its centre of curvature $A(8a, 4\sqrt{2}a)$ also on the parabola, as in figure 3.38.

If the cusp of the evolute is $C(2a, 0)$ then the length of arc AC is the difference of the radii of curvature at A′ and O, so that:

$$
\begin{aligned}
\text{arc AC} = \text{A'A} - \text{OC} &= \sqrt{(8a - 2a)^2 + (4\sqrt{2}a + 2\sqrt{2}a)^2} - 2a \\
&= (\sqrt{108} - 2)a = 2(\sqrt{27} - 1)a.
\end{aligned}
$$

Therefore arc $\text{ACB} = 4\left(\sqrt{27} - 1\right)a \approx 16.8a$.

EXERCISE 3H

1 Find the total length of the evolute of the ellipse $\dfrac{x^2}{a^2} + \dfrac{y^2}{b^2} = 1$.

2 Draw a sketch showing the astroid $x = a\cos^3\theta$, $y = a\sin^3\theta$ and its evolute (as in Exercise 3G, Question 4). Let these curves meet the line $y = x$ in the first quadrant at the points H and K. Prove that $\text{HK} = \frac{3}{2}a$. Use this to find the total length of:

(i) the evolute **(ii)** the original astroid.

3 The point C on the evolute corresponds to the point P on the original curve. Prove that the radius of curvature of the evolute at C equals the value of $\dfrac{d^2s}{d\psi^2}$ at P.

4 Explain why all the involutes of a given circle are congruent. Prove that, for the circle $x^2 + y^2 = a^2$, one of the involutes through $(a, 0)$ has parametric equations:

$$x = a\cos\theta + a\theta\sin\theta \qquad y = a\sin\theta - a\theta\cos\theta.$$

Find similar equations for the other involute through $(a, 0)$.

5 Involute gears

(i) The diagram shows two wheels with centres A and B, and radii a and b, connected by a crossed drive belt. Show that if the upper wheel turns anticlockwise with angular speed Ω_A then the lower wheel turns clockwise with angular speed Ω_B, where $\Omega_B : \Omega_A = a : b$.

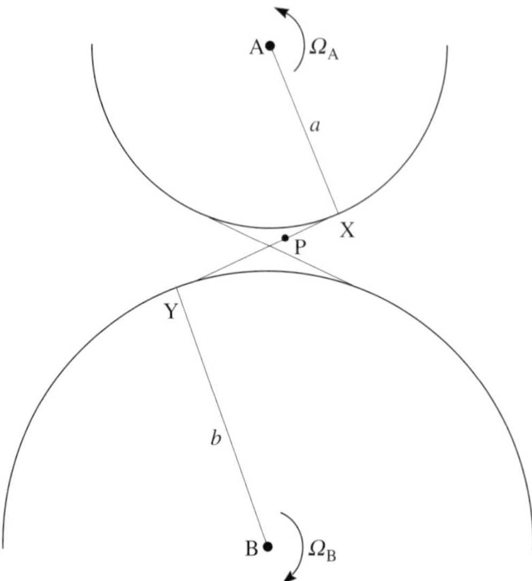

(ii) Suppose that P is a fixed point of the drive belt. Explain why the locus of P *as seen by an observer fixed to either wheel* is an involute of that wheel. This means that the drive belt can be replaced by gear teeth of which the faces are involutes of the two circles, as in the diagram below. These gear wheels will roll on each other without sliding (thus minimising wear), and the velocity ratio of the gear wheels remains as before.

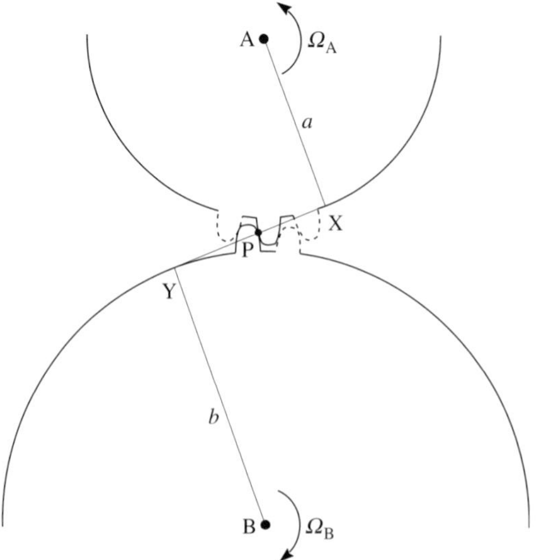

The tractrix

Figure 3.39 shows the catenary $y = c\cosh\frac{x}{c}$ together with an involute which passes through A(0, c). The point C(X, Y) on the catenary corresponds to the point P(x, y) on this involute, and the arc length of the catenary from A to C is s.

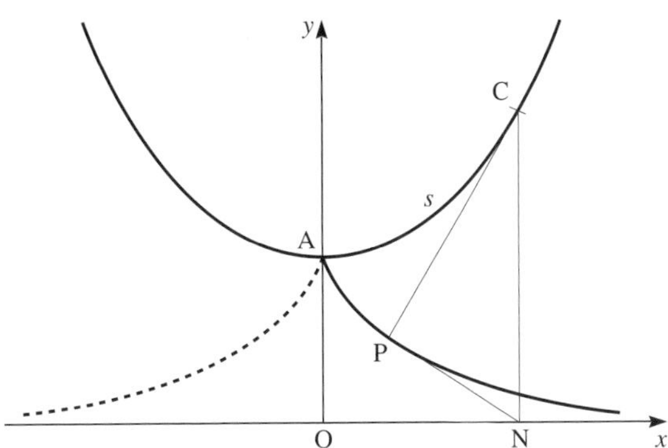

Figure 3.39

Let the tangent to the involute meet the line $x = X$ at N.

(i) Prove that angle CNP $= \psi$, and deduce from the intrinsic equation of the catenary $s = c\tan\psi$ that PN $= c$.

(ii) Prove from the intrinsic and cartesian equations that $s^2 + c^2 = Y^2$, and deduce that NC $= Y$, so that N is on the x axis.

(The fact that the length of the tangent to the involute between P and N is always c shows that if a small object placed at A is attached by a string of length c with its other end initially at O, and this end is slowly moved along the x axis, then the object moves along the involute. This curve plus its reflection in the y axis is therefore called the *tractrix* (the pulling curve), a name coined by Huygens in 1693. He also called it the 'dog curve' because it reminded him of dragging a reluctant dog for a walk.)

(iii) Prove that the tractrix has parametric equations:

$$x = c\ln(\sec\psi + \tan\psi) - c\sin\psi$$

$$y = c\cos\psi$$

for $-\frac{\pi}{2} < \psi < \frac{\pi}{2}$.

(iv) By considering a small displacement of the line PN as P moves along the tractrix in figure 3.39, show that the area between the tractrix and its asymptote can be found as $\int_{-\pi/2}^{\pi/2} \frac{1}{2}c^2 \, d\psi$, and evaluate this integral.

(v) The solid of revolution (an infinitely long double trumpet) obtained by rotating the tractrix about its asymptote is called the *pseudosphere*; it plays an important part in non-Euclidean geometry. Prove that the pseudosphere has volume $\frac{2}{3}\pi c^3$ and surface area $4\pi c^2$.

The cycloidal pendulum

Figure 3.40 shows a pendulum consisting of a bob P attached to a point B by a string BQP. As it swings the string wraps around the arcs AB and BC which are two half-arches of a cycloid. The length of the string is $4a$, which is half the arc length of one complete arch of the standard cycloid (as in Exercise 3B, Question 5).

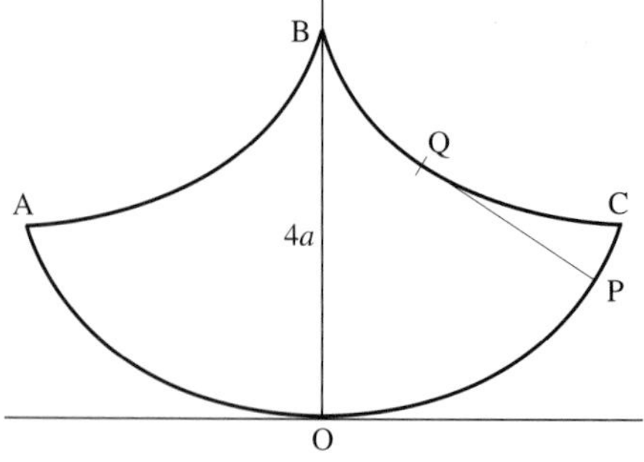

Figure 3.40

(i) Use Exercise 3G, Question 6 to show that P moves along an equal cycloid AOC.

(ii) With O as the origin the intrinsic equation of cycloid AOC is $s = 4a \sin \psi$ (Exercise 3D, Question 4). Use this, and Exercise 3G, Question 7, with Newton's second law of motion, to show that the equation of tangential motion of P is $\dfrac{\mathrm{d}^2 s}{\mathrm{d}t^2} = -\dfrac{g}{4a}s$, where g is the acceleration due to gravity.

(iii) Hence show that P moves with *exact* simple harmonic motion along its path, with period $4\pi\sqrt{\dfrac{a}{g}}$ independent of the amplitude of the swing.

Note

In 1673 Huygens proposed this as a method of improving pendulum clocks on ships, where accurate timekeeping is needed for navigation. It is remarkable that the cycloid is both the path needed to produce exact simple harmonic motion and the means of making the bob move on this path. Such clocks were made, but because of other mechanical difficulties the cycloidal pendulum did not actually improve accuracy.

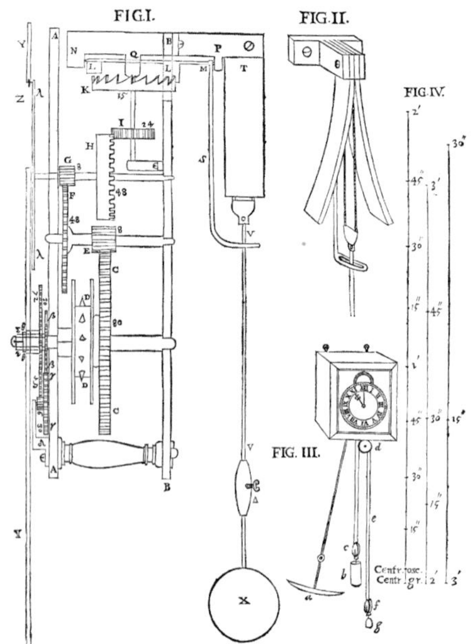

Figure 3.41 Diagrams from Huygens' Horologium Oscillatorium (1673). Fig II shows the cycloidal 'cheeks'.

EXERCISE 3I

1 **(i)** For the point P(0, 1) on the curve $y = e^{2x}$, calculate

(a) the radius of curvature

(b) the co-ordinates of the centre of curvature.

(ii) **(a)** Find the equation of the straight line passing through the points $(t, 0)$ and $(0, t^3)$.

(b) As t varies, these straight lines define an envelope. Find the cartesian equation of the envelope.

[MEI]

2 A curve has parametric equations $x = 4t - \frac{1}{3}t^3,\ y = 2t^2 - 8$.

(i) Show that the radius of curvature at a general point $(4t - \frac{1}{3}t^3, 2t^2 - 8)$ on the curve is $\frac{1}{4}(4 + t^2)^2$.

(ii) Find the centre of curvature corresponding to the point on the curve given by $t = 3$.

The arc of the curve given by $0 \leqslant t \leqslant 2\sqrt{3}$ is denoted by C.

(iii) Find the length of the arc C.

(iv) Find the area of the curved surface generated when the arc C is rotated about the y axis.

[MEI]

3 A curve is given parametrically by

$$x = e^{\theta}(2 \sin 2\theta + \cos 2\theta),\ y = e^{\theta}(\sin 2\theta - 2 \cos 2\theta).$$

P is the point corresponding to $\theta = 0$, and Q is the point corresponding to $\theta = \alpha$ (where $\alpha > 0$).

(i) Show that the gradient of the curve at Q is $\tan 2\alpha$, and find the length of the arc of the curve between P and Q.

(ii) Using intrinsic co-ordinates (s, ψ), where s is the arc length of the curve measured from P and $\tan\psi = \dfrac{dy}{dx}$, show that $s = 5(e^{\psi/2} - 1)$.

(iii) Find the radius of curvature at the point Q.

(iv) Show that the centre of curvature corresponding to the point Q is

$$\left(\tfrac{1}{2}e^{\alpha}(2 \cos 2\alpha - \sin 2\alpha), \tfrac{1}{2}e^{\alpha}(2 \sin 2\alpha + \cos 2\alpha)\right).$$

[MEI]

4 **(i)** Show that the arc length of the polar curve $r = \sin^3\frac{1}{3}\theta$, for $0 \leqslant \theta \leqslant 3\pi$, is $\frac{3}{2}\pi$.

(ii) A family of curves in the x–y plane is given by

$$y = \lambda x^2 + 3x - \lambda^2, \qquad \text{where } \lambda > 0.$$

For the point $(0, -\lambda^2)$ on the curve $y = \lambda x^2 + 3x - \lambda^2$, find (in terms of λ)

(a) the radius of curvature

(b) the co-ordinates of the centre of curvature.

As λ varies, the curves in the family define an envelope.

(c) Find the equation of this envelope.

[MEI]

5 The equation of a curve is $y = a\cosh\left(\dfrac{x}{a}\right)$, where a is a positive constant.

The arc of this curve for which $0 \leqslant x \leqslant a\ln 3$ is denoted by C.

(i) Find the length of the arc C.

(ii) Show that, when C is rotated through 2π radians about the x axis, the curved surface area generated is $\pi a^2\left(\ln 3 + \frac{20}{9}\right)$.

(iii) Find the equation of the normal to the curve $y = a\cosh\left(\dfrac{x}{a}\right)$ at a general point $(a\theta, a\cosh\theta)$. Hence find parametric equations for the evolute of the curve.

[MEI]

KEY POINTS

1 The equation of the envelope of a family of curves can be found by elimination from the equations $f(x, y, p) = 0$ and $\frac{\partial f}{\partial p}(x, y, p) = 0$.

2 Arc length s can be found by integrating:

$$\frac{ds}{dp} = \sqrt{\left(\frac{dx}{dp}\right)^2 + \left(\frac{dy}{dp}\right)^2}$$

$$\text{or } \frac{ds}{dx} = \sqrt{1 + \left(\frac{dy}{dx}\right)^2} \text{ or } \frac{ds}{dy} = \sqrt{\left(\frac{dx}{dy}\right)^2 + 1}$$

$$\text{or (for polar equations) } \frac{ds}{d\theta} = \sqrt{\left(\frac{dr}{d\theta}\right)^2 + r^2}.$$

3 The volume of a solid of revolution formed by rotating about the x axis is $\int_a^b \pi y^2 \, dx$ and its surface area is $\int_A^B 2\pi y \, ds$.

The corresponding results for a solid formed by rotating about the y axis are $\int_c^d \pi x^2 \, dy$ and $\int_C^D 2\pi x \, ds$.

4 The intrinsic equation of a curve is the equation linking its arc length s and the inclination ψ of the tangent.

5 The curvature of a curve is:

$$\kappa = \frac{d\psi}{ds} = \frac{x'y'' - y'x''}{(x'^2 + y'^2)^{3/2}} = \frac{\frac{d^2y}{dx^2}}{\left[1 + \left(\frac{dy}{dx}\right)^2\right]^{3/2}}.$$

6 The radius of curvature is $\rho = \frac{1}{\kappa} = \frac{ds}{d\psi}$.

7 The tangential and normal unit vectors are $\hat{\mathbf{t}} = \begin{pmatrix} \cos\psi \\ \sin\psi \end{pmatrix}$ and $\hat{\mathbf{n}} = \begin{pmatrix} -\sin\psi \\ \cos\psi \end{pmatrix}$.

8 The centre of curvature has position vector $\mathbf{c} = \mathbf{r} + \rho\hat{\mathbf{n}}$.

9 The evolute of a curve is the locus of the centre of curvature; it is also the envelope of the normals to the curve. An involute of a given curve is a curve which has the given curve as its evolute.

4 Groups

Premature abstraction falls on deaf ears whether they belong to mathematicians or to students.

Morris Kline (1908–92)

Sets and operations

Anyone who knows how to add two-dimensional column vectors can easily learn how to add 3×3 matrices or complex numbers. In each case the basic idea is to add corresponding pairs of components: the process is 'the same but different'. This recognition of the underlying structure in different situations is an essential skill, since otherwise mathematics comes to be seen as an incoherent bag of tricks. Of course it is equally important to recognise when structures are *not* the same (for example, when forming products of vectors, of matrices or of complex numbers).

From your earliest stages in mathematics you have been dealing with sets of mathematical objects and operations on these objects. Obvious examples include:

- sets of numbers (e.g. counting numbers, rational numbers, integers, complex numbers) with the 'four rules' ($+, -, \times, \div$) or the process of taking square roots
- sets of vectors (e.g. in two or three or, perhaps, n dimensions) with vector addition or the scalar or vector product or the operation of finding the modulus of the vector
- sets of functions (e.g. polynomial functions, rational functions, functions f such that $f(0) = f(1) = 0$, exponential functions) combined by composition of functions ('function of a function') or changed by differentiation
- sets of matrices (e.g. 2×3 matrices, non-singular matrices, 2×2 matrices with determinant 1) with matrix addition or matrix multiplication or the process of finding the inverse
- sets of points with the operations of finding the mid-point of two given points or finding the distance between two points.

? From these examples, pick out cases where:

(i) the operation cannot be applied at all in the set mentioned

(ii) the operation can be applied to general elements of the set, but not to some particular elements.

Most of these operations take *two* elements of the set and combine them in some way to give a definite result; such a rule of combination is called a *binary operation*. Many binary operations are denoted by conventional symbols, such as + for addition (though this could mean addition of numbers or vectors or matrices according to the context) and ÷ or / for division. Other symbols such as $\ast$ or $\bullet$ can be used to show binary operations, so that $x \ast y$ or $x \bullet y$ means the result of combining x and y. The elements to be combined do not have to be distinct: it is usually possible to combine an element with itself, as with $x \ast x$ or $x \bullet x$.

Other operations (for example, taking the square root of a number or finding the inverse of a matrix) act on a single element; these are called *unary operations*.

ACTIVITY 4.1

(i) Identify two other unary operations from the examples above.
(ii) Give two examples of *ternary operations* (which combine three elements).

Here you will concentrate on some properties which a particular binary operation may or may not possess. Suppose that $\bullet$ is a binary operation on elements $x, y, z, \ldots$ of the set S.

Closure

If the result of the operation is always in the original set S, i.e. $x \bullet y \in S$ for all $x, y \in S$, then the operation is said to be *closed*. (In set notation, $\in$ means 'belongs to' or 'is a member of'.) For example, within the set of positive integers, multiplication is closed (since the product of two positive integers is always a positive integer) but division is not (since for example $2 \div 3$ is not a positive integer).

Commutativity

If changing the order of the elements has no effect on the result, i.e. if $y \bullet x = x \bullet y$ for all $x, y \in S$, then the operation is said to be *commutative*. For example, if S is the set of three-dimensional vectors, then the scalar product is commutative ($\mathbf{a} . \mathbf{b} = \mathbf{b} . \mathbf{a}$ for all $\mathbf{a}, \mathbf{b} \in S$), but the vector product is not (since $\mathbf{a} \times \mathbf{b}$ and $\mathbf{b} \times \mathbf{a}$ have opposite directions for all non-parallel $\mathbf{a}$ and $\mathbf{b}$).

Associativity

If the operation is closed then the result of combining x and y can be combined with another element, z say, to give $(x \bullet y) \bullet z$. Alternatively you can form $x \bullet (y \bullet z)$, where the bracketing now shows that x is combined with the result of combining y and z. If the bracketing has no effect, i.e. if $(x \bullet y) \bullet z = x \bullet (y \bullet z)$ for all $x, y, z \in S$, then the operation is said to be *associative*. For example, addition of real numbers is associative, but subtraction is not (since for example $(10 - 6) - 2 \neq 10 - (6 - 2)$). More is said about associativity on page 136.

ACTIVITY 4.2 From the examples on page 130, select a set and a binary operation which is:

(i) non-closed, commutative
(ii) closed, non-commutative, associative
(iii) closed, commutative, non-associative
(iv) closed, non-commutative, non-associative.

Modular arithmetic

Within the set of integers, two numbers are said to be *congruent modulo m* if the difference between them is a multiple of m. For example, since

$$77 - 29 = 48 = 12 \times 4,$$

77 and 29 are congruent modulo 12; this can be abbreviated to $77 = 29 \pmod{12}$.

ACTIVITY 4.3

(i) Give three other integers, one of them negative, which are congruent to 77 modulo 12.
(ii) Give three other positive integers m such that $77 = 29 \pmod{m}$.

If the remainder when a is divided by m is b, then $a = b + hm$ for some integer h, and so $a = b \pmod{m}$. The only possible remainders are 0, 1, 2, …, $m - 1$, and so every integer is congruent to one of these. *Modular arithmetic* (with modulus m) is carried out on the set $\{0, 1, 2, \ldots, m - 1\}$ using the binary operations $+_m$ and $\times_m$, which are like ordinary addition and multiplication respectively, except that if the sum or product falls outside the set then the answer is the remainder when this is divided by m.

EXAMPLE 4.1 Find $8 +_{12} 11$ and $8 \times_{12} 11$.

SOLUTION

The modulus is 12.

$8 + 11 = 19 = 12 \times 1 + \underline{7}$, so that $8 +_{12} 11 = 7$.

$8 \times 11 = 88 = 12 \times 7 + \underline{4}$, so that $8 \times_{12} 11 = 4$.

The theory of congruences and modular arithmetic has far-reaching consequences, but here it is used only to provide examples in the development of the main topic, groups.

EXERCISE 4A

1 Write out:

(i) the addition table for $\{0, 1, 2, 3, 4\}$ under $+_5$

(ii) the multiplication table for $\{0, 1, 2, 3, 4, 5, 6\}$ under $\times_7$.

2 Answer these questions, and explain the connections with modular arithmetic.

(i) If today is Monday, what day of the week will it be after 100 days?

(ii) If a train departs at 21.37 and the journey takes 5 hours 40 minutes, at what time (on the 24-hour clock) does the train arrive?

(iii) Is 48 902 918 529 263 a perfect square?

3 Prove or disprove each of these statements.

(i) $x + 2 = y + 4 \pmod{12} \Rightarrow x = y + 2 \pmod{12}$

(ii) $2x = 4y \pmod{12} \Rightarrow x = 2y \pmod{12}$.

4 **(i)** Prove that: $a = b \pmod m$ and $c = d \pmod m \Rightarrow a + c = b + d \pmod m$.
[**Hint:** If $a = b \pmod m$ and $c = d \pmod m$ then there are integers h and k such that $a = b + hm$ and $c = d + km$.]

(ii) Prove that: $a = b \pmod m$ and $c = d \pmod m \Rightarrow ac = bd \pmod m$.

(iii) Investigate whether the converses of **(i)** and **(ii)** are true.

5 The integer x written as '$a_n a_{n-1} \ldots a_2 a_1 a_0$', has units digit a_0, tens digit a_1, hundreds digit a_2, and so on. Prove that:

$$x = a_n + a_{n-1} + \ldots + a_2 + a_1 + a_0 \pmod 9.$$

Deduce that x is divisible by 9 if and only if the digit sum $a_n + a_{n-1} + \ldots + a_2 + a_1 + a_0$ is divisible by 9. State and prove a similar test for divisibility by 3.

6 Prove that $10^k = (-1)^k \pmod{11}$ for all integers $k \geqslant 0$.

Using the notation of Question 5, deduce that x is divisible by 11 if and only if the alternating digit sum $\sum_{r=0}^{n} (-1)^r a_r$ is divisible by 11.

7 Prove that each of the operations of $+_m$ and $\times_m$ on the set $\{0, 1, 2, \ldots, m-1\}$ is closed, commutative and associative.

Groups

Here are four examples for you to work through; keep your results so that you can refer to them as the chapter develops.

Example A

Write out the addition table for $\{0, 1, 2, 3, 4, 5\}$ under $+_6$ (addition modulo 6).

Example B

Draw an equilateral triangle on a piece of card, and cut it out. Then draw the three axes u, v and w on the card, and put distinguishing marks on the corners of the triangle, as in figure 4.1, with the same marks in corresponding positions on the back of the triangle too. The triangle can be fitted into the hole in the card in various ways, and can be moved by the following transformations:

P: rotation 120° anticlockwise about the axis through the centre perpendicular to the plane of the card

Q: rotation 120° clockwise about the same axis

U: half-turn about axis u

V: half-turn about axis v

W: half-turn about axis w.

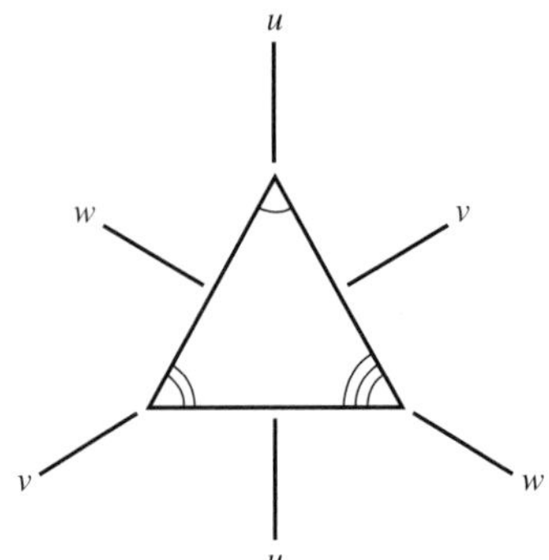

Figure 4.1

Applying P and then U gives: 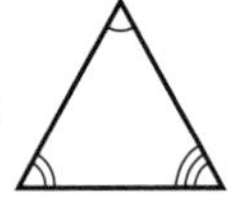 $\overset{P}{\mapsto}$ 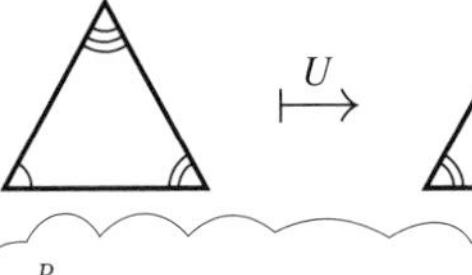 $\overset{U}{\mapsto}$

$\overset{P}{\mapsto}$ means 'is mapped by P to'.

But  $\overset{V}{\mapsto}$ 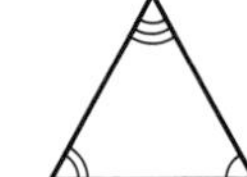, so P followed by U is equivalent to V, and you write $UP = V$. Notice that, as is usually the case when combining mappings, the first transformation P is written on the right of the second transformation U; it is important to be clear about this, since the same transformations applied in the other order have a different effect: $PU \neq UP$.

ACTIVITY 4.4 Which transformation is equivalent to PU? Try combining other pairs of transformations, and record your results. You will find that some combinations are equivalent to the 'stay put' identity transformation I.

The following table gives the results of combining these six transformations.

	First transformation					
followed by	*I*	*P*	*Q*	*U*	*V*	*W*
I	*I*	*P*	*Q*	*U*	*V*	*W*
P	*P*	*Q*	*I*	*W*	*U*	*V*
Q	*Q*	*I*	*P*	*V*	*W*	*U*
U	*U*	*V*	*W*	*I*	*P*	*Q*
V	*V*	*W*	*U*	*Q*	*I*	*P*
W	*W*	*U*	*V*	*P*	*Q*	*I*

(Rows: Second transformation)

Notice that the entry for UP is written in row U and column P.

Example C

A *permutation* of a finite set of objects is a mapping of the set on to itself. For example, if the objects are $\clubsuit, \diamondsuit, \heartsuit, \spadesuit$ then one possible permutation is the mapping $\clubsuit \mapsto \diamondsuit, \diamondsuit \mapsto \spadesuit, \heartsuit \mapsto \heartsuit, \spadesuit \mapsto \clubsuit$, which can be written more compactly as:

$$\begin{pmatrix} \clubsuit & \diamondsuit & \heartsuit & \spadesuit \\ \diamondsuit & \spadesuit & \heartsuit & \clubsuit \end{pmatrix}$$

With three objects, called 1, 2, 3, say, there are $3! = 6$ permutations, as follows.

$$i = \begin{pmatrix} 1 & 2 & 3 \\ 1 & 2 & 3 \end{pmatrix} \quad p = \begin{pmatrix} 1 & 2 & 3 \\ 2 & 3 & 1 \end{pmatrix} \quad q = \begin{pmatrix} 1 & 2 & 3 \\ 3 & 1 & 2 \end{pmatrix}$$

$$u = \begin{pmatrix} 1 & 2 & 3 \\ 1 & 3 & 2 \end{pmatrix} \quad v = \begin{pmatrix} 1 & 2 & 3 \\ 3 & 2 & 1 \end{pmatrix} \quad w = \begin{pmatrix} 1 & 2 & 3 \\ 2 & 1 & 3 \end{pmatrix}$$

Permutations can be combined in the same way as any other functions. For example, under the permutation up (meaning p followed by u), 1 goes to 2 which goes to 3 (i.e. $1 \mapsto 2 \mapsto 3$) and similarly $2 \mapsto 3 \mapsto 2$ and $3 \mapsto 1 \mapsto 1$, so that:

$$up = \begin{pmatrix} 1 & 2 & 3 \\ 3 & 2 & 1 \end{pmatrix} = v.$$

ACTIVITY 4.5 Show that $pu = w$. Make a table like the one in Example B to show all the results of combining two of these permutations.

Example D

Let $\omega = \cos\left(\frac{2\pi}{3}\right) + j\sin\left(\frac{2\pi}{3}\right)$, one of the complex cube roots of unity.

ACTIVITY 4.6

(i) Find the set of all the complex numbers which can be obtained by multiplying together any of the numbers ω, $-\omega$, and previous products.

(ii) Make a multiplication table for this set of numbers.

Comparing the examples

ACTIVITY 4.7 List the common features shared by the four examples, A, B, C and D.

Now compare your list with the following items.

- In each example there is a set of elements: numbers (mod 6), transformations, permutations or complex numbers.
- Each set has six elements.

- In each example there is a binary operation, combining any two elements of the set. In Example *A* the binary operation is addition modulo 6, in Examples *B* and *C* the binary operation is the composition of successive transformations or permutations, and in Example *D* it is multiplication. The same binary operation can be used to combine an element with itself.
- In each example the binary operation is *closed* in the set.
- The results of combining elements can be shown in a table, such as the one given in Example *B*, which is called a *Cayley table.*
- Each Cayley table is a *Latin square*, which means that every element occurs just once in each row or column of the body of the table.
- In each example there is just one element in the set which, when combined with any element of the set, leaves that element unchanged: this element is called the *identity* or *neutral element.* In Examples *A*, *B*, *C* and *D* the identities are, respectively, the number 0, the 'stay put' transformation *I*, the permutation $i = \begin{pmatrix} 1 & 2 & 3 \\ 1 & 2 & 3 \end{pmatrix}$ and the number 1.
- In each example for each element in the set there is just one element (called the *inverse*) which combines with it to produce the identity. Sometimes an element is its own inverse, in which case it is called a *self-inverse* element.
- Each binary operation is *associative.*

Associativity

Most of the points listed above are easy to verify, but associativity cannot be seen immediately from a Cayley table.

The obvious way to test for associativity is to use particular elements. For example, using the Cayley table in Example *B* gives $U(QV) = UW = Q$ and $(UQ)V = WV = Q$, so that $U(QV) = (UQ)V$. The problem with this approach is that to prove associativity you have to check all possible combinations, in this case $6^3 = 216$ of them! Happily this is not necessary, because it is easy to show that the operation of composition of mappings (in this case transformations) is always associative.

To see this, suppose that *X*, *Y* and *Z* are mappings, and that • denotes composition of mappings. Let *a* be any element in the domain of *Z*, and suppose that *Z* maps *a* to *b*, *Y* maps *b* to *c*, and *X* maps *c* to *d*, as in figure 4.2.

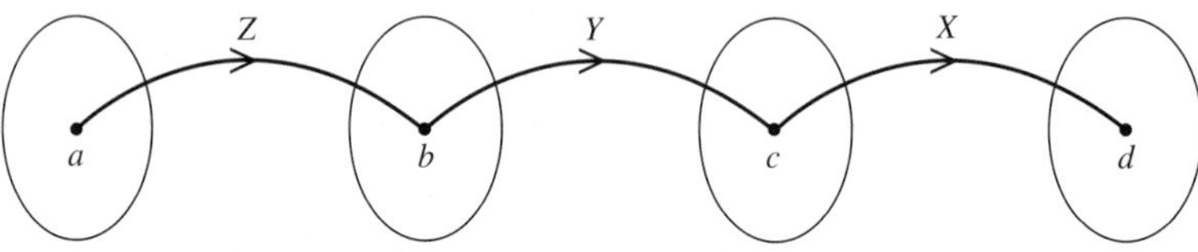

Figure 4.2

So you have a set of (unary) operations (the mappings X, Y, ...) which are the elements combined by a (binary) operation (composition of mappings $\bullet$), and in order to prove associativity you have to 'look inside' the mappings to see what happens to the elements (a, b, ...) upon which they act.

The mapping $(X \bullet Y) \bullet Z$ means 'Z followed by the composition of Y and X', under which a maps to b which then maps straight to d, as shown in figure 4.3.

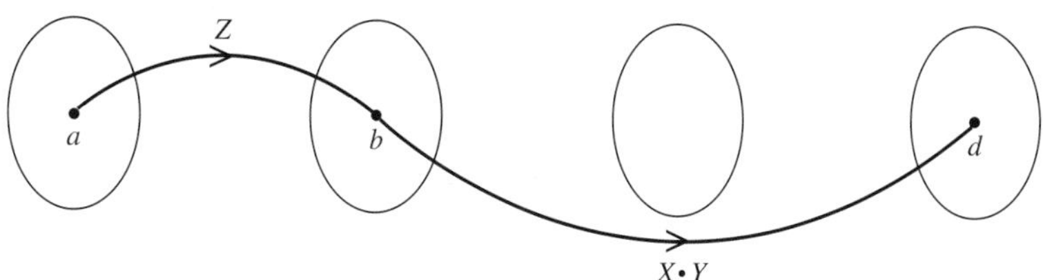

Figure 4.3

Similarly $X \bullet (Y \bullet Z)$ means 'the composition of Z and Y, followed by X', under which a maps straight to c which then maps to d, as in figure 4.4.

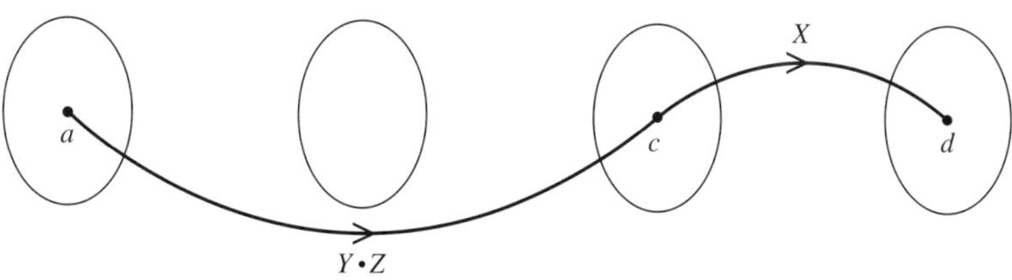

Figure 4.4

The 'by-passing' indicated by the bracketing has no effect on the overall result, which in each case is to map a to d. Therefore $(X \bullet Y) \bullet Z = X \bullet (Y \bullet Z)$. This proves that any binary operation which can be interpreted as the composition of mappings is associative.

This argument establishes associativity in Examples B and C. In Examples A and D there is no problem since modular addition and multiplication of complex numbers are both associative operations.

ACTIVITY 4.8 Which of the binary operations $+$, $-$, $\div$, $\wedge$ applied to real numbers (where $x \wedge y$ means x^y) are associative?

EXERCISE 4B

1 The *absolute difference* between two numbers x and y is written as $x \sim y$, so that $x \sim y = |x - y|$.

(i) Make a Cayley table showing the results of applying the binary operation $\sim$ to the set $S = \{0, 1, 2, 3, 4\}$.

(ii) Is S closed under $\sim$?

(iii) Is the operation $\sim$ associative?

(iv) Is there an identity or neutral element? If so, what is it?

(v) Does each element have an inverse? If so, what are they?

2 A binary operation, $\circ$, is defined on the set $\mathbb{R}$ of real numbers by:

$$a \quad b = \begin{cases} \text{maximum of } a \text{ and } b & \text{if } a \neq b \\ a & \text{if } a = b \end{cases}$$

State whether $\circ$ is **(i)** closed, **(ii)** associative, giving your reasons.

Show that $\mathbb{R}$ does not contain an identity element for this operation.

Suggest a set S on which this operation can be defined which does contain an identity. Does every element of your set S have an inverse in S?

[MEI]

3 The *union* of two sets A and B is the set $A \cup B$ of elements belonging to A or B or both. The *intersection* $A \cap B$ is the set of elements belonging to both A and B. Investigate whether the operations $\cup$ and $\cap$ are associative.

4 **(i)** The operation $\bullet$ is defined on the set of complex numbers by:

$$m \bullet n = (m^2 + n^2)^{1/2}.$$

Investigate closure, associativity, and the existence of an identity and inverses.

(ii) How do your answers to part **(i)** differ when the operation is applied to the set of non-negative real numbers?

(iii) If the operation is applied to the set $\mathbb{Z}^+$ of positive integers show that $m \bullet n \in \mathbb{Z}^+$ if $n = \frac{1}{2}(m^2 - 1)$ and state the condition this imposes on m. Find the relation between the integers p, q and r if $m = p + q$, $n = q + r$ and $m \bullet n = p + q + r$.

[MEI, *adapted*]

5 Prove that the operation $\bullet$ defined on the real numbers by:

$$x \bullet y = \frac{xy + k^2}{x + y} \quad (x + y \neq 0)$$

is associative for all values of the constant k. Show that there are in general no solutions to the equation $x \bullet y = y$, and discuss any exceptional cases.

6 Suppose that f is a function with an inverse and that $\bullet$ is an associative binary operation. A new binary operation $\diamond$ is defined by $x \diamond y = \mathrm{f}^{-1}(\mathrm{f}(x) \bullet \mathrm{f}(y))$. Prove that $\diamond$ is associative. Find $x \diamond y$ in the following particular cases:

(i) $\mathrm{f}(x) = x + 3$, $\quad \bullet = \times$

(ii) $\mathrm{f}(x) = \dfrac{2x - 1}{x - 1}$, $\quad \bullet = +$

(iii) $\mathrm{f}(x) = \arctan x$, $\quad \bullet = +$.

7 The operation $\circ$ is defined on the number pairs $A = (a_1, a_2)$ and $B = (b_1, b_2)$ so that $A \circ B = (a_1 + b_2, a_2 + b_1)$ and $A = B$ if and only if $a_1 = b_1$ and $a_2 = b_2$. Find whether the operation is associative.

Find P such that $A \circ P = A$, and Q such that $Q \circ A = A$, and determine whether I, J can be found such that, for all A, $A \circ I = A$ and $J \circ A = A$.

Given that $A^* = (-a_2, -a_1)$, discuss the following:

$$B \circ A = C \circ A \Rightarrow B \circ A \circ A^* = C \circ A \circ A^*$$
$$\Rightarrow B \circ (0, 0) = C \circ (0, 0)$$
$$\Rightarrow B = C.$$

[MEI]

Group axioms

Your collection of the four examples A, B, C and D shows in a small way that there are many similarities between the various systems formed by particular sets of mathematical objects and their operations. This interested mathematicians increasingly during the nineteenth century, when the emphasis moved from concentrating on particular systems (such as the algebra of complex numbers, or matrix algebra, or vector algebra, or the algebra of transformations) to *abstract algebra*. In abstract algebra you assume certain basic statements (called *axioms*) about unspecified objects and operations, and then see what can be deduced from these. One abstract theorem can then be interpreted in many ways by taking particular objects and operations which satisfy the axioms. Thus abstract methods have great generality and often reveal connections between the properties of apparently quite separate systems.

Of course, much depends on the choice of axioms: one of the simplest but most productive abstract systems is the *group*, which is defined as follows.

A group $(S, \bullet)$ is a non-empty set S with a binary operation $\bullet$ such that

(C) $\bullet$ is *closed* in S, i.e. $a \bullet b \in S$ for all $a, b \in S$

(A) $\bullet$ is *associative*, i.e. $(a \bullet b) \bullet c = a \bullet (b \bullet c)$ for all $a, b, c \in S$

(N) there is an *identity* or *neutral* element $e \in S$ such that:

$$a \bullet e = e \bullet a = a \text{ for all } a \in S$$

(I) each $a \in S$ has an *inverse* element $a^{-1} \in S$ such that:

$$a \bullet a^{-1} = a^{-1} \bullet a = e.$$

ACTIVITY 4.9 Check that each of the examples A, B, C and D satisfies all four group axioms.

Note that the group axioms do not require $\bullet$ to be commutative, and in the case of Examples B and C it is not. If the binary operation $\bullet$ is commutative, i.e. if $a \bullet b = b \bullet a$ for all $a, b \in S$, then the group is said to be commutative or *Abelian*, named after one of the pioneers of group theory, the Norwegian Niels Abel (1802–29). Examples A and D are Abelian groups, since modular addition and the multiplication of complex numbers are commutative operations.

Note

One way of remembering this and the four axioms (C), (A), (N), (I) is to think of the biblical brothers Cain and Abel. Of course, the initials only work if you use 'neutral' rather than 'identity', though for most purposes the latter seems to be more common.

The order of a group

In each of the examples, A, B, C and D there are six distinct elements in the set. You will meet many examples of groups where the set S has a finite number of elements (not necessarily six). These are called *finite* groups and the number of elements of S is called the *order* of the group. There are also many *infinite* groups, where S has infinitely many distinct elements: simple examples are the set of integers under the operation of addition (for which the neutral element is 0 and the inverse of a is $-a$), or the set of all rotations about a fixed centre under the operation of combination of transformations.

ACTIVITY 4.10 Explain why:

(i) the set of rational numbers forms a group under addition but not under multiplication

(ii) the set of positive real numbers forms a group under multiplication but not under addition.

Notation

From now on the symbol $\bullet$, or whatever has been used to show the binary operation, will often be left out and $a \bullet b$ will be written as ab. This fits with the usual way of showing the multiplication of numbers or matrices or the composition of mappings, and is considerably quicker to write. But you must remember to distinguish between ab and ba unless you specifically know that the operation is commutative.

Indices can be used to show repeated combination of the same element, for example

$$a^2 = a \bullet a \qquad \text{and} \qquad a^3 = a \bullet (a \bullet a) = (a \bullet a) \bullet a.$$

If the operation is addition (of numbers, vectors, matrices, or in modular arithmetic) + will continue to be used, with the inverse of a denoted by $-a$.

EXAMPLE 4.2

Let a, b and c be the functions defined (for all x except 0 and 1) by:

$$a(x) = x \qquad b(x) = 1 - x \qquad c(x) = \frac{1}{x}.$$

Show that the set of functions formed by combining any two of these (including repetitions) forms a finite non-Abelian group under the operation of composition of functions. Give the Cayley table of this group.

SOLUTION

Stage 1

Clearly a is the identity function, and $bb(x) = cc(x) = x$, so that $bb = cc = a$.

Also $bc(x) = b(c(x)) = 1 - \dfrac{1}{x} = \dfrac{x-1}{x} = d(x)$, say, so that $bc = d$,

whereas $cb(x) = c(b(x)) = \dfrac{1}{1-x} = e(x)$, say, so that $cb = e$.

The fact that $bc \neq cb$ shows that the operation is not commutative.

Next find cd:

$$cd(x) = \frac{x}{x-1} = f(x), \text{ say, so that } cd = f.$$

Stage 2

You could find dc and the other entries by substitution in a similar way, but it is quicker to make use of what is already known (including the fact that composition of functions is associative):

$$dc = (bc)c = b(cc) = ba = b.$$

Several other results can be found in a similar way. In what follows frequent use is made of associativity, but the working is condensed by leaving out the details of the bracketing.

$bd = bbc = ac = c$ $\quad$ $ce = ccb = ab = b$ $\quad$ $cf = ccd = ad = d$

$de = bccb = bab = bb = a$ $\quad$ $df = dcd = bd = c$ $\quad$ $eb = cbb = ca = c$

$ed = cbbc = cac = cc = a$ $\quad$ $fc = cdc = cb = e$ $\quad$ $ff = cdcd = cbd = cc = a$

Stage 3

To make further progress you need one more substitution:

$$ee(x) = \frac{1}{1 - \dfrac{1}{1-x}} = \frac{1-x}{1-x-1} = \frac{x-1}{x} = d(x), \text{ so that } ee = d.$$

Stage 4

Everything else follows from this.

$dd = dee = ae = e$ $\quad$ $be = bdd = cd = f$ $\quad$ $bf = bbe = ae = e$

$db = bcb = be = f$ $\quad$ $ec = ddc = db = f$ $\quad$ $ef = ddf = dc = b$

$fb = beb = bc = d$ $\quad$ $fd = bed = ba = b$ $\quad$ $fe = fdd = bd = c$

This shows that the set of six functions is closed under the operation of composition of functions. The remaining axiom (existence of inverses) is easily checked from the Cayley table overleaf, so this is a non-Abelian group of order 6. (In the table the entries obtained at stages 1, 2, 3 and 4 are shown by the type faces *k*, *<u>k</u>*, **k**, **<u>k</u>** respectively).

		First function					
	followed by	a	b	c	d	e	f
Second function	a	a	b	c	d	e	f
	b	b	a	d	c	**f**	**e**
	c	c	e	a	f	b	d
	d	d	**f**	b	**e**	a	c
	e	e	c	**f**	a	**d**	**b**
	f	f	**d**	e	**b**	**c**	a

Immediate consequences of the axioms

Other properties common to all groups can be deduced from the group axioms; here are a few important simple ones. Notice the rather formal style of argument which is needed to show how the property links back to the axioms.

The identity element is unique

Proof
Suppose that a group has two identity elements, e and f.

Then $\quad ef = e \quad$ (since f is an identity)

and $\quad ef = f \quad$ (since e is an identity).

Therefore $e = f$.

So there is only one identity.

Each element has a unique inverse

Proof
Suppose that e is the identity, and that an element a has two inverses, p and q, so that $ap = pa = e$ and $aq = qa = e$.

$$\begin{aligned}
\text{Then } p &= pe && (e \text{ is the identity})\\
&= p(aq) && (aq = e)\\
&= (pa)q && (\text{associativity})\\
&= eq && (pa = e)\\
&= q && (e \text{ is the identity}).
\end{aligned}$$

Therefore the inverse of a is unique. A consequence of this result is that there is no ambiguity in using the notation a^{-1} for the inverse of a.

The cancellation laws

Suppose that a, b, h are elements of a group such that $ha = hb$. Then you can 'cancel h on the left' to obtain $a = b$.

Similarly $ah = bh \quad \Rightarrow \quad a = b$ ('cancelling on the right').

Proof

$$
\begin{aligned}
& ha = hb & \\
\Rightarrow \quad & h^{-1}(ha) = h^{-1}(hb) & \text{(using the unique inverse of } h\text{)} \\
\Rightarrow \quad & (h^{-1}h)a = (h^{-1}h)b & \text{(associativity)} \\
\Rightarrow \quad & ea = eb & (h^{-1}h = e) \\
\Rightarrow \quad & a = b & (e \text{ is the identity}).
\end{aligned}
$$

ACTIVITY 4.11 **(i)** Prove similarly that $ah = bh \Rightarrow a = b$.
(ii) Produce an example to show that $ha = bh$ does not imply that $a = b$.

The solution of ax = b

If a and b are elements of a group then the equation $ax = b$ has the unique solution $x = a^{-1}b$.

Proof

$$
\begin{aligned}
& ax = b & \\
\Leftrightarrow \quad & a^{-1}(ax) = a^{-1}b & (a^{-1} \text{ exists since each element has an inverse}) \\
\Leftrightarrow \quad & (a^{-1}a)x = a^{-1}b & \text{(associativity)} \\
\Leftrightarrow \quad & ex = a^{-1}b & (a^{-1}a = e) \\
\Leftrightarrow \quad & x = a^{-1}b & (e \text{ is the identity}).
\end{aligned}
$$

Note that $a^{-1}b$ is an element of the group, by the closure axiom.

ACTIVITY 4.12 Solve the following equations.
(i) $xa = b$ **(ii)** $axb = c$

Historical note

The idea of an abstract algebraic system developed gradually throughout the nineteenth century. Galois, Abel and Cauchy worked with particular groups, and Arthur Cayley wrote about the notion of an abstract group as early as 1849, attracting no attention at the time (see Kline's comment at the start of the chapter), though he is remembered by his name being given to the *Cayley table*, which shows how the elements of a finite group combine. The first axiomatic definitions of a group were given by Heinrich Weber and Walther von Dyck in independent papers which appeared in the same journal in 1882. The subject grew rapidly, and many mathematicians in the early twentieth century came to believe that all worthwhile mathematics would ultimately be included in the theory of groups: in 1921 Poincaré wrote, '... the theory of groups is, so to say, the whole of mathematics divested of its matter and reduced to pure form'.

EXERCISE 4C

1 Write out the Cayley table for combining the symmetry transformations of a square, using I for the identity transformation, R, H, S for rotations 90° anticlockwise, 180° and 90° clockwise about O respectively, X, Y, A, B for half-turns about axes x, y, a, b respectively.

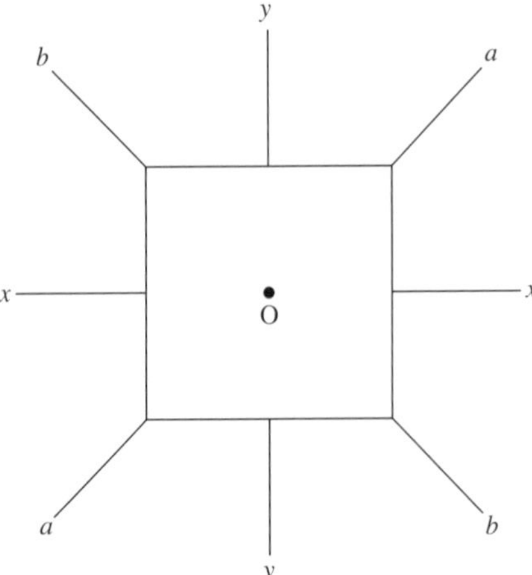

Check that all the group axioms are satisfied.

2 Prove that the Cayley table of a finite group has the Latin square property, i.e. each element occurs just once in each row and in each column. Give an example of a 4×4 Latin square which is not a group table, stating which axioms are not satisfied.

3 Prove that if a and b are elements of a group then $(ab)^{-1} = b^{-1}a^{-1}$.

4 In the Cayley table of a group with identity e the following rectangles occur:

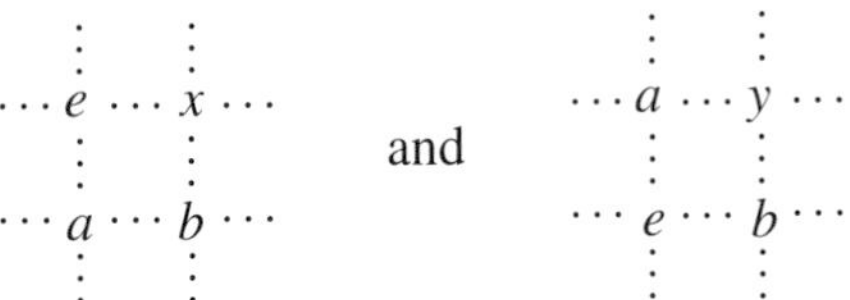

Express x and y in terms of a and b.

5 Which of the following sets of 2×2 matrices form a group under the operation of matrix multiplication? Which of these groups are Abelian?

(i) those with rational elements

(ii) those with integer elements and unit determinant

(iii) those of the form $\begin{pmatrix} \cos\theta & -\sin\theta \\ \sin\theta & \cos\theta \end{pmatrix}$

(iv) those of the form $\begin{pmatrix} z & -w^* \\ w & z^* \end{pmatrix}$ where z and w are complex numbers, not both zero.

6 If A and B are sets, the *symmetric difference* $A \triangle B$ is defined as:

$$A \triangle B = (A \cap B') \cup (A' \cap B)$$

as shown in this Venn diagram.

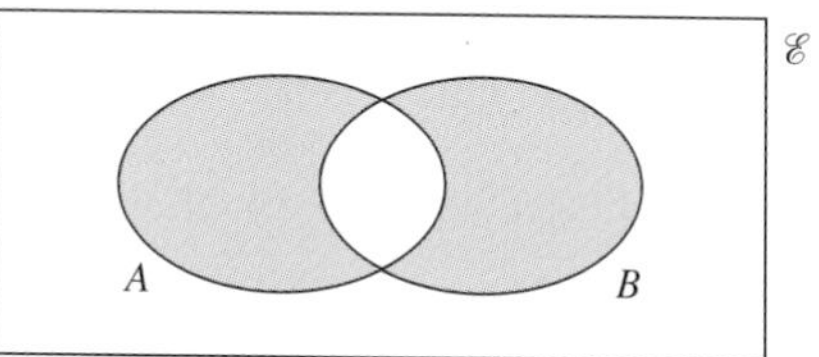

(i) Prove that the set of all subsets of the set $\mathscr{E}$ forms an Abelian group under the operation $\triangle$.

(ii) Given that $\mathscr{E} = \{1, 2, 3, 4, 5, 6, 7, 8, 9\}$, $A = \{1, 2, 3\}$ and $B = \{2, 4, 6, 8\}$, solve the equation $A \triangle X = B$.

7 Prove that if $a^2 = e$ (the identity) for every element a of a group then the group is Abelian. Give an example of such a group.

8 (i) Show that the sets $\{1, 4, 7, 13\}$ and $\{3, 6, 9, 12\}$ form Abelian groups under multiplication modulo 15, but $\{2, 5, 8, 14\}$ does not.

(ii) Write out the multiplication table for $\{1, 2, 3, 4, 5, 6, 7\}$ under multiplication modulo 8, and explain why this is not a group. Find subsets of this set which, under the same operation, give groups of order 2 and 4.

9 G is a group and $D(G)$ is the set of ordered pairs of elements (g, ε) where g is an element of G and $\varepsilon = \pm 1$. Show that $D(G)$ together with the binary operation $(g, \varepsilon) \bullet (h, \delta) = (gh^{\varepsilon}, \varepsilon\delta)$ is a group if and only if G is Abelian. (Here (h, δ) denotes another element of $D(G)$.)

Find the condition on G which makes $D(G)$ an Abelian group and show that, if this condition is satisfied, then $D(D(G))$ is also an Abelian group.

[MEI]

10 The Lorentz group

(i) In the special theory of relativity as applied to motion along a straight line a central problem is to find the linear transformations

$$\begin{pmatrix} x' \\ t' \end{pmatrix} = \begin{pmatrix} p & q \\ r & s \end{pmatrix} \begin{pmatrix} x \\ t \end{pmatrix}$$

for which $x'^2 - c^2t'^2 = x^2 - c^2t^2$, where c is the speed of light.

Show that this leads to the conditions $p^2 - c^2r^2 = 1$, $pq = c^2rs$ and $c^2s^2 - q^2 = c^2$. Verify that these are all satisfied if:

$$p = \frac{1}{\alpha}, \quad q = -\frac{v}{\alpha}, \quad r = -\frac{v}{c^2\alpha}, \quad s = \frac{1}{\alpha},$$

where v is any number with $|v| < c$ and $\alpha = \sqrt{1 - \frac{v^2}{c^2}}$.

(ii) Let $\mathbf{L}(v) = \begin{pmatrix} \frac{1}{\alpha} & -\frac{v}{\alpha} \\ -\frac{v}{c^2\alpha} & \frac{1}{\alpha} \end{pmatrix}$.

Show that $(\mathbf{L}(v))^{-1} = \mathbf{L}(-v)$ and that

$\mathbf{L}(v_1)\mathbf{L}(v_2) = \mathbf{L}(v_3)$ where $v_3 = \dfrac{v_1 + v_2}{1 + \frac{v_1 v_2}{c^2}}$.

(This gives the rule for adding velocities in the special theory of relativity.)

(iii) Show that the set of matrices $\mathbf{L}(v)$ with $|v| < c$ forms an Abelian group under matrix multiplication; this is called the Lorentz group.

Isomorphism

You may have already noticed that the Cayley tables of Examples *B* and *C* on pages 134–135 are very similar. In fact you can change one into the other merely by replacing capital letters by small letters, or vice versa: both tables show exactly the same pattern of elements. When this happens we say that the mapping:

capital letter $\leftrightarrow$ small letter

preserves the structure of the two groups. The mapping is called an *isomorphism*, and the groups are said to be *isomorphic* (from the Greek *isos* meaning 'equal' and *morphe* meaning 'form' or 'shape'). Isomorphic groups are essentially the same, differing only in the notation used to describe them, and so any property of a particular group can immediately be translated into the corresponding property of any other isomorphic group.

ACTIVITY 4.13 Show that the vertices of the equilateral triangle in Example *B* and their original positions on the surrounding card can be numbered 1, 2, 3 in such a way that each transformation in Example *B* produces the corresponding permutation in Example *C*.

To put this more formally, two groups $(S, \bullet)$ and $(T, \diamondsuit)$ are *isomorphic* if there is a one-to-one mapping (called an *isomorphism*) which associates each of the elements $a, b, c, \ldots$ of S with one of the elements $x, y, z, \ldots$ of T in such a way that, if a maps to x and b maps to y, then the result of combining a and b under $\bullet$ maps to the result of combining x and y under $\diamondsuit$, i.e.

$$a \leftrightarrow x \text{ and } b \leftrightarrow y \text{ (where } a, b \in S \text{ and } x, y \in T) \Rightarrow a \bullet b \leftrightarrow x \diamondsuit y.$$

This is shown diagrammatically in figure 4.5.

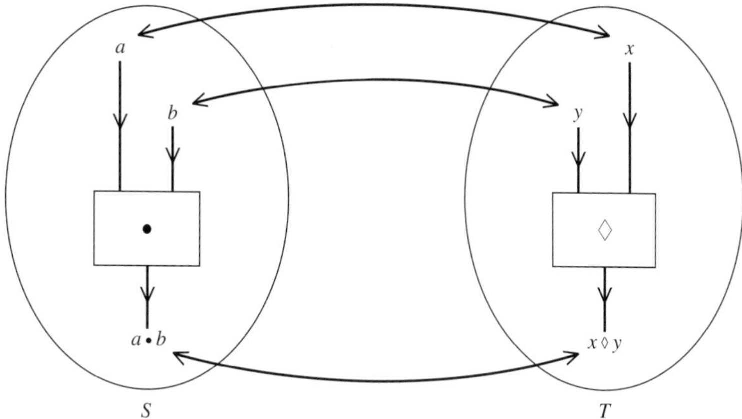

Figure 4.5

How can you find whether two groups are isomorphic? Sometimes there may be an obvious isomorphism, or an obvious way to construct one (as in the activity above). Otherwise the search can be aided by the following simple theorems.

(A) *Two isomorphic groups are either both finite and of the same order or both infinite*

Proof

If one group is finite and of order n then so is the other, since there is a one-to-one mapping between them; the only alternative is that both groups are infinite.

(B) *The identity elements of isomorphic groups are mapped to each other by the isomorphism*

Proof

Suppose that $a \leftrightarrow x$ and $e \leftrightarrow u$, where e is the identity of $(S, \bullet)$. Then $a \bullet e \leftrightarrow x \diamond u$. But $a \bullet e = a$ so $a \bullet e \leftrightarrow x$. Therefore $x \diamond u = x$, and so u is the identity of $(T, \diamond)$.

(C) *The inverses of corresponding elements are mapped to each other by the isomorphism*

Proof

Suppose that $a \leftrightarrow x$ and $a^{-1} \leftrightarrow y$. Then $a \bullet a^{-1} \leftrightarrow x \diamond y$.

But $a \bullet a^{-1} = e \leftrightarrow u$. Therefore $x \diamond y = u$, and so $y = x^{-1}$ (the inverse of x in $(T, \diamond)$).

ACTIVITY 4.14

(i) An element a is *self-inverse* if $a^{-1} = a$. Prove that two isomorphic groups must have equal numbers of self-inverse elements.

(ii) Are the groups in Examples B and D isomorphic?

EXAMPLE 4.3

Investigate whether there is an isomorphism between the group B and the group of functions given in Example 4.2 (which we shall call group E).

SOLUTION

The Cayley tables for groups B and E are shown below.

	I	P	Q	U	V	W
I	I	P	Q	U	V	W
P	P	Q	I	W	U	V
Q	Q	I	P	V	W	U
U	U	V	W	I	P	Q
V	V	W	U	Q	I	P
W	W	U	V	P	Q	I

Group *B*

	a	b	c	d	e	f
a	a	b	c	d	e	f
b	b	a	d	c	f	e
c	c	e	a	f	b	d
d	d	f	b	e	a	c
e	e	c	f	a	d	b
f	f	d	e	b	c	a

Group *E*

The identities of the two groups are I and a, and so in any isomorphism these elements must correspond. The leading diagonals show that in each group there are four self-inverse elements (including the identities). The elements which are not self-inverse are P and Q in B and d and e in E, and these too must correspond in an isomorphism, giving two possible pairings. Suppose for example that $P \leftrightarrow d$; then it follows that $Q \leftrightarrow e$, but we still have to link the remaining self-inverse elements, U, V, W and b, c, f. Choosing one pairing arbitrarily, suppose that $U \leftrightarrow f$. Then if the mapping is an isomorphism, $V = UP \leftrightarrow fd = b$ and $W = UQ \leftrightarrow fe = c$. So the mapping given by the table:

I	P	Q	U	V	W
a	d	e	f	b	c

may be an isomorphism. To decide whether it is, rewrite the Cayley table for group E with the elements arranged in this order.

	a	d	e	f	b	c
a	a	d	e	f	b	c
d	d	e	a	c	f	b
e	e	a	d	b	c	f
f	f	b	c	a	d	e
b	b	c	f	e	a	d
c	c	f	b	d	e	a

It is now easy to check that the pattern of entries here is the same as the pattern in the Cayley table for group B, so that these two groups are isomorphic.

ACTIVITY 4.15 Two of the steps of the solution of this example involved making arbitrary choices. Work through the solution again, making different choices at these two points, and show that you still get an isomorphism. How many different isomorphisms between these two groups are there?

EXERCISE 4D

1 Find two different isomorphisms between the group of integers under addition and the group of multiples of 5 under addition.

2 Investigate whether there is an isomorphism between group A and group D in the examples on pages 133–135.

3 Show that the following groups are all isomorphic.

(i) The set of complex numbers $a + b\text{j}$, where a and b are integers, under addition.

(ii) The set of rational numbers of the form $5^m 7^n$, where m and n are integers, under multiplication.

(iii) The set of translations which map an infinite lattice grid of rectangles to itself, under composition of transformations.

4 Prove that the group of symmetry transformations of a non-square rectangle is isomorphic to the group of symmetry transformations of a non-square rhombus:

(i) by defining the transformations and writing out the Cayley table for each group

(ii) by joining the mid-points of the edges of the rectangle.

5 **(i)** Prove that all groups of order 2 are isomorphic.

(ii) Show that there is only one way of completing this Latin square.

e	a	b
a	...	...
b	...	...

Deduce that all groups of order 3 are isomorphic. Give a specific example of one such group.

6 Prove that it is impossible for an Abelian group to be isomorphic to a non-Abelian group.

7 Prove that the group of positive real numbers under multiplication is isomorphic to the group of all real numbers under addition.
[**Hint:** Use logarithms.]

8 Prove that the group of matrices $\begin{pmatrix} a & 0 \\ 0 & a \end{pmatrix}$ under matrix addition and the group of matrices $\begin{pmatrix} 1 & 0 \\ b & 1 \end{pmatrix}$ under matrix multiplication, where a and b are real numbers, are isomorphic.

9 Show that each of the following sets of four elements with the stated operation forms a group, and sort these six groups into isomorphic sets.

(i) $1, -1, \mathrm{j}, -\mathrm{j}$; multiplication of complex numbers

(ii) functions $\mathrm{e}(x) = x$, $\mathrm{f}(x) = -\frac{1}{x}$, $\mathrm{g}(x) = \frac{x-1}{x+1}$, $\mathrm{h}(x) = \frac{1+x}{1-x}$; composition of functions

(iii) 1, 2, 3, 4; multiplication modulo 5

(iv) 1, 3, 5, 7; multiplication modulo 8

(v) $\begin{pmatrix} 1 & 0 \\ 0 & 1 \end{pmatrix}, \begin{pmatrix} 1 & 0 \\ 0 & -1 \end{pmatrix}, \begin{pmatrix} -1 & 0 \\ 0 & 1 \end{pmatrix}, \begin{pmatrix} -1 & 0 \\ 0 & -1 \end{pmatrix}$; matrix multiplication

(vi) $\begin{pmatrix} 1 & 0 \\ 0 & 1 \end{pmatrix}, \begin{pmatrix} 0 & 1 \\ -1 & 0 \end{pmatrix}, \begin{pmatrix} -1 & 0 \\ 0 & -1 \end{pmatrix}, \begin{pmatrix} 0 & -1 \\ 1 & 0 \end{pmatrix}$; matrix multiplication

10 Suppose that a group of order 4 has the distinct elements e, a, b, c, where e is the identity.

(i) Explain why ab cannot equal a or b.

(ii) Deduce that there are four possibilities:

(a) $ab = ba = e$ **(b)** $ab = e, ba = c$

(c) $ab = c, ba = e$ **(d)** $ab = ba = c$.

(iii) By trying to complete the Cayley table, show that cases **(b)** and **(c)** lead to contradictions, that **(a)** gives the Cayley table for one group, and that **(d)** gives the Cayley tables for three groups.

(iv) Show that the groups in part **(iii)** are isomorphic to those in Question 9.

(This shows that there are essentially only two groups of order 4; the *cyclic group* (with two self-inverse elements) and the *Klein 4-Group* (with four self-inverse elements), named after Felix Klein (1849–1925).)

Subgroups

The symmetry transformations of the equilateral triangle are of two types, rotations (including the identity transformation) and reflections. In Example *B* on page 134 these are *I*, *P*, *Q* and *U*, *V*, *W* respectively. From the Cayley table for this group you can see that the set of rotations is closed, contains the identity, and contains the inverse of each rotation. Therefore $\{I, P, Q\}$ forms a group under the same operation (composition of transformations); this is called a *subgroup*.

	I	**P**	**Q**	U	V	W
I	**I**	**P**	**Q**	U	V	W
P	**P**	**Q**	**I**	W	U	V
Q	**Q**	**I**	**P**	V	W	U
U	U	V	W	I	P	Q
V	V	W	U	Q	I	P
W	W	U	V	P	Q	I

The set of reflections $\{U, V, W\}$ is not a subgroup, since it does not contain the identity, but the subsets $\{I, U\}$, $\{I, V\}$ and $\{I, W\}$ are other subgroups.

ACTIVITY 4.16 Find whether $\{I, U, V, W\}$ is a subgroup.

The formal definition is as follows.

> A *subgroup* of a group $(S, \bullet)$ is a non-empty subset of *S* which forms a group under the same binary operation $\bullet$.

Every group has its *trivial subgroup* $\{e\}$, the subset consisting of just the identity. Since it is usual to count the set *S* as a subset of itself, the whole group is technically also a subgroup. Sometimes you want to exclude these two extremes, so you use the terms *proper subgroup* for any subgroup which is not the whole group, and *non-trivial subgroup* for any subgroup other than $\{e\}$.

EXAMPLE 4.4

Let S_4 be the group of permutations of four elements. Find a subgroup of S_4 which is isomorphic to the group *G* formed by the set $\{1, 2, 3, 4\}$ under $\times_5$ (multiplication mod 5).

SOLUTION

The Cayley table for *G* is as follows.

$\times_5$	1	2	3	4	permutation
1	1	2	3	4	*e*
2	2	4	1	3	*a*
3	3	1	4	2	*b*
4	4	3	2	1	*c*

Each row of this table is a permutation of the set {1, 2, 3, 4}. Label these permutations as shown, so that:

$$e = \begin{pmatrix} 1 & 2 & 3 & 4 \\ 1 & 2 & 3 & 4 \end{pmatrix} \quad a = \begin{pmatrix} 1 & 2 & 3 & 4 \\ 2 & 4 & 1 & 3 \end{pmatrix}$$

$$b = \begin{pmatrix} 1 & 2 & 3 & 4 \\ 3 & 1 & 4 & 2 \end{pmatrix} \quad c = \begin{pmatrix} 1 & 2 & 3 & 4 \\ 4 & 3 & 2 & 1 \end{pmatrix}.$$

It is easy to check that the set $\{e, a, b, c\}$ (which contains four of the 24 permutations in S_4) forms a subgroup isomorphic to G, with the following Cayley table.

	e	a	b	c
e	e	a	b	c
a	a	c	e	b
b	b	e	c	a
c	c	b	a	e

Direct comparison with the Cayley table for G shows that the subgroup $\{e, a, b, c\}$ of S_4 is isomorphic to G.

Exactly the same method is used in the proof of the following general result connecting any finite group with a subgroup of permutations.

Cayley's theorem

Let S_n be the group of permutations of n elements, and let G be any group of order n. Then G is isomorphic to a subgroup of S_n.

Proof

Let the elements of G be $a_1, a_2, \ldots, a_n$. By the Latin square property, each row of the Cayley table of G is a permutation of these n elements: the row corresponding to a_i is $(a_ia_1 \quad a_ia_2 \quad \ldots \quad a_ia_n)$.

Let p_i be the permutation $\begin{pmatrix} a_1 & a_2 & \cdots & a_n \\ a_ia_1 & a_ia_2 & \cdots & a_ia_n \end{pmatrix}$, so that p_i maps a_k to a_ia_k, which you can write as $p_i(a_k) = a_ia_k$. Then the mapping $a_i \leftrightarrow p_i$ gives a one-to-one correspondence linking the elements of G with a subset of S_n.

Now let • be the operation of combination of permutations, so that $p_j \bullet p_i$ means p_i followed by p_j. Then:

$$\begin{aligned}(p_j \bullet p_i)(a_k) &= p_j(p_i(a_k)) \\ &= p_j(a_ia_k) \\ &= a_j(a_ia_k) \\ &= (a_ja_i)a_k \qquad \text{(using associativity).}\end{aligned}$$

So under the permutation $p_j \bullet p_i$ the general element a_k maps to $(a_j a_i)a_k$ and therefore:

$$a_j a_i \leftrightarrow p_j \bullet p_i.$$

This shows that the mapping $a_i \leftrightarrow p_i$ is an isomorphism. Therefore G is isomorphic to a subgroup of S_n.

This completes the proof of Cayley's theorem.

EXERCISE 4E

1 Find all the proper subgroups of the symmetry group of a square. (Use the notation of Exercise 4C, Question 1.)

2 (i) List the elements of a subgroup of S_4 (the group of permutations of four elements) which is isomorphic to the symmetry group of a non-square rectangle.

(ii) List the elements of a subgroup of S_8 which is isomorphic to the symmetry group of a square.

3 Prove that if H and K are two subgroups of a group G then $H \cap K$ is also a subgroup. Give an example to show that $H \cup K$ need not be a subgroup.

4 Show that the symmetry group of a regular n-sided polygon has $2n$ elements, comprising n rotations (including the identity) and n reflections. (When dealing with the reflections, take separately the cases when n is odd and when n is even.) This is called the *dihedral* group, D_n. Show that if k is any factor of $2n$ then D_n has a subgroup of order k.

5 (i) Show that successive half-turns about the centres (a, b) and (c, d) are equivalent to the translation $2\begin{pmatrix} c-a \\ d-b \end{pmatrix}$.

(ii) Show that the set of rotations and translations of a plane under the composition of transformations forms a group.

(iii) Show that the set of translations is a subgroup and explain why the set of rotations is not a subgroup. Find two subgroups of which all of the elements are rotations.

6 Let G be a group and let H be any non-empty subset of the elements of G. Prove that H is a subgroup of G if and only if $xy^{-1} \in H$ for all $x, y \in H$.

The centre C of a group G is defined to be the set of all elements of G which commute with every element of G (that is, $c \in C$ if and only if $gc = cg$ for all $g \in G$). Prove that C is a subgroup of G.

Show that the set of matrices of the form $\begin{pmatrix} 1 & p & q \\ 0 & 1 & r \\ 0 & 0 & 1 \end{pmatrix}$, where p, q, r are rational numbers, forms a group under matrix multiplication. Find the centre of this group.

[SMP]

7 The table shows a Latin square for $\{E, A, B, C, D\}$ under the operation $\bullet$, together with the permutations e, a, b, c, d defined by the rows of this square.

$\bullet$	E	A	B	C	D	permutation
E	E	A	B	C	D	e
A	A	C	D	B	E	a
B	B	D	C	E	A	b
C	C	E	A	D	B	c
D	D	B	E	A	C	d

Show that the set of permutations is not closed, and deduce that $\{E, A, B, C, D\}$ does not form a group under $\bullet$.

Lagrange's theorem

The symmetry group of the equilateral triangle (i.e. Example B from page 134) is a finite group of order 6, and has subgroups of order 1 ($\{I\}$), order 2 (three of them, $\{I, U\}$, $\{I, V\}$, $\{I, W\}$), order 3 ($\{I, P, Q\}$), and order 6 (group B itself). The order of each subgroup is a factor of the order of the group.

ACTIVITY 4.17 Use the answer to Question 1 of Exercise 4E to check that the order of each subgroup of the symmetry group of a square is a factor of the order of the group.

The purpose of this section is to prove that what happens in these cases must always happen: the order of each subgroup of a finite group is a factor of the order of the group. This result is known as *Lagrange's theorem*.

As a tool for proving this (and an important idea in its own right) the idea of a *coset* is introduced. Suppose that $H = \{h_1, h_2, h_3, \ldots, h_m\}$ is a subgroup of a group $(S, \bullet)$, and that x is any element of S. Then the set of elements $\{x \bullet h_1, x \bullet h_2, x \bullet h_3, \ldots, x \bullet h_m\}$ is called the *left coset* of H by x, and is denoted by xH.

For example, if $S = \{I, P, Q, U, V, W\}$ and $H = \{I, P, Q\}$ as in Example B then $PH = \{PI, PP, PQ\} = \{P, Q, I\} = H$ and $UH = \{UI, UP, UQ\} = \{U, V, W\}$.

ACTIVITY 4.18
(i) Find the other four left cosets IH, QH, VH and WH. How many distinct left cosets of H are there? What is the union of all these cosets?
(ii) Let $K = \{I, U\}$. Show that there are only three distinct left cosets of K, each containing two elements, and that the union of these is the whole set S.

The *right coset* Hx is defined similarly as $\{h_1 \bullet x, h_2 \bullet x, h_3 \bullet x, \ldots, h_m \bullet x\}$. If the group is Abelian then $xH = Hx$, but this need not be true in other cases: for example, in Activity 4.18, $PK = \{P, W\}$ but $KP = \{P, V\}$. The arguments that follow use left cosets throughout, even when the word 'left' is omitted.

The behaviour in the last activity is typical of the general case: the left cosets of a subgroup $H = \{h_1, h_2, h_3, \ldots, h_m\}$ of a group $(S, \bullet)$ have the following properties.

Property 1

Every coset has m distinct elements, where m is the order of H.

Proof

In the coset $xH = \{x \bullet h_1, x \bullet h_2, x \bullet h_3, \ldots, x \bullet h_m\}$ all the elements are distinct, since $x \bullet h_i = x \bullet h_j \Rightarrow h_i = h_j$ by the left cancellation rule.

Property 2

If $y \notin xH$ then xH and yH are disjoint (i.e. have no common element).

Proof

Suppose that xH and yH do have a common element, a say.
Then $a = x \bullet h_i = y \bullet h_j$, and so $y = x \bullet h_i \bullet h_j^{-1}$.
But since H is a subgroup $h_j^{-1} \in H$ and so (by closure) $h_i \bullet h_j^{-1} \in H$.
Therefore $x \bullet h_i \bullet h_j^{-1} \in xH$, i.e. $y \in xH$, which is a contradiction.
Therefore there can be no common element.

These properties are now used to prove the main result.

Lagrange's theorem

The order of any subgroup of a finite group is a factor of the order of the group.

Proof

Let H be a subgroup of a finite group $(S, \bullet)$, where H has order m and S has order n.

If $H = S$ then $m = n$ and the theorem is true.

If H is a proper subgroup then choose an element of S which is not in H: let this element be x, say. From property **1** the coset xH has m elements, and from property **2** H and xH are disjoint.

Therefore $H \cup xH$ has $2m$ elements.

If $H \cup xH = S$ then $n = 2m$ and the theorem is true.

If $H \cup xH \neq S$ then choose an element of S which is not in $H \cup xH$: let this element be y, say. From property **1** the coset yH has m elements and from property **2** H, xH and yH are all disjoint.

Therefore $H \cup xH \cup yH$ has $3m$ elements.

If $H \cup xH \cup yH = S$ then $n = 3m$ and the theorem is true.

If $H \cup xH \cup yH \neq S$ then proceed as before, choosing an element of S not in the union of the cosets used so far, and forming its left coset. At each stage this brings m extra elements into the union of cosets, so the total number of elements remains a multiple of m. This process must terminate, since S is finite, so at some stage the union of cosets equals S. If this occurs when there are k cosets (including H itself) then $n = km$, which proves the theorem.

Historical note

During his (unsuccessful) search for a formula for the roots of a quintic equation, Joseph Louis de Lagrange (1736–1813) found a result in the theory of equations which is a special case of the theorem which now bears his name. Although this was before the concept of a group was recognised, Lagrange's method of proving his result was essentially the same as the proof above, using the equivalents of cosets to partition the set whose elements he wanted to count.

EXERCISE 4F

1 Find the left cosets XK, AK and RK, where K is the subgroup $\{I, A, H, B\}$ of the symmetry group of a square (as in Question 1 of Exercise 4E).

2 Let C_n be the subgroup of rotations of the dihedral group D_n (as in Question 4 of Exercise 4E), and let $R \in D_n$ be any reflection. Prove that $D_n = C_n \cup RC_n$.

3 Let G be a group in which every element x satisfies the equation $x^2 = e$ (where e is the identity element of G). Show that G is Abelian. If, in addition, G is finite and contains more than two elements, show that G contains a subgroup H of order four, and deduce that the number of elements of G is of the form $4k$, where k is an integer.

By considering cosets of the form gH (where g denotes an element of G), prove that the product of all the elements of G is equal to e.

[MEI]

4 A subgroup H of a finite group G is said to be a *normal subgroup* if, for each element $h \in H$ and each element $g \in G$, the element $g^{-1}hg \in H$.

Prove that:

(i) G and $\{e\}$ (where e is the identity element of G) are normal subgroups of G

(ii) if G is a commutative group, then every subgroup of G is a normal subgroup

(iii) H is a normal subgroup if and only if every left coset of H is a right coset of H (that is, $gH = Hg$, for all $g \in G$)

(iv) if the order of G is twice the order of H, then H is a normal subgroup of G. Give (and justify) an example of a finite group G and a subgroup H which is *not* a normal subgroup.

[MEI]

INVESTIGATION

Change ringing

The object of change ringing a peal of n bells is to ring all the $n!$ possible permutations of the bells without any omissions or repetitions. Clearly it is quite a task to organise this, and to ring the permutations in a sequence which makes it relatively easy for a particular ringer to remember what to do. This investigation shows one method for a peal of four bells, for which there are $4! = 24$ permutations.

(i) For an ordered set of four objects, let A be the operation of interchanging the first and second and interchanging the third and fourth objects, and let B be the operation of interchanging the second and third objects, as shown diagrammatically in figure 4.6.

Figure 4.6

Show that A: $(1\ \ 2\ \ 3\ \ 4) \rightarrow (2\ \ 1\ \ 4\ \ 3)$
and B: $(2\ \ 1\ \ 4\ \ 3) \rightarrow (2\ \ 4\ \ 1\ \ 3)$
as shown in figure 4.7.

Copy and complete the diagram to show that the sequence A, B, A, B, A, B, A, B produces a loop of eight permutations.

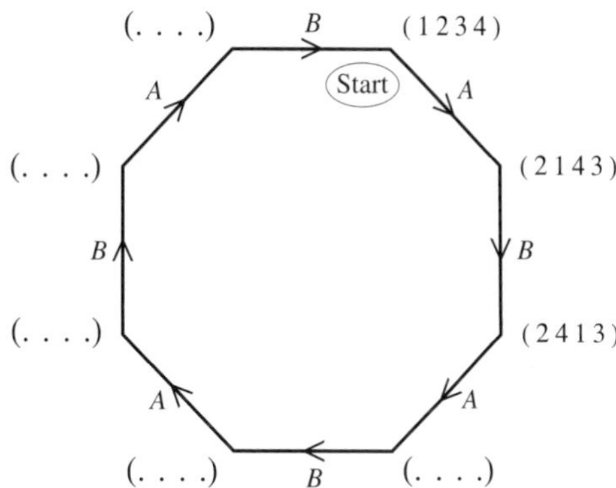

Figure 4.7

(ii) Using, for example, $(2\ \ 1\ \ 4\ \ 3)$ as shorthand for the permutation $\begin{pmatrix} 1 & 2 & 3 & 4 \\ 2 & 1 & 4 & 3 \end{pmatrix}$, show that the eight permutations in part **(i)** form a subgroup H of the permutation group S_4.

(iii) Now suppose that the final operation B in part **(i)** is replaced by the operation C which interchanges the third and fourth objects, as in figure 4.8.

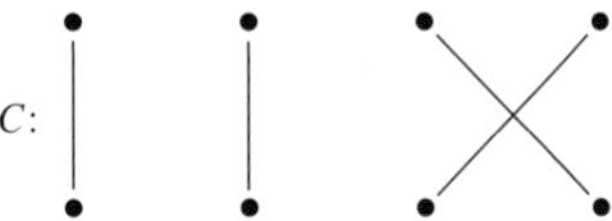

Figure 4.8

This leads to $(1\ \ 3\ \ 4\ \ 2)$ instead of $(1\ \ 2\ \ 3\ \ 4)$, thus stopping the loop from closing. Applying the sequence A, B, A, B, A, B, A, B again now gives another loop of eight permutations, which is a coset of H.

(iv) Again replacing the final B by C gives a third loop containing the final eight permutations; these form a second coset of H. And if the last B in this loop is replaced by C you get back to (1 2 3 4), the starting point. This is shown in figure 4.9, which you should copy and complete.

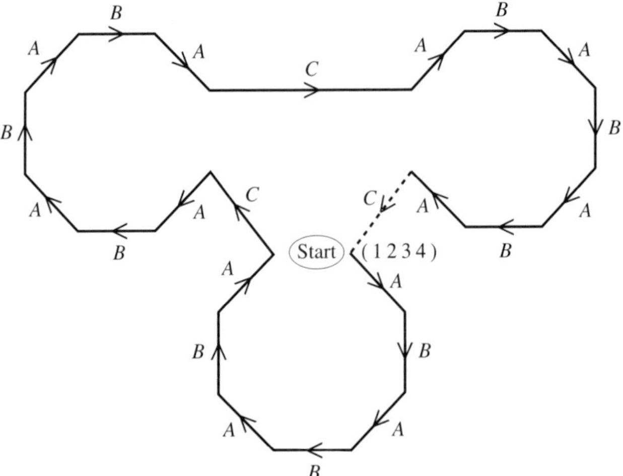

Figure 4.9

(v) Now that you have found this sequence of all 24 permutations you can see how each individual bell ringer can know where to ring in each permutation. This is shown for the ringers of bells 1 and 2 in figure 4.10. Ringer 1 has the easiest task, moving steadily through the order of ringing from first to last and then from last to first ('hunting'). Ringer 2 does mostly the same, but with a variant each time C is used ('dodging').

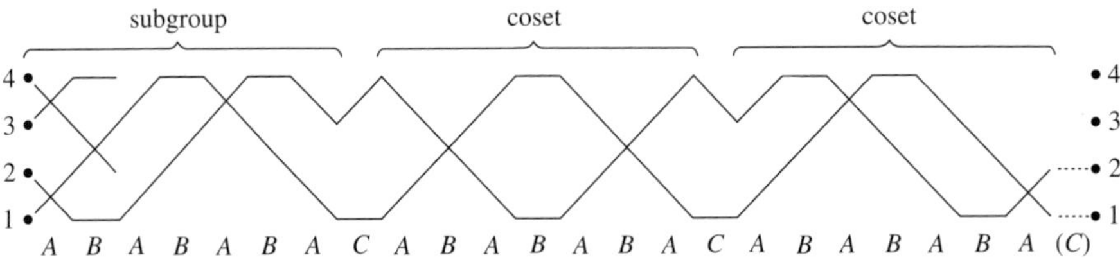

Figure 4.10

Copy figure 4.10 and complete the patterns for ringers 3 and 4. (It is actually easier to draw the whole diagram from scratch, since it consists of the patterns for A, B and C (above) turned upright for convenience and put together in the correct order.)

Cyclic groups

ACTIVITY 4.19 See what happens when you work out successive powers of each element of the group $\{1, 2, 4, 8\}$ under $\times_{15}$.

Let x be an element of a finite group $(S, \bullet)$, and consider the set of powers of x, $P = \{x, x^2, x^3, \ldots\}$, where $x^r = x \bullet x \bullet x \bullet \ldots \bullet x$ with r factors.

By closure, all the elements of P belong to S, which is finite. Therefore P must be finite, and so at some stage in the list of powers of x there must be an element which has occurred earlier in the list. Suppose that the first time this happens the earlier element is x^j and the later element is x^{j+k}, so that $x^{j+k} = x^j$. Multiplying both sides of this by $(x^{-1})^j$ gives $x^k = e$, where e is the identity element. Therefore P contains e.

The smallest positive power k such that $x^k = e$ is called the *order* (or *period*) of the element x. This shows that every element of a finite group has a finite order.

ACTIVITY 4.20 Referring yet again to the examples on pages 133–135, find the order of

(i) 5 in A **(ii)** U in B **(iii)** q in C **(iv)** $-\omega$ in D.

If the element x of $(S, \bullet)$ has order k then $P = \{e, x, x^2, \ldots, x^{k-1}\}$. To see this, note that:

(i) any higher index r can be written in the form $r = ak + b$, where $0 \leqslant b \leqslant k - 1$, so that $x^r = (x^k)^a x^b = x^b$ (since $x^k = e$), which is already listed

(ii) the elements listed are all distinct, since if two were equal then k would not be the *smallest* positive power for which $x^k = e$.

The set P is closed under the group operation since if the result of combining two elements is x^r with $r \geqslant k$ the procedure in **(i)** gives $x^r = x^{r-k}$, which is in P. Moreover, the inverse of each element of P is also in P, since the inverse of x^b $(0 < b \leqslant k - 1)$ is x^{k-b}. Therefore P is a subgroup of S; this is called the subgroup *generated* by x.

ACTIVITY 4.21 List the elements of the subgroups of Example D generated by:

(i) 1 **(ii)** -1 **(iii)** ω **(iv)** $-\omega$.

The subgroup generated by x has order k, where k is the order of the element x. Therefore, by Lagrange's theorem, the order of each element of a group is a factor of the order of the group.

A group generated by a single element is called a *cyclic* group. The cyclic group of order n is denoted by C_n, and is isomorphic to the group generated by the rotation of a plane through $\dfrac{2\pi}{n}$ about a fixed point. Therefore cyclic groups of all orders do exist.

ACTIVITY 4.22 Are there any cyclic groups among the examples A, B, C and D?

Finally, if the order of a finite group is a *prime* number p then the only possible orders for the elements of the group are 1 and p. Only the identity element e has order 1, so every other element must have order p, and must generate the whole of the group. The group is therefore isomorphic to C_p, the cyclic group of order p. This show that all groups of prime order are cyclic.

EXAMPLE 4.5

Prove that there are only two non-isomorphic groups of order 4.

SOLUTION

One method has already been outlined in Question 10 of Exercise 4D, but here is a more economical solution.

In a group G of order 4 each element, except for the identity e, must have order 2 or 4. There are two possibilities.

1 If G contains an element a of order 4 then the elements e, a, a^2, a^3 are distinct, and so G is C_4, the cyclic group of order 4.

2 If G contains no element of order 4 then each element, except for e, has order 2. Suppose e, a, b are distinct elements of G, with $a^2 = b^2 = e$.

The element ab does not equal any of these, since:

$$ab = e = a^2 \Rightarrow b = a, \quad ab = a \Rightarrow b = e, \quad ab = b \Rightarrow a = e$$

all of which contradict the supposition that e, a, b are distinct.

Therefore ab is the fourth element of G. Similarly:

$$ba = e = a^2 \Rightarrow b = a, \quad ba = a \Rightarrow b = e, \quad ba = b \Rightarrow a = e$$

all of which are contradictory. Therefore $ba = ab$. It is now easy to complete the Cayley table (using, for example, $b(ab) = b(ba) = b^2a = ea = a$): which shows that G is V, the Klein 4-Group.

	e	a	b	ab
e	e	a	b	ab
a	a	e	ab	b
b	b	ab	e	a
ab	ab	b	a	e

EXERCISE 4G

1 List the orders of all the elements of D_4, the symmetry group of a square, and find all the cyclic subgroups.

2 Prove that in a group the elements ab and ba have the same order.

3 Prove by induction that, in a group, $(b^{-1}ab)^n = b^{-1}a^nb$. Deduce that $b^{-1}ab$ has the same order as a.

4 **(i)** Show that C_5 (the cyclic group of order 5) can be generated by every one of its elements except for the identity. Show that the corresponding statement about C_6 is not true.

(ii) Investigate similar statements about C_7 and C_8.

(iii) Given that a is a generator of C_n, find a necessary and sufficient condition for a^k to generate C_n.

5 The Big Wheel at a fairground has 20 seats spaced equally around the rim. At the end of the ride the machinery automatically advances the wheel through successive angles of $\frac{\pi}{10}$ radians so that passengers may dismount in turn. On one occasion, to the dismay of all the passengers except one, the machinery develops a fault at the end of the ride and begins to advance the wheel through successive angles of $\frac{n\pi}{10}$, where n is an integer. The remaining passenger, a mathematician, notices that $n = 9$ and patiently awaits his turn to dismount. Explain his confidence. What other values of n would leave him unperturbed? [MEI]

6 Let a and b be distinct elements of a finite group G. Show that the set of elements obtained by taking all possible products of a finite number of a's and b's, including repetitions (for example aba^2b^3a), is a subgroup H of G. (a and b are said to be generators of H.)

7 With the notation of Question 1 of Exercise 4C, for the group D_4:

(i) by expressing H, S, Y, A, B in terms of R and/or X show that R and X are generators of the group

(ii) show that $R^4 = X^2 = I$ and $RX = XR^3$ (these are called *defining relations*).

8 Show that D_n is generated by two elements R and X with $R^n = X^2 = I$ and $RX = XR^{n-1}$.

9 Let $p = 2^k + 1$ be a prime number, and let G be the group of integers $1, 2, \ldots, p - 1$, with multiplication defined modulo p.

(i) Show that if $0 < m < k$ then $0 < 2^m - 1 < p$ and deduce that $2^m \neq 1 \pmod{p}$.

(ii) Show that if $k < m < 2k$ then $2^m = 1 \pmod{p} \Rightarrow 2^{2k-m} = -1 \pmod{p}$ and deduce that $2^m \neq 1 \pmod{p}$.

(iii) Use parts **(i)** and **(ii)** to show that the order of the element 2 in G is $2k$.

(iv) Deduce that k is a power of 2.

10 A set G consists of 1 and all positive integers having no squared factors.

Prove that G is a group with respect to the law of composition, $a \bullet b = \frac{m}{d}$, where m is the least common multiple of a and b, and d is the greatest common divisor.

Prove that the subgroup generated by the distinct elements $a_1, a_2, \ldots, a_k$ has order 2^t, $1 \leqslant t \leqslant k$ and that $t = k$ if $a_1, a_2, \ldots, a_k$ are coprime in pairs. (The pair a, b is *coprime* if and only if $d = 1$.) [MEI]

INVESTIGATION

The symmetries of the five platonic solids

You will find it a great help to have models of the five platonic solids (tetrahedron, cube, octahedron, dodecahedron and icosahedron) available to handle as you work through this investigation. Here you will be concerned only with regular solids.

(i) The tetrahedron

Any particular vertex can be moved to any one of the four vertices of the tetrahedron, and then the other three vertices can be permuted in any of six ways. Therefore the tetrahedron has $4 \times 6 = 24$ symmetries, corresponding to the 24 permutations of the four vertices, and so the group of symmetries of the tetrahedron is isomorphic to S_4. Some of these are *opposite* symmetries, which involve a change of handedness. It is not possible to perform these operations on a three-dimensional solid in the space of three dimensions, though it could be done if the solid were embedded in four-dimensional space (just as reflecting a rigid two-dimensional shape in a line cannot be done without using a half-turn about this line, which moves the shape into the third dimension and then back into its plane). How many of these opposite symmetries are reflections?

The others are *direct* symmetries, which are rotations, and can be done physically with a model. There are two distinct types of axis of rotation:

(a) a line joining a vertex to the centre of the opposite face,

(b) a line joining the mid-points of opposite edges.

Find how many rotations of type **(a)** there are, giving the angles of rotation, and do the same with type **(b)**. Hence show that the direct symmetries (including the identity) form a subgroup of order 12, which is often denoted by A_4. Explain why the opposite symmetries form a coset of A_4.

(ii) The cube

Any particular vertex A can be moved to any one of the eight vertices of the cube, and then the three vertices nearest to A can be permuted in any of six ways. The position of the whole cube is determined by the positions of these four vertices, so there are $8 \times 6 = 48$ symmetries. Some of these are direct symmetries (rotations). Describe the possible axes of rotation (there are three types) and give the possible angles of rotation. Hence show that the direct symmetries form a group of order 24; this is called the *octahedral* group (see part **(iv)**).

(iii) Show that the octahedral group is isomorphic to S_4, the group of permutations of four objects. **Hint:** Don't make this difficult – consider the effects of the rotations on the space diagonals of the cube.

(iv) The octahedron

Show that the mid-points of the faces of a cube are the vertices of an octahedron, and that the mid-points of the faces of an octahedron are the vertices of a cube. Hence these two solids have the same symmetry properties – if one is transformed into itself then so is the other. Thus the symmetry group of the octahedron is also of order 48, and the rotations form a subgroup (the octahedral group) of order 24, isomorphic to S_4. Check that you can find these 24 rotations of an octahedron.

(v) The dodecahedron

The dodecahedron has 12 pentagonal faces, with three faces meeting at each of the 20 vertices. By adapting the argument for the cube given in part **(ii)**, show that the dodecahedron has $20 \times 6 = 120$ symmetries. Describe the possible axes of rotation (there are again three types) and give the possible angles of rotation. Hence show that the direct symmetries form a group of order 60; this is called the *dodecahedral* group.

(vi) The dodecahedron has the property that it is possible to choose one diagonal of each pentagonal face so that these 12 lines are the edges of a cube, as in figure 4.11. By using each of the five diagonals of one particular face in turn you obtain five cubes inscribed in the dodecahedron.

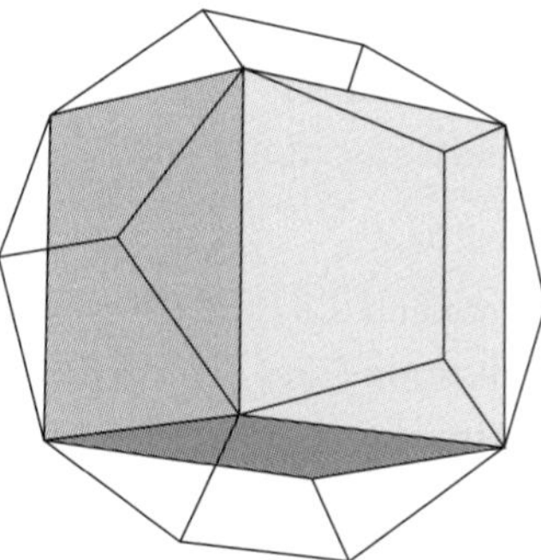

Figure 4.11

By considering the effect of the symmetry transformations on these cubes, show that the symmetry group of the dodecahedron is isomorphic to S_5, with the dodecahedral group of rotations forming a subgroup A_5, and the set of opposite symmetries forming a coset of A_5.

(vii) The icosahedron

Show that the centres of the 12 faces of a dodecahedron may be joined to form an icosahedron, having 12 vertices and 20 triangular faces, and that the mid-points of the faces of an icosahedron are the vertices of a dodecahedron. Deduce that an icosahedron has the same symmetry group as a dodecahedron.

e Fields

The real number system is an example of a more complicated algebraic structure with a set $\mathbb{R}$ of real numbers and two basic binary operations, addition (+) and multiplication (×). This system has the following properties:

1 $(\mathbb{R}, +)$ is an Abelian group, with identity 0

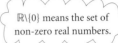

2 $(\mathbb{R}\backslash\{0\}, \times)$ is an Abelian group, with identity 1

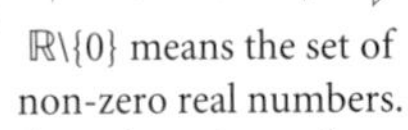

$\mathbb{R}\backslash\{0\}$ means the set of non-zero real numbers.

3 multiplication is *distributive* over addition; that is:

$a \times (b + c) = (a \times b) + (a \times c)$ for all $a, b, c \in \mathbb{R}$.

The other two operations, subtraction (−) and division (÷), are defined by:

$a - b = a + (-b)$, where $-b$ is the additive inverse of b

$a \div b = a \times b^{-1}$, where b^{-1} is the multiplicative inverse of b.

Note that − and ÷ are neither commutative nor associative.

 Are there any other distributive properties involving +, −, ×, ÷?

There are other sets which have these properties, and you say that a set S with two binary operations which has all the properties **1**, **2** and **3** forms a *field* $(S, +, \times)$.

The product $a \times b$ is often written as ab, and the usual convention that multiplication takes precedence over addition saves writing some brackets: thus the distributive property can be written as

$$a(b + c) = ab + ac.$$

ACTIVITY 4.23 Check that the set of rational numbers under addition and multiplication forms a field, and explain why the set of irrational numbers does not.

The rational numbers and the real numbers both have all the field properties, and yet some statements (for example 'there is a number x such that $x^2 = 2$') are true for real numbers but false for rational numbers. So the field properties are not sufficient to determine the behaviour of a set of numbers completely. However, all the standard algebraic processes of simplifying, expanding, factorising and solving equations (but not extracting roots or using inequalities) can be derived from the field axioms.

EXAMPLE 4.6 Prove that, in every field, $a \times 0 = 0$.

SOLUTION

$$
\begin{aligned}
& & 1 + 0 = 1 & \quad \text{(0 is neutral)} \\
&\Rightarrow & a \times (1 + 0) = a \times 1 & \\
&\Rightarrow & a \times 1 + a \times 0 = a \times 1 & \quad \text{(distributivity)} \\
&\Rightarrow & a + a \times 0 = a & \quad \text{(1 is neutral)} \\
&\Rightarrow & a \times 0 + a = a & \quad \text{(commutativity)} \\
&\Rightarrow & (a \times 0 + a) + (-a) = a + (-a) & \\
&\Rightarrow & a \times 0 + (a + (-a)) = a + (-a) & \quad \text{(associativity)} \\
&\Rightarrow & a \times 0 + 0 = 0 & \quad \text{(use of inverse)} \\
&\Rightarrow & a \times 0 = 0 & \quad \text{(0 is neutral).}
\end{aligned}
$$

ACTIVITY 4.24 Prove that, in every field, $ab = 0 \Rightarrow a = 0$ or $b = 0$.

Note

This is the fundamental result needed for the method of solving equations by factorising.

The field of complex numbers

It is easy to check that the set of enlargement matrices $\begin{pmatrix} x & 0 \\ 0 & x \end{pmatrix}$, where $x \in \mathbb{R}$, forms a field under the operations of matrix addition and matrix multiplication with the matrices $\mathbf{O} = \begin{pmatrix} 0 & 0 \\ 0 & 0 \end{pmatrix}$ and $\mathbf{I} = \begin{pmatrix} 1 & 0 \\ 0 & 1 \end{pmatrix}$ as the identities. Moreover, the mapping $x \leftrightarrow \begin{pmatrix} x & 0 \\ 0 & x \end{pmatrix}$ is an isomorphism between the field of real numbers and the field of enlargement matrices, preserving the structure of both addition and multiplication.

ACTIVITY 4.25 Check this.

This idea can be extended by considering matrices of the form $\begin{pmatrix} x & -y \\ y & x \end{pmatrix}$, where $x, y \in \mathbb{R}$; these are called *spiral* matrices.

ACTIVITY 4.26 Account for this name by describing the geometrical transformation represented by this matrix and check that the set of spiral matrices forms a field under matrix addition and matrix multiplication.

This field has the set of enlargement matrices as a *subfield* (i.e. subset which is itself a field under the same operations), isomorphic to the real numbers. But it also has a crucial property which the real numbers lack, for if **J** denotes the particular spiral matrix $\begin{pmatrix} 0 & -1 \\ 1 & 0 \end{pmatrix}$ then $\mathbf{J}^2 = -\mathbf{I}$.

ACTIVITY 4.27 Check this. What transformation does **J** represent?

Every spiral matrix $\mathbf{Z} = \begin{pmatrix} x & -y \\ y & x \end{pmatrix}$ can be written in the form $\mathbf{Z} = x\mathbf{I} + y\mathbf{J}$, and such expressions can be manipulated by 'ordinary' algebra, using $\mathbf{I}^2 = -\mathbf{J}^2 = \mathbf{I}$, $\mathbf{IJ} = \mathbf{JI} = \mathbf{J}$.

As a further simplification you can write 1 for **I** and j for **J** to obtain expressions of the form $z = x + y\text{j}$, where $x, y \in \mathbb{R}$, which behave as if they were real numbers with the extra property that $\text{j}^2 = -1$. This is exactly the *Bold Hypothesis* with which complex numbers were introduced on page 48 of *AS Further Pure Mathematics* (*FP1*), but now you can be sure that the complex numbers form a field (isomorphic to the field of spiral matrices). This resolves the longstanding (though probably forgotten) question of whether the Bold Hypothesis might lead to a contradiction.

EXERCISE 4H

1 Prove that, in every field, if $a \neq 0$ then:

$$ax + b = c \Leftrightarrow x = (c - b) \div a,$$

making clear which field property is used at each step.

2 Prove that the usual 'rules of signs':

$$(-a)b = a(-b) = -(ab), \qquad (-a)(-b) = ab$$

hold in every field.

3 Prove that the set of numbers $p + q\sqrt{2}$, where p and q are rational, forms a field under ordinary addition and multiplication.

4 Investigate the circumstances in which the set $\{0, 1, 2, \ldots, m - 1\}$ forms a field under the operations of addition and multiplication modulo m.

5 The set Z consists of all integers (positive, zero and negative). The operations of 'addition', $\oplus$, and 'multiplication', $\otimes$, are defined on Z as follows:

$$m \oplus n = m + n - 1 \qquad m \otimes n = m + n - mn.$$

Show that the system $(Z, \oplus, \otimes)$ is closed, commutative, and associative with respect to each operation, and that 'multiplication' is distributive over 'addition'. Show also that each operation has an identity element in Z, and find them. Determine whether each element of Z has an inverse with respect to each operation.

[MEI]

6 Use the isomorphism between spiral matrices and complex numbers to write the matrix equation:

$$\begin{pmatrix} 2 & -1 \\ 1 & 2 \end{pmatrix}\mathbf{Z} + \begin{pmatrix} 4 & 5 \\ -5 & 4 \end{pmatrix} = \begin{pmatrix} 1 & -3 \\ 3 & 1 \end{pmatrix}\mathbf{Z}$$

in terms of complex numbers, and hence find the matrix **Z**.

7 Use complex numbers to find two matrices **Z** for which:

$$\mathbf{Z}^2 + \begin{pmatrix} -9 & -2 \\ 2 & -9 \end{pmatrix}\mathbf{Z} + \begin{pmatrix} 23 & 7 \\ -7 & 23 \end{pmatrix} = \begin{pmatrix} 0 & 0 \\ 0 & 0 \end{pmatrix}.$$

8 Find $\mathbf{P}^6$ if $\mathbf{P} = \begin{pmatrix} \frac{\sqrt{3}}{2} & -\frac{1}{2} \\ \frac{1}{2} & \frac{\sqrt{3}}{2} \end{pmatrix}$.

9 **(i)** What operation on complex numbers corresponds to transposing (i.e. interchanging rows and columns) spiral matrices?

(ii) Establish the result $zz^* = |z|^2$ by using matrices.

(iii) What property of determinants corresponds to the fact that $|z_1z_2| = |z_1||z_2|$?

10 **(i)** Show that the set of matrices

$$\mathbf{Q} = \begin{pmatrix} z & -w^* \\ w & z^* \end{pmatrix}$$

where z and w are complex numbers, satisfies all the field axioms under matrix addition and multiplication, except that multiplication is not commutative.

(ii) Show that if $z = a + b\mathrm{j}$ and $w = c + d\mathrm{j}$ then $\mathbf{Q} = a\mathbf{I} + b\mathbf{E} + c\mathbf{F} + d\mathbf{G}$, where:

$$\mathbf{I} = \begin{pmatrix} 1 & 0 \\ 0 & 1 \end{pmatrix} \quad \mathbf{E} = \begin{pmatrix} \mathrm{j} & 0 \\ 0 & -\mathrm{j} \end{pmatrix} \quad \mathbf{F} = \begin{pmatrix} 0 & -1 \\ 1 & 0 \end{pmatrix} \quad \mathbf{G} = \begin{pmatrix} 0 & \mathrm{j} \\ \mathrm{j} & 0 \end{pmatrix}.$$

(iii) Show that $\mathbf{E}^2 = \mathbf{F}^2 = \mathbf{G}^2 = -\mathbf{I}$, $\mathbf{EF} = -\mathbf{FE} = -\mathbf{G}$, $\mathbf{FG} = -\mathbf{GF} = -\mathbf{E}$, $\mathbf{GE} = -\mathbf{EG} = -\mathbf{F}$.

Show also that the same relations can be written more compactly as $\mathbf{E}^2 = \mathbf{F}^2 = \mathbf{G}^2 = -\mathbf{EFG} = -\mathbf{I}$.

(iv) By writing 1, e, f and g in place of **I**, **E**, **F** and **G** show that the system in part **(i)** is isomorphic to the system of expressions of the form $q = a + be + cf + dg$, where a, b, c and d are real and the elements e, f and g act like real numbers with the additional properties:

$$e^2 = f^2 = g^2 = -1$$

$$ef = -fe = -g, \qquad fg = -gf = -e, \qquad ge = -eg = -f.$$

('Super-complex' numbers of this form are called *quaternions*. Invented by William Rowan Hamilton in 1843, quaternions are the earliest example of a non-commutative algebraic system. They were studied extensively in the nineteenth century (usually being written in the form $a + b\mathrm{i} + c\mathrm{j} + d\mathrm{k}$) and were found to have many applications which would now be handled by vectors.)

EXERCISE 4I

1 G is a finite group which is commutative (i.e. $ab = ba$ for all $a, b \in G$). S and T are subgroups of G, and $S \cap T = \{e\}$, where e is the identity element of G.

We define ST to be the set of all elements of the form st, where $s \in S$ and $t \in T$

(i) Show that ST is a subgroup of G.

(ii) Show that if $s_1t_1 = s_2t_2$ where $s_1, s_2 \in S$ and $t_1, t_2 \in T$, then $s_1 = s_2$ and $t_1 = t_2$.

(iii) Deduce that if S contains k elements and T contains m elements, then ST contains km elements.

Now let $G = \{1, 5, 7, 11, 13, 17, 19, 23, 25, 29, 31, 35\}$, where the binary operation is multiplication modulo 36. You may assume that G is a commutative group.

Three cyclic subgroups of G are

$$S = \{1, 13, 25\}, T = \{1, 17\} \text{ and } U = \{1, 35\}.$$

(iv) List the elements of the subgroup ST. Show that ST is cyclic.

(v) List the elements of the subgroup TU. Show that TU is not cyclic.

[MEI]

2 A non-Abelian group G consists of eight 2×2 matrices, and the binary operation is matrix multiplication. The eight distinct elements of G can be written as

$$G = \{\mathbf{I}, \mathbf{A}, \mathbf{A}^2, \mathbf{A}^3, \mathbf{B}, \mathbf{AB}, \mathbf{A}^2\mathbf{B}, \mathbf{A}^3\mathbf{B}\}, \quad ⊛$$

where $\mathbf{I}$ is the identity matrix, and $\mathbf{A}$, $\mathbf{B}$ are 2×2 matrices such that

$$\mathbf{A}^4 = \mathbf{I}, \qquad \mathbf{B}^2 = \mathbf{I}, \qquad \text{and} \qquad \mathbf{BA} = \mathbf{A}^3\mathbf{B}.$$

(i) Show that $(\mathbf{A}^2\mathbf{B})(\mathbf{AB}) = \mathbf{A}$ and $(\mathbf{AB})(\mathbf{A}^2\mathbf{B}) = \mathbf{A}^3$.

(ii) Evaluate the following products, giving each one as an element of G as listed in ⊛: $(\mathbf{AB})(\mathbf{A})$, $(\mathbf{AB})(\mathbf{AB})$, $(\mathbf{B})(\mathbf{A}^2)$.

(iii) Find the order of each element of G.

(iv) Show that $\{\mathbf{I}, \mathbf{A}^2, \mathbf{B}, \mathbf{A}^2\mathbf{B}\}$ is a subgroup of G.

(v) Find the other two subgroups of G which have order 4.

(vi) For each of the three subgroups of order 4, state whether or not it is a cyclic subgroup.

[MEI]

3 The notation

$$\begin{bmatrix} 1 & 2 & 3 & 4 \\ 2 & 4 & 1 & 3 \end{bmatrix}$$

denotes the permutation, or mapping of {1, 2, 3, 4} into itself, in which 1 has image 2, 2 has image 4, 3 has image 1, 4 has image 3. Permutations are combined in the usual way by composition of mappings.

Show that the set of permutations

$$\left\{ \begin{bmatrix} 1 & 2 & 3 & 4 \\ 1 & 2 & 3 & 4 \end{bmatrix}, \begin{bmatrix} 1 & 2 & 3 & 4 \\ 2 & 1 & 4 & 3 \end{bmatrix}, \begin{bmatrix} 1 & 2 & 3 & 4 \\ 3 & 4 & 1 & 2 \end{bmatrix}, \begin{bmatrix} 1 & 2 & 3 & 4 \\ 4 & 3 & 2 & 1 \end{bmatrix} \right\}$$

and the set of matrices

$$\left\{ \begin{pmatrix} 1 & 0 \\ 0 & 1 \end{pmatrix}, \begin{pmatrix} 1 & 0 \\ 0 & -1 \end{pmatrix}, \begin{pmatrix} -1 & 0 \\ 0 & 1 \end{pmatrix}, \begin{pmatrix} -1 & 0 \\ 0 & -1 \end{pmatrix} \right\}$$

under matrix multiplication are isomorphic groups,
and that the set of complex numbers

$\{1, -1, \text{j}, -\text{j}\}$

(usual multiplication) is a group not isomorphic with the others.

For each group give the order of each element, say whether the group is cyclic, and list all its proper subgroups.

Indicate briefly how you would show that these are the only two types of group of order 4.

[MEI]

4 The set $G = \{1, 3, 7, 9, 11, 13, 17, 19\}$ is a group under the binary operation of multiplication modulo 20.

(i) Give the combination table for G.

(ii) State the inverse of each element of G.

(iii) Find the order of each element of G.

(iv) List all the subgroups of G.
Identify those subgroups which are isomorphic to one another.

(v) For each of the following, state, giving reasons, whether or not the given set and binary operation is a group. If it is a group, state, giving a reason, whether or not it is isomorphic to G.

(a) $J = \{0, 1, 2, 3, 4, 5, 6, 7\}$ under multiplication modulo 8

(b) $K = \{0, 1, 2, 3, 4, 5, 6, 7\}$ under addition modulo 8

[MEI]

5 (i) State Lagrange's theorem for finite groups, and use it to show that every group of order $n \leqslant 5$ is Abelian. Give an example of a non-Abelian group of order 6, and prove that it is non-Abelian.

(ii) Let $p = 2^k + 1$ be a prime number, and let G be the group of integers $1, 2, \ldots, p - 1$, with multiplication defined modulo p. Show that the order of the element 2 is $2k$, and deduce that k is a power of 2.

[MEI]

6 The set $G = \{\mathbf{P}, \mathbf{Q}, \mathbf{R}, \mathbf{S}\}$ consists of the four matrices

$$\mathbf{P} = \begin{pmatrix} 1 & 0 \\ 0 & 1 \end{pmatrix}, \mathbf{Q} = \begin{pmatrix} -1 & 0 \\ 0 & -1 \end{pmatrix}, \mathbf{R} = \begin{pmatrix} 0.6 & 0.8 \\ 0.8 & -0.6 \end{pmatrix}, \mathbf{S} = \begin{pmatrix} -0.6 & -0.8 \\ -0.8 & 0.6 \end{pmatrix}.$$

(i) Show that G is a group under matrix multiplication. (You may assume that matrix multiplication is associative.)

(ii) State the order of each of the elements of G.

A fifth matrix is $\mathbf{T} = \begin{pmatrix} 1 & 0 \\ 0 & -1 \end{pmatrix}$.

(iii) Prove that $\mathbf{P}, \mathbf{Q}, \mathbf{R}, \mathbf{S}, \mathbf{T}$ cannot be 5 of the elements in a group of order 8.

[MEI, *part*]

KEY POINTS

1 A *group* $(S, \bullet)$ is a non-empty set S with a binary operation $\bullet$ which is closed and associative, which has an identity element, and in which each element has an inverse element. The group is *Abelian* if and only if $\bullet$ is commutative.

2 Two groups $(S, \bullet)$ and $(T, \diamond)$ are *isomorphic* if there is a one-to-one mapping between them which preserves their structure, i.e.

$$a \leftrightarrow x \text{ and } b \leftrightarrow y \Rightarrow a \bullet b \leftrightarrow x \diamond y.$$

3 A *subgroup* of a group $(S, \bullet)$ is a non-empty subset of S which forms a group under the same binary operation $\bullet$.

4 Lagrange's theorem states: the order (i.e. number of elements) of any subgroup of a finite group is a factor of the order of the group.

5 The *order* of an element x of a group is the smallest positive power k such that $x^k = e$ (the identity element). The set of powers of x forms a subgroup of order k, called the *cyclic* group *generated* by x.

5 Markov chains

I can see looming ahead one of those terrible exercises in probability where six men have white hats and six men have black hats and you have to work out by mathematics how likely it is that the hats will get mixed up and in what proportions.

Agatha Christie (1890–1976)

This chapter is based on the assumption that you have a calculator that can handle matrices.

In November 2004 the people of the USA re-elected a Republican President for a second term. The two previous presidential terms, each of length four years, were held by the Democrats. For the past 140 years the President of the USA has come from either the Democratic or Republican Party. Each time there is an election, how likely is the current government to remain in power and how likely is the party in power to change?

The results of the last 36 presidential elections in the USA have resulted in the following pattern of results (where **D** represents Democratic and **R** represents Republican).

R R R R R D R D R R R R
D D R R R D D D D D R R
D D R R D R R R D D R R

When you look at the 35 handovers of power from one president to the next the following pattern emerges.

		From	
		Democratic	**Republican**
To	**Democratic**	7	7
	Republican	7	14
	Total	14	21

These results can be used to generate *empirical probabilities* for the four types of handover.

		From	
		Democratic	**Republican**
To	**Democratic**	$\frac{1}{2}$	$\frac{1}{3}$
	Republican	$\frac{1}{2}$	$\frac{2}{3}$
	Total	1	1

What does empirical mean?

The table is very informative, since it tells you that over the last 140 years, whenever the Democrats have held office, on about half the occasions they have lost the presidency at the next election. However, when there has been a Republican president, the party retained the presidency on average two times out of three.

The fractions in the table are called *transition probabilities*, since they give the probabilities of moving from one state (a Democratic or Republican president) to the next state (a Democratic or Republican president). An alternative representation of these probabilities is a *transition state diagram*.

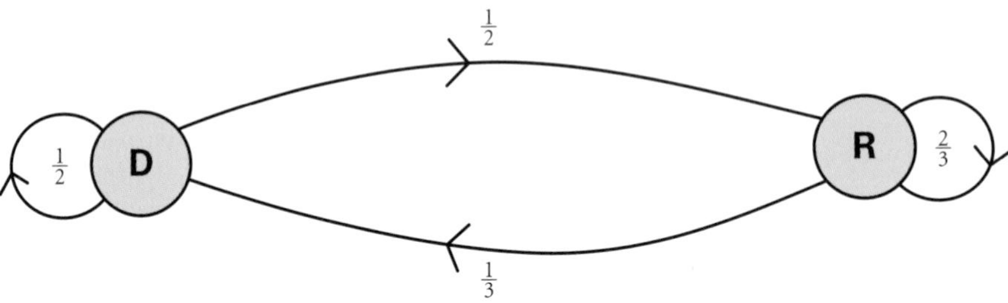

Figure 5.1

Building a Markov chain

Transition probabilities can be used to find the probability of states in the future, beyond the next state. This is illustrated by the following example.

Tony is an amateur weather forecaster. For the last year he has kept a record of whether any particular day is *fine* or *wet*. If it rains during daylight hours he classifies the day as *wet*, otherwise the day is said to be *fine*. He notes that, if it is fine one day it is often fine the next day. Similarly, a wet day is often followed by another wet day.

From his records over the past year, Tony suggests the following model.

> If a day is fine, then the probability that the next day is fine is $\frac{2}{3}$.
>
> If a day is wet, then the probability that the next day is wet is $\frac{3}{4}$.

Monday is fine. The possible weather for the next few days can then be illustrated by a tree diagram.

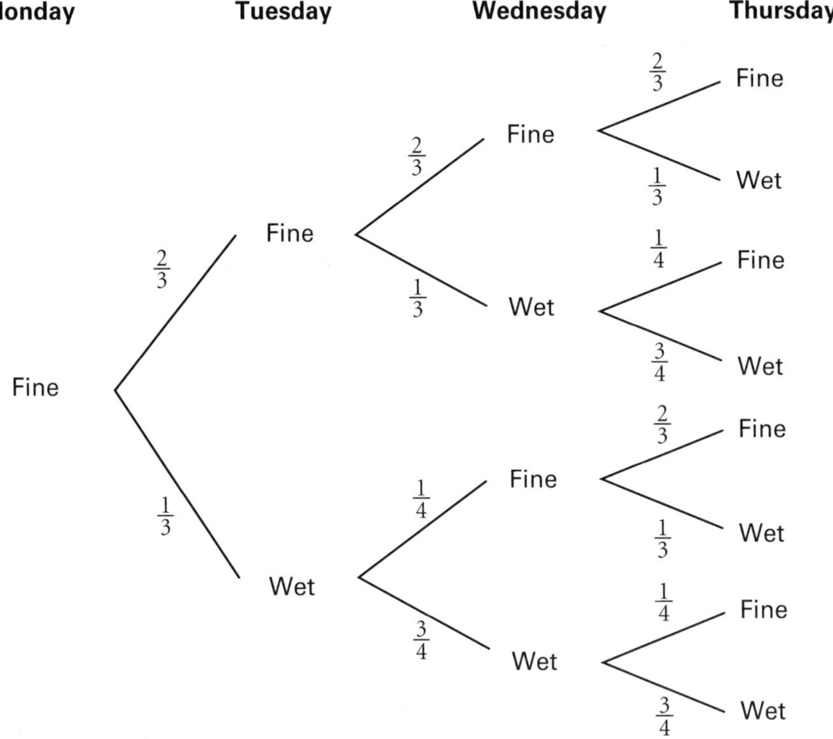

Figure 5.2

Given that Monday is fine, the probability that it is wet on Wednesday can be found from the diagram.

$$\tfrac{2}{3}\times\tfrac{1}{3}+\tfrac{1}{3}\times\tfrac{3}{4}=\tfrac{17}{36}$$

Similarly, the probability that it is fine on Thursday is

$$\tfrac{2}{3}\times\tfrac{2}{3}\times\tfrac{2}{3}+\tfrac{2}{3}\times\tfrac{1}{3}\times\tfrac{1}{4}+\tfrac{1}{3}\times\tfrac{1}{4}\times\tfrac{2}{3}+\tfrac{1}{3}\times\tfrac{3}{4}\times\tfrac{1}{4}=\tfrac{203}{432}.$$

In the example above it was assumed that the probability of a day being fine or wet depends only on the previous day's weather. This is an example of a *Markov chain*, where the probability of a particular outcome, or state, at a given time, such as fine or wet tomorrow, is dependent only on the state at the previous time, in this case, fine or wet today.

The four conditional probabilities:

$$\text{P(fine tomorrow} \mid \text{today is fine)} = \tfrac{2}{3} \qquad \text{P(fine tomorrow} \mid \text{today is wet)} = \tfrac{1}{4}$$

$$\text{P(wet tomorrow} \mid \text{today is fine)} = \tfrac{1}{3} \qquad \text{P(wet tomorrow} \mid \text{today is wet)} = \tfrac{3}{4}$$

are the *transition probabilities.*

It is convenient to summarise this information by arranging such probabilities into a matrix, called a *transition matrix*, which is denoted by **P**.

$$\begin{array}{ccc} & & \textbf{Today} \\ & & \begin{array}{cc} \textit{Fine} & \textit{Wet} \end{array} \\ \textbf{Tomorrow} & \begin{array}{c} \textit{Fine} \\ \textit{Wet} \end{array} & \begin{pmatrix} \frac{2}{3} & \frac{1}{4} \\ \frac{1}{3} & \frac{3}{4} \end{pmatrix} = \mathbf{P} \end{array}$$

The entries in the first column correspond to the possible weather conditions tomorrow, given that it is fine today and the entries in the second column correspond to the possible weather conditions tomorrow, given that it is wet today. Each column of a transition matrix is known as a *probability vector* and it is not difficult to see that the sum of the terms in each column must equal 1.

There are two conventions for writing transition matrices.

- This book uses the conventions used elsewhere in matrix work, and developed in earlier books in the series, *AS Further Pure Mathematics* (*FP1*) and *A2 Further Pure Mathematics* (*FP2*). This is the right to left notation in which the product **ABC** is evaluated by working out $\mathbf{B} \times \mathbf{C}$ first and then pre-multiplying the answer by **A**. So **ABC** reads 'First **C**, then **B**, then **A**'. This is consistent with function notation where $\mathrm{fg}(x)$ means 'start with x, work out $\mathrm{g}(x)$ and then work out f of your answer'.
- Statisticians use a different convention, reading from left to right as you do in a tree diagram. If you are using this notation, the transition matrix is transposed. In this case it would be $\begin{pmatrix} \frac{2}{3} & \frac{1}{3} \\ \frac{1}{4} & \frac{3}{4} \end{pmatrix}$.

If your motivation for studying this chapter is as an interesting application of the matrices you have learnt so far in pure mathematics, the notation used is fine. If, however, you want to study statistics in some depth, you would be better working with the alternative notation.

Given that it is fine on Monday, the probability that it is fine on Wednesday is given by

$$\tfrac{2}{3} \times \tfrac{2}{3} + \tfrac{1}{3} \times \tfrac{1}{4} = \boxed{\tfrac{19}{36}}$$

Similarly, given that it is fine on Monday, the probability that it is wet on Wednesday is given by

$$\tfrac{2}{3} \times \tfrac{1}{3} + \tfrac{1}{3} \times \tfrac{3}{4} = \boxed{\tfrac{17}{36}}$$

To complete the picture, suppose that Monday is wet. The corresponding probabilities of it being fine or wet on Wednesday are given by

$\tfrac{1}{4} \times \tfrac{2}{3} + \tfrac{3}{4} \times \tfrac{1}{4} = \boxed{\tfrac{17}{48}}$ and $\tfrac{1}{4} \times \tfrac{1}{3} + \tfrac{3}{4} \times \tfrac{3}{4} = \boxed{\tfrac{31}{48}}$ respectively.

The four circled probabilities are the entries in the two-step transition matrix, which can easily be found by squaring matrix **P**, i.e. by multiplying **P** by itself.

$$\mathbf{P} \times \mathbf{P} = \begin{pmatrix} \frac{2}{3} & \frac{1}{4} \\ \frac{1}{3} & \frac{3}{4} \end{pmatrix} \begin{pmatrix} \frac{2}{3} & \frac{1}{4} \\ \frac{1}{3} & \frac{3}{4} \end{pmatrix} = \begin{pmatrix} \frac{19}{36} & \frac{17}{48} \\ \frac{17}{36} & \frac{31}{48} \end{pmatrix} = \mathbf{P}^2$$

Notice that each column of $\mathbf{P}^2$ satisfies the condition to be a probability vector since the sum of the terms in each column equals 1.

A natural extension of the analysis is to cube the transition matrix to give the three-step transition matrix, which gives the various probabilities for Thursday.

$$\mathbf{P} \times \mathbf{P} \times \mathbf{P} = \begin{pmatrix} \frac{2}{3} & \frac{1}{4} \\ \frac{1}{3} & \frac{3}{4} \end{pmatrix} \begin{pmatrix} \frac{2}{3} & \frac{1}{4} \\ \frac{1}{3} & \frac{3}{4} \end{pmatrix} \begin{pmatrix} \frac{2}{3} & \frac{1}{4} \\ \frac{1}{3} & \frac{3}{4} \end{pmatrix} = \begin{pmatrix} \frac{2}{3} & \frac{1}{4} \\ \frac{1}{3} & \frac{3}{4} \end{pmatrix} \begin{pmatrix} \frac{19}{36} & \frac{17}{48} \\ \frac{17}{36} & \frac{31}{48} \end{pmatrix} = \begin{pmatrix} \frac{203}{432} & \frac{229}{576} \\ \frac{229}{432} & \frac{347}{576} \end{pmatrix} = \mathbf{P}^3$$

? Check that each column of $\mathbf{P}^3$ is a probability vector.

Amongst others, the probability of it being fine on Thursday, given that it was fine on Monday, as found earlier, is given by the top left-hand entry of matrix $\mathbf{P}^3$.

? Check that the bottom left-hand entry of matrix $\mathbf{P}^3$ gives the probability of it being wet on Thursday, given that it was fine on Monday.

Once again, to complete the picture, suppose that Monday was wet. Then, the corresponding probabilities of it being fine or wet on Thursday are given by the top right-hand and bottom right-hand entries of $\mathbf{P}^3$ respectively.

Although the tree diagram only extends to Thursday, higher powers of matrix **P** ($\mathbf{P}^4$, $\mathbf{P}^5$, etc.) can be used to calculate conditional weather probabilities for succeeding days.

EXERCISE 5A

1 For each of the following transition matrices, work out $\mathbf{P}^2$, $\mathbf{P}^3$ and $\mathbf{P}^4$.

(i) $\mathbf{P} = \begin{pmatrix} \frac{5}{8} & \frac{3}{4} \\ \frac{3}{8} & \frac{1}{4} \end{pmatrix}$ **(ii)** $\mathbf{P} = \begin{pmatrix} \frac{1}{3} & \frac{3}{4} \\ \frac{2}{3} & \frac{1}{4} \end{pmatrix}$

(iii) $\mathbf{P} = \begin{pmatrix} \frac{1}{6} & \frac{5}{6} \\ \frac{5}{6} & \frac{1}{6} \end{pmatrix}$ **(iv)** $\mathbf{P} = \begin{pmatrix} 0.7 & 0.1 \\ 0.3 & 0.9 \end{pmatrix}$

2 Ruth also studies the weather. She classifies each day as either *sunny* or *cloudy*. If today is sunny, she thinks there is a 70% chance that tomorrow will be sunny. If today is cloudy, she suggests that there is an 80% chance that tomorrow will be cloudy.

(i) Form a 2×2 transition matrix, **P**.

(ii) One Saturday it is sunny. Use suitable powers of **P** to find the probability that it is

(a) sunny on the following Monday

(b) cloudy on the following Tuesday

(c) sunny on the following Wednesday.

3 (i) Write the probabilities for the handovers of presidents in the USA as a transition matrix, **P**.

(ii) Given that a Republican president was re-elected in November, 2004, find the probability that

(a) a Republican president will be elected in 2008

(b) a Democratic president will be elected in 2012.

4 On a Saturday night Tina either goes to the disco or to the cinema. If she has been to the disco on the previous Saturday, then there is a probability of 0.5 that she will go to the disco again. However, if she has been to the cinema on the previous Saturday, there is a probability of 0.75 that she will go to the disco.

(i) Write down the transition matrix, **P**, for this problem.

(ii) On the first Saturday in February Tina went to the disco. Find the probability that Tina goes to

(a) the disco on the third Saturday in February

(b) the cinema on the fourth Saturday in February.

(iii) On the first Saturday in March Tina went to the cinema. Find the probability that Tina goes to the disco on the first Saturday in April. [**Note:** There are two possible answers.]

5 A tennis player hits either to his opponent's forehand or to his opponent's backhand. If he has previously hit to the forehand, then he has a probability of $\frac{4}{5}$ of hitting to the backhand on the next shot. If, however, he has previously hit to the backhand, there is a probability of $\frac{2}{3}$ that he will again hit to the backhand.

(i) Write down the transition matrix for this problem.

(ii) If his first shot is to his opponent's backhand, calculate the probability that the third shot will also be to the backhand.

(iii) What is the probability that his fourth shot will be to his opponent's backhand if his first shot is to

(a) the backhand

(b) the forehand?

6 Since the Boat Race began, whenever Oxford win there seems to be a probability of $\frac{3}{5}$ that they will also win the following year. For Cambridge the corresponding probability is $\frac{2}{3}$.

(i) Write down the transition matrix for this problem.

(ii) Find out which team won the last race and so calculate the probability of each team winning the race after next.

7 If I am late for school, I make a greater effort to arrive on time the next school day. If I arrive on time, I am liable to be less careful the next day. Consequently, if I am late one day, the probability that I am on time the next day is 0.75. If I am on time one day, the probability that I am late the next day is 0.5.

(i) Write down the transition matrix for this problem.

(ii) I am on time on Monday. Calculate the probability that, in the same week, I am on time

(a) on Wednesday **(b)** on Friday.

8 A 2×2 transition matrix, $\mathbf{P}$, is given by $\begin{pmatrix} a & c \\ b & d \end{pmatrix}$, where $0 \leqslant a, b, c, d \leqslant 1$.

(i) Write down two equations satisfied by some of a, b, c, d.

(ii) Find $\mathbf{P}^2$ in terms of a, b, c, d and hence show that each column of $\mathbf{P}^2$ is a probability vector, i.e. that $\mathbf{P}^2$ is a transition matrix.

(iii) Show that $\mathbf{P}^3$ is also a transition matrix.

3 × 3 transition matrices

Markov chains can have two, three or more states at each stage of the process. If there are, say, three possible outcomes, then a 3×3 matrix will be required to store the nine possible transition probabilities.

EXAMPLE 5.1

Bob has a very unreliable car. Every morning he goes out hopefully to start it: some days it starts by itself, some days it starts if he gets a push from a neighbour, other days no amount of pushing is effective and the garage must be called out. If it starts one day, the probabilities for the next day are $\frac{1}{2}$ that it will start, $\frac{1}{3}$ that it must be pushed and $\frac{1}{6}$ that the garage must be called out. If it is pushed one day, the probabilities are $\frac{1}{3}$ that it will start and $\frac{2}{3}$ that the garage must be called out the next day. It is never pushed two days in a row. If the garage is called out one day, the probabilities are $\frac{5}{6}$ that it will start and $\frac{1}{6}$ that it must be pushed the next day.

On Monday morning the car started by itself. What is the probability that it will start by itself on

(i) Wednesday morning **(ii)** Friday morning?

SOLUTION

The situation may be represented by a transition state diagram.

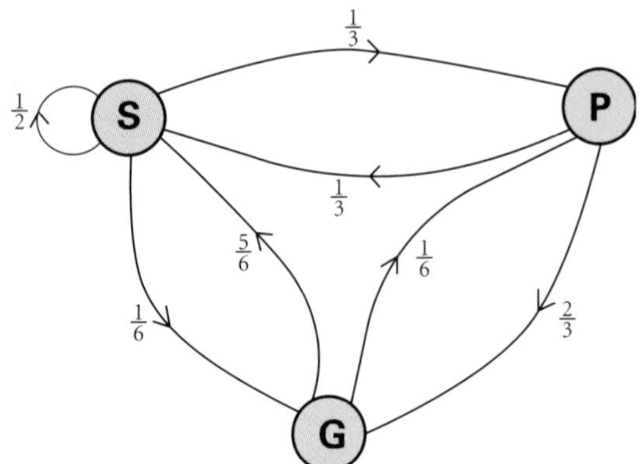

Figure 5.3

The 3×3 transition matrix for the situation is as follows.

$$\begin{array}{ccc} & & \textbf{Today} \\ & & \begin{array}{ccc} \textit{Starts} & \textit{Push} & \textit{Garage} \end{array} \\ \textbf{Tomorrow} & \begin{array}{c} \textit{Starts} \\ \textit{Push} \\ \textit{Garage} \end{array} & \begin{pmatrix} \frac{1}{2} & \frac{1}{3} & \frac{5}{6} \\ \frac{1}{3} & 0 & \frac{1}{6} \\ \frac{1}{6} & \frac{2}{3} & 0 \end{pmatrix} = \mathbf{P} \end{array}$$

(i) To find Wednesday's probabilities you need the two-step transition matrix, found by squaring matrix $\mathbf{P}$.

$$\mathbf{P} \times \mathbf{P} = \begin{pmatrix} \frac{1}{2} & \frac{1}{3} & \frac{5}{6} \\ \frac{1}{3} & 0 & \frac{1}{6} \\ \frac{1}{6} & \frac{2}{3} & 0 \end{pmatrix} \begin{pmatrix} \frac{1}{2} & \frac{1}{3} & \frac{5}{6} \\ \frac{1}{3} & 0 & \frac{1}{6} \\ \frac{1}{6} & \frac{2}{3} & 0 \end{pmatrix} = \begin{pmatrix} \frac{1}{2} & \frac{13}{18} & \frac{17}{36} \\ \frac{7}{36} & \frac{2}{9} & \frac{5}{18} \\ \frac{11}{36} & \frac{1}{18} & \frac{1}{4} \end{pmatrix} = \mathbf{P}^2$$

Therefore the probability that the car will start by itself on Wednesday morning is still $\frac{1}{2}$.

(ii) Will the probability remain the same for Friday morning? To find out you need to compute the four-step transition matrix, $\mathbf{P}^4$. This is done in two stages, by first calculating $\mathbf{P}^3$ and then $\mathbf{P}^4$.

$$\mathbf{P} \times \mathbf{P}^2 = \begin{pmatrix} \frac{1}{2} & \frac{1}{3} & \frac{5}{6} \\ \frac{1}{3} & 0 & \frac{1}{6} \\ \frac{1}{6} & \frac{2}{3} & 0 \end{pmatrix} \begin{pmatrix} \frac{1}{2} & \frac{13}{18} & \frac{17}{36} \\ \frac{7}{36} & \frac{2}{9} & \frac{5}{18} \\ \frac{11}{36} & \frac{1}{18} & \frac{1}{4} \end{pmatrix} = \begin{pmatrix} \frac{41}{72} & \frac{13}{27} & \frac{29}{54} \\ \frac{47}{216} & \frac{1}{4} & \frac{43}{216} \\ \frac{23}{108} & \frac{29}{108} & \frac{19}{72} \end{pmatrix} = \mathbf{P}^3$$

$$\mathbf{P} \times \mathbf{P}^3 = \begin{pmatrix} \frac{1}{2} & \frac{1}{3} & \frac{5}{6} \\ \frac{1}{3} & 0 & \frac{1}{6} \\ \frac{1}{6} & \frac{2}{3} & 0 \end{pmatrix} \begin{pmatrix} \frac{41}{72} & \frac{13}{27} & \frac{29}{54} \\ \frac{47}{216} & \frac{1}{4} & \frac{43}{216} \\ \frac{23}{108} & \frac{29}{108} & \frac{19}{72} \end{pmatrix} = \begin{pmatrix} \frac{77}{144} & \frac{355}{648} & \frac{719}{1296} \\ \frac{73}{324} & \frac{133}{648} & \frac{289}{1296} \\ \frac{311}{1296} & \frac{20}{81} & \frac{2}{9} \end{pmatrix} = \mathbf{P}^4$$

From the top left-hand entry of $\mathbf{P}^4$ you can see that the probability of the car starting by itself has increased slightly to $\frac{77}{144} \approx 0.535$.

The most useful aspect of computing successive transition matrices is that, at a glance, you can see what happens to the probabilities over a period of time. For example, if Bob needs to call out the garage on Monday morning, the probability that he needs to call it out on Tuesday morning is zero; the probability that he needs to call it out on Wednesday, however, is $\frac{1}{4} = 0.25$; for Thursday it is $\frac{19}{72} \approx 0.264$ and for Friday it is $\frac{2}{9} \approx 0.222$.

Using a calculator to multiply matrices

You can use the matrix facilities of a calculator to cut down the time you take to multiply matrices. This enables you to explore the properties of powers of transition matrices, $\mathbf{P}^n$, for large values of n.

ACTIVITY 5.1

The matrices **P** and **Q** are given by

$$\mathbf{P} = \begin{pmatrix} 0 & 1 & 0.3 & 0 \\ 0.4 & 0 & 0 & 0 \\ 0.6 & 0 & 0 & 1 \\ 0 & 0 & 0.7 & 0 \end{pmatrix} \quad \text{and} \quad \mathbf{Q} = \begin{pmatrix} 0 \\ 1 \\ 0 \\ 0 \end{pmatrix}.$$

Use your calculator to find **(i)** $\mathbf{PQ}$ **(ii)** $\mathbf{P}^2\mathbf{Q}$ **(iii)** $\mathbf{P}^{99}\mathbf{Q}$ **(iv)** $\mathbf{P}^{100}\mathbf{Q}$.

Note

To enable sensible viewing of the matrices in decimal form, you can set the format to, say, 4 decimal place accuracy.

EXERCISE 5B

1 For each of the following transition matrices, work out $\mathbf{P}^2$, $\mathbf{P}^3$ and $\mathbf{P}^4$.

(i) $\mathbf{P} = \begin{pmatrix} 0 & \frac{3}{4} & \frac{5}{6} \\ \frac{1}{2} & 0 & 0 \\ \frac{1}{2} & \frac{1}{4} & \frac{1}{6} \end{pmatrix}$ **(ii)** $\mathbf{P} = \begin{pmatrix} 0.5 & 0.25 & 0.3 \\ 0.45 & 0.5 & 0.3 \\ 0.05 & 0.25 & 0.4 \end{pmatrix}$ **(iii)** $\mathbf{P} = \begin{pmatrix} \frac{1}{2} & \frac{1}{3} & \frac{1}{6} \\ \frac{1}{3} & \frac{1}{3} & \frac{1}{3} \\ \frac{1}{6} & \frac{1}{3} & \frac{1}{2} \end{pmatrix}$

2 Every year the Smith family goes on holiday: either a camping trip (preferred by the children), a city break (preferred by Mrs Smith) or a winter holiday (preferred by Mr Smith). They never take the same kind of holiday two years in a row. Each year they flip a coin to decide which of the two types of holiday they did not take the previous year they will take that year.

(i) Form a 3×3 transition matrix, **P**.

(ii) This year the Smith family took a city break.
Use suitable powers of **P** to find the probability that

(a) the year after next the Smiths take a city break

(b) the year after next they go on a camping trip

(c) the Smiths go on a winter holiday in three years' time.

3 In a particular area, three weekly newspapers, the *Herald*, the *Tribune* and the *Gazette* have, between them, a fixed number of subscribers. During any month the *Herald* retains $\frac{7}{8}$ of its subscribers and loses $\frac{1}{8}$ of them to the *Tribune*; the *Tribune* retains $\frac{1}{12}$ of its subscribers, loses $\frac{3}{4}$ of them to the *Herald* and the rest to the *Gazette*; the *Gazette* retains $\frac{1}{3}$ of its subscribers, loses $\frac{1}{2}$ of them to the *Herald* and the rest to the *Tribune*.

(i) Write down the transition matrix, **P**, for this problem.

(ii) On 1st September, Lisa is a *Tribune* subscriber. Find the probability that

(a) on 1st October, she subscribes to the *Gazette*

(b) on 1st November, she subscribes to the *Tribune*

(c) on 1st January, she subscribes to the *Tribune*.

4 A sports correspondent has to write a background article each day in a daily paper. He writes about either athletics or cricket or tennis, and arranges his writing as follows.

He never writes about athletics on two consecutive days; after a day writing about athletics, he writes about cricket the next day with probability $\frac{3}{5}$. After a day writing about cricket, he has probability $\frac{1}{3}$ of again writing about cricket the next day and probability $\frac{1}{2}$ of writing about tennis the next day. After a day writing about tennis, he writes about athletics the next day with probability $\frac{1}{2}$ and is otherwise equally likely to write again about tennis or about cricket.

(i) Form a 3×3 transition matrix, **P**, for this problem.

(ii) On the Tuesday of a certain week, he writes about athletics. Find the probabilities of his writing about each sport on

(a) the Thursday of that week

(b) the Friday of that week.

[MEI]

5 Consider the following simple model of the demand for cars. There are three makes *A*, *B* and *C* of similar type. Market research has estimated that owners who buy a new car every year do so according to the following scheme.

		Old car		
		A	*B*	*C*
New car	*A*	$\frac{1}{2}$	$\frac{1}{6}$	$\frac{1}{4}$
	B	$\frac{1}{4}$	$\frac{1}{2}$	$\frac{1}{4}$
	C	$\frac{1}{4}$	$\frac{1}{3}$	$\frac{1}{2}$

(i) Which make of car is a person most likely to own in 1999 if he owned a car of make *B* in 1996?

(ii) In a certain district there are 1000 such owners of make *A*, 600 of make *B* and 400 of make *C* in 1996. What are the total sales of each make from 1996 to 1999 inclusive?

[MEI]

6 A 3×3 transition matrix, $\mathbf{P}$, is given by $\begin{pmatrix} a & d & g \\ b & e & h \\ c & f & i \end{pmatrix}$ where $0 \leqslant a, b, c, d, e, f, g, h, i \leqslant 1$.

(i) Write down three equations satisfied by some of $a, b, c, d, e, f, g, h, i$.

(ii) Find $\mathbf{P}^2$ in terms of $a, b, c, d, e, f, g, h, i$ and hence show that $\mathbf{P}^2$ is a transition matrix.

INVESTIGATIONS

1 Take the 2×2 transition matrix $\mathbf{P}$ as $\begin{pmatrix} \frac{2}{3} & \frac{1}{4} \\ \frac{1}{3} & \frac{3}{4} \end{pmatrix}$, as used by Tony for his weather forecasting.

Use your calculator to find successive powers of matrix $\mathbf{P}$, i.e. $\mathbf{P}^2$, $\mathbf{P}^3$, $\mathbf{P}^4$, $\mathbf{P}^5$, $\mathbf{P}^6$, ….

Continuing the sequence on page 175, you should be able to obtain these matrices.

Friday : $\mathbf{P}^4 = \begin{pmatrix} 0.4457 & 0.4156 \\ 0.5542 & 0.5843 \end{pmatrix}$ **Saturday :** $\mathbf{P}^5 = \begin{pmatrix} 0.4357 & 0.4231 \\ 0.5642 & 0.5768 \end{pmatrix}$

Sunday : $\mathbf{P}^6 = \begin{pmatrix} 0.4315 & 0.4263 \\ 0.5684 & 0.5736 \end{pmatrix}$ **Monday :** $\mathbf{P}^7 = \begin{pmatrix} 0.4298 & 0.4276 \\ 0.5701 & 0.5723 \end{pmatrix}$

(For convenience the probabilities are given as decimals to 4 decimal places.)

By inspecting matrix $\mathbf{P}^7$ you will see that the pair of probabilities in the two columns are roughly equal. Show that, by taking successively higher powers of matrix $\mathbf{P}$, the two columns do in fact become closer to each other.

Show that the probabilities in each column tend towards 0.4286 and 0.5714 (to 4 decimal places).

Using transition probabilities from $\mathbf{P}$ evaluate: $\dfrac{\frac{1}{4}}{\frac{1}{3}+\frac{1}{4}}$ and $\dfrac{\frac{1}{3}}{\frac{1}{3}+\frac{1}{4}}$ as fractions and decimals. What do you notice?

2 Now take the 3×3 transition matrix $\mathbf{P}$ as $\begin{pmatrix} \frac{1}{2} & \frac{1}{3} & \frac{5}{6} \\ \frac{1}{3} & 0 & \frac{1}{6} \\ \frac{1}{6} & \frac{2}{3} & 0 \end{pmatrix}$, used to model the behaviour of Bob's car.

Use your calculator to find successive powers of matrix $\mathbf{P}$, i.e. $\mathbf{P}^2$, $\mathbf{P}^3$, $\mathbf{P}^4$, $\mathbf{P}^5$, $\mathbf{P}^6$, ….

Check that you obtain the following matrices for Saturday and Sunday.

$\mathbf{P}^5 = \begin{pmatrix} 0.5424 & 0.5480 & 0.5369 \\ 0.2182 & 0.2237 & 0.2219 \\ 0.2393 & 0.2281 & 0.2411 \end{pmatrix}$ $\mathbf{P}^6 = \begin{pmatrix} 0.5434 & 0.5387 & 0.5433 \\ 0.2207 & 0.2207 & 0.2191 \\ 0.2358 & 0.2405 & 0.2374 \end{pmatrix}$

Show that, by taking successively higher powers of matrix **P**, the probabilities in the three columns become closer to each other.

By taking high enough powers of **P**, show that the probabilities in each column tend towards 0.5424, 0.2203 and 0.2373 (to 4 decimal places).

Equilibrium probabilities

The limiting probabilities you met in the investigations above are known as *equilibrium probabilities*. In the example about Bob's old car they indicate that, in the long run, the probability of any of the three events (the car starts on its own, the car needs a push, or the garage must be called out) are independent of what happened on the first day.

 Why would you expect this to happen?

In the problems discussed so far it has been assumed that, initially, a particular state exists and the probabilities of future events, based on the initial state, have been calculated. In other words, you have found *conditional probabilities*, dependent on the initial state.

- In the first example, the initial state was that it was *fine* on Monday.
- In Exercise 5A, Question 2, the initial state was that it was *sunny* on Saturday.
- In Example 5.1, the initial state was that Bob's car *started by itself* on Monday.
- In Exercise 5B, Question 2, the initial state was that the Smiths *took a city break* this year.

Now consider the situation where probabilities are attached to the initial states. These may be 1 or 0, reflecting a known initial state, or values between 0 and 1, reflecting an uncertain initial state.

Returning to Tony's weather forecasting, it was stated that it was fine on Monday, so

$$\text{P(Fine on Monday)} = 1 \quad \text{and} \quad \text{P(Wet on Monday)} = 0.$$

These two 'probabilities' can be represented by a *probability vector*; this is the column matrix $\begin{pmatrix} 1 \\ 0 \end{pmatrix}$. Now multiply the transition matrix by this column matrix to obtain a second column matrix.

$$\begin{pmatrix} \frac{2}{3} & \frac{1}{4} \\ \frac{1}{3} & \frac{3}{4} \end{pmatrix} \begin{pmatrix} 1 \\ 0 \end{pmatrix} = \begin{pmatrix} \frac{2}{3} \\ \frac{1}{3} \end{pmatrix}$$

Note

In the statisticians' convention this is written $\begin{pmatrix}1 & 0\end{pmatrix}\begin{pmatrix}\frac{2}{3} & \frac{1}{3}\\ \frac{1}{4} & \frac{3}{4}\end{pmatrix} = \begin{pmatrix}\frac{2}{3} & \frac{1}{3}\end{pmatrix}$

Notice how it is read from left to right, as in a tree diagram.

The second column matrix simply gives the probabilities of it being fine or wet on Tuesday. By repeating the process, to obtain further column matrices, you automatically generate probabilities of it being fine or wet on Wednesday, Thursday and beyond.

$$\begin{pmatrix}\frac{2}{3} & \frac{1}{4}\\ \frac{1}{3} & \frac{3}{4}\end{pmatrix}\begin{pmatrix}\frac{2}{3}\\ \frac{1}{3}\end{pmatrix} = \begin{pmatrix}\frac{19}{36}\\ \frac{17}{36}\end{pmatrix}$$

$$\begin{pmatrix}\frac{2}{3} & \frac{1}{4}\\ \frac{1}{3} & \frac{3}{4}\end{pmatrix}\begin{pmatrix}\frac{19}{36}\\ \frac{17}{36}\end{pmatrix} = \begin{pmatrix}\frac{203}{432}\\ \frac{229}{432}\end{pmatrix}$$

Notice that, since the first column matrix was $\begin{pmatrix}1\\ 0\end{pmatrix}$, successive column matrices are just the left-hand columns of $\mathbf{P}$, $\mathbf{P}^2$, $\mathbf{P}^3$, etc. If it had been wet on Monday, the initial column matrix would have been $\begin{pmatrix}0\\ 1\end{pmatrix}$, with successive column matrices being the right-hand columns of $\mathbf{P}$, $\mathbf{P}^2$, $\mathbf{P}^3$, etc.

$$\begin{pmatrix}\frac{2}{3} & \frac{1}{4}\\ \frac{1}{3} & \frac{3}{4}\end{pmatrix}\begin{pmatrix}0\\ 1\end{pmatrix} = \begin{pmatrix}\frac{1}{4}\\ \frac{3}{4}\end{pmatrix}$$

$$\begin{pmatrix}\frac{2}{3} & \frac{1}{4}\\ \frac{1}{3} & \frac{3}{4}\end{pmatrix}\begin{pmatrix}\frac{1}{4}\\ \frac{3}{4}\end{pmatrix} = \begin{pmatrix}\frac{17}{48}\\ \frac{31}{48}\end{pmatrix}$$

$$\begin{pmatrix}\frac{2}{3} & \frac{1}{4}\\ \frac{1}{3} & \frac{3}{4}\end{pmatrix}\begin{pmatrix}\frac{17}{48}\\ \frac{31}{48}\end{pmatrix} = \begin{pmatrix}\frac{229}{576}\\ \frac{347}{576}\end{pmatrix}$$

Now suppose that there is a fifty-fifty chance of it being fine or wet on Monday. In this case the initial probabilities, in column matrix form, become $\begin{pmatrix}\frac{1}{2}\\ \frac{1}{2}\end{pmatrix}$. These can be used to generate further column matrices as follows.

$$\begin{pmatrix}\frac{2}{3} & \frac{1}{4}\\ \frac{1}{3} & \frac{3}{4}\end{pmatrix}\begin{pmatrix}\frac{1}{2}\\ \frac{1}{2}\end{pmatrix} = \begin{pmatrix}\frac{11}{24}\\ \frac{13}{24}\end{pmatrix}$$

$$\begin{pmatrix}\frac{2}{3} & \frac{1}{4}\\ \frac{1}{3} & \frac{3}{4}\end{pmatrix}\begin{pmatrix}\frac{11}{24}\\ \frac{13}{24}\end{pmatrix} = \begin{pmatrix}\frac{127}{288}\\ \frac{161}{288}\end{pmatrix}$$

Converting to decimal notation for the column matrices, the next four column matrices are as follows.

$$\begin{pmatrix} \frac{2}{3} & \frac{1}{4} \\ \frac{1}{3} & \frac{3}{4} \end{pmatrix}\begin{pmatrix} 0.4410 \\ 0.5590 \end{pmatrix} = \begin{pmatrix} 0.4337 \\ 0.5663 \end{pmatrix} \quad \begin{pmatrix} \frac{2}{3} & \frac{1}{4} \\ \frac{1}{3} & \frac{3}{4} \end{pmatrix}\begin{pmatrix} 0.4337 \\ 0.5663 \end{pmatrix} = \begin{pmatrix} 0.4307 \\ 0.5693 \end{pmatrix}$$

$$\begin{pmatrix} \frac{2}{3} & \frac{1}{4} \\ \frac{1}{3} & \frac{3}{4} \end{pmatrix}\begin{pmatrix} 0.4307 \\ 0.5693 \end{pmatrix} = \begin{pmatrix} 0.4295 \\ 0.5705 \end{pmatrix} \quad \begin{pmatrix} \frac{2}{3} & \frac{1}{4} \\ \frac{1}{3} & \frac{3}{4} \end{pmatrix}\begin{pmatrix} 0.4295 \\ 0.5705 \end{pmatrix} = \begin{pmatrix} 0.4289 \\ 0.5711 \end{pmatrix}$$

By continuing in this way, notice that the probabilities in the column matrices seem to be converging towards particular values. These are the equilibrium probabilities. By continuing the sequence of column matrices you will see that the probabilities converge towards $\begin{pmatrix} 0.4286 \\ 0.5714 \end{pmatrix}$, with entries given correct to 4 decimal places. Therefore, multiplying the transition matrix by this column matrix leaves the column matrix unchanged.

$$\begin{pmatrix} \frac{2}{3} & \frac{1}{4} \\ \frac{1}{3} & \frac{3}{4} \end{pmatrix}\begin{pmatrix} 0.4286 \\ 0.5714 \end{pmatrix} = \begin{pmatrix} 0.4286 \\ 0.5714 \end{pmatrix}$$

It can be shown that whatever the values of the probabilities in the initial column matrix, the sequence of column matrices generated by repeated pre-multiplication by **P**, the transition matrix, converge on the same equilibrium column matrix.

The equilibrium column matrix has the property that it remains unchanged when it is multiplied by the transition matrix. Using this property you can calculate the equilibrium column matrix directly, rather than by iteration, as follows.

Let the equilibrium probability vector be $\begin{pmatrix} p_1 \\ p_2 \end{pmatrix}$, then

$$\begin{pmatrix} \frac{2}{3} & \frac{1}{4} \\ \frac{1}{3} & \frac{3}{4} \end{pmatrix}\begin{pmatrix} p_1 \\ p_2 \end{pmatrix} = \begin{pmatrix} p_1 \\ p_2 \end{pmatrix}.$$

Multiplying out gives

$$\tfrac{2}{3}p_1 + \tfrac{1}{4}p_2 = p_1$$
$$\tfrac{1}{3}p_1 + \tfrac{3}{4}p_2 = p_2$$

Collecting like terms

$$-\tfrac{1}{3}p_1 + \tfrac{1}{4}p_2 = 0$$
$$\tfrac{1}{3}p_1 - \tfrac{1}{4}p_2 = 0$$

Notice that both equations give the same information! However, you also know that $p_1 + p_2 = 1$, so you can solve the simultaneous equations

$$\tfrac{1}{3}p_1 - \tfrac{1}{4}p_2 = 0 \qquad ①$$

$$p_1 + p_2 = 1 \qquad ②$$

$$\Rightarrow p_1 = \tfrac{3}{7}, \quad p_2 = \tfrac{4}{7}.$$

Check that these values for p_1 and p_2 correspond to the equilibrium probabilities found by iteration above.

If you are using the statisticians' convention, repeat this work with the equilibrium matrix written $(p_1 \quad p_2)$ and check that you get the same answer.

An equilibrium probability vector is an example of a steady state in which the probability vector remains the same from one state to the next. There are, however, matrices which give rise to steady states but not equilibrium. The matrix $\begin{pmatrix} 0 & 1 \\ 1 & 0 \end{pmatrix}$ does not have an equilibrium probability vector but, since $\begin{pmatrix} 0 & 1 \\ 1 & 0 \end{pmatrix}\begin{pmatrix} \frac{1}{2} \\ \frac{1}{2} \end{pmatrix} = \begin{pmatrix} \frac{1}{2} \\ \frac{1}{2} \end{pmatrix}$, an initial probability vector of $\begin{pmatrix} \frac{1}{2} \\ \frac{1}{2} \end{pmatrix}$ remains unaltered and so represents a steady state. An equilibrium probability vector represents the limiting probabilities from any initial state.

A similar technique can be used to find the equilibrium probabilities for a 3×3 transition matrix directly. The transition matrix for Bob's unreliable car leads to this equilibrium situation.

$$\begin{pmatrix} \frac{1}{2} & \frac{1}{3} & \frac{5}{6} \\ \frac{1}{3} & 0 & \frac{1}{6} \\ \frac{1}{6} & \frac{2}{3} & 0 \end{pmatrix}\begin{pmatrix} p_1 \\ p_2 \\ p_3 \end{pmatrix} = \begin{pmatrix} p_1 \\ p_2 \\ p_3 \end{pmatrix}$$

Multiplying out gives

$$\begin{aligned} \tfrac{1}{2}p_1 + \tfrac{1}{3}p_2 + \tfrac{5}{6}p_3 &= p_1 \\ \tfrac{1}{3}p_1 \qquad\quad + \tfrac{1}{6}p_3 &= p_2 \\ \tfrac{1}{6}p_1 + \tfrac{2}{3}p_2 \qquad\quad &= p_3 \end{aligned}$$

Collecting like terms

$$\begin{aligned} -\tfrac{1}{2}p_1 + \tfrac{1}{3}p_2 + \tfrac{5}{6}p_3 &= 0 \\ \tfrac{1}{3}p_1 - p_2 + \tfrac{1}{6}p_3 &= 0 \\ \tfrac{1}{6}p_1 + \tfrac{2}{3}p_2 - p_3 &= 0 \end{aligned}$$

These three equations are dependent on each other; any one of them can be obtained from a linear combination of the other two, so only two of them can be used to find p_1, p_2 and p_3.

However, you also know that $p_1 + p_2 + p_3 = 1$, therefore you can solve the following simultaneous equations to find p_1, p_2 and p_3.

$$\tfrac{1}{3}p_1 - p_2 + \tfrac{1}{6}p_3 = 0 \quad ①$$
$$\tfrac{1}{6}p_1 + \tfrac{2}{3}p_2 - p_3 = 0 \quad ②$$
$$p_1 + p_2 + p_3 = 1 \quad ③$$

First eliminate p_1 from equations ①, ② and ③.

$$③ - 3 \times ① \Rightarrow \quad 4p_2 + \tfrac{1}{2}p_3 = 1 \quad ④$$
$$③ - 6 \times ② \Rightarrow \quad -3p_2 + 7p_3 = 1 \quad ⑤$$

Now eliminate p_2 from equations ④ and ⑤.

$$3 \times ④ + 4 \times ⑤ \Rightarrow \tfrac{59}{2}p_3 = 7$$
$$\Rightarrow p_3 = \tfrac{14}{59}$$

Substituting for p_3 in ④ gives

$$4p_2 + \tfrac{1}{2} \times \tfrac{14}{59} = 1$$
$$\Rightarrow 4p_2 = 1 - \tfrac{7}{59}$$
$$\Rightarrow p_2 = \tfrac{13}{59}.$$

Substituting for p_2 and p_3 in ③ gives

$$p_1 + \tfrac{13}{59} + \tfrac{14}{59} = 1$$
$$\Rightarrow p_1 = 1 - \tfrac{27}{59}$$
$$\Rightarrow p_1 = \tfrac{32}{59}.$$

Therefore the equilibrium probabilities are

$$p_1 = \tfrac{32}{59} \approx 0.5424, \quad p_2 = \tfrac{13}{59} \approx 0.2203, \quad p_3 = \tfrac{14}{59} \approx 0.2373.$$

Comparing these probabilities with the values obtained in the investigation, you can see that this direct method gives the equilibrium probabilities, irrespective of the values of the initial-state column matrix.

Using a calculator to find equilibrium probabilities

You can use the matrix facilities of a calculator to evaluate matrix products.

Using the transition matrix $\mathbf{P} = \begin{pmatrix} \frac{2}{3} & \frac{1}{4} \\ \frac{1}{3} & \frac{3}{4} \end{pmatrix}$, together with the initial-state probability vector $\mathbf{p}_0 = \begin{pmatrix} 1 \\ 0 \end{pmatrix}$, the products $\begin{pmatrix} \frac{2}{3} & \frac{1}{4} \\ \frac{1}{3} & \frac{3}{4} \end{pmatrix}^n \begin{pmatrix} 1 \\ 0 \end{pmatrix}$, for $n = 1, 2, 3, \ldots$ can be evaluated.

ACTIVITY 5.2 Check that you get the following matrices on your calculator.

$$\mathbf{Pp}_0 = \begin{pmatrix} 0.6667 \\ 0.3333 \end{pmatrix} \qquad \mathbf{P}^2\mathbf{p}_0 = \begin{pmatrix} 0.5278 \\ 0.4722 \end{pmatrix}$$

$$\mathbf{P}^{11}\mathbf{p}_0 = \begin{pmatrix} 0.4286 \\ 0.5714 \end{pmatrix} \qquad \mathbf{P}^{12}\mathbf{p}_0 = \begin{pmatrix} 0.4286 \\ 0.5714 \end{pmatrix}$$

The matrix facilities are also useful to solve systems of linear equations, when seeking equilibrium probabilities. On page 185, the equations for the equilibrium situation for the transition matrix, $\begin{pmatrix} \frac{2}{3} & \frac{1}{4} \\ \frac{1}{3} & \frac{3}{4} \end{pmatrix}$, were written algebraically as follows.

$$\tfrac{1}{3}p_1 - \tfrac{1}{4}p_2 = 0 \qquad ①$$

$$p_1 + p_2 = 1 \qquad ②$$

These equations can be written in matrix form as

$$\begin{pmatrix} \frac{1}{3} & -\frac{1}{4} \\ 1 & 1 \end{pmatrix}\begin{pmatrix} p_1 \\ p_2 \end{pmatrix} = \begin{pmatrix} 0 \\ 1 \end{pmatrix},$$

giving

$$\begin{pmatrix} p_1 \\ p_2 \end{pmatrix} = \begin{pmatrix} \frac{1}{3} & -\frac{1}{4} \\ 1 & 1 \end{pmatrix}^{-1}\begin{pmatrix} 0 \\ 1 \end{pmatrix} = \begin{pmatrix} \frac{3}{7} \\ \frac{4}{7} \end{pmatrix}.$$

ACTIVITY 5.3 Check that you get the same result on your calculator.

EXERCISE 5C

1 Look back at the transition matrix for each of the following and, using the direct method, calculate the equilibrium probabilities.

Exercise 5A, Questions 1 to 5
Exercise 5B, Questions 1 to 4

2 In the community of Gardenville, each year 5% of the residents in the city move to the suburbs and 2% of the people in the suburbs move to the city.

(i) Write down the transition matrix to describe this situation.

(ii) Assuming that the total number of people in the community remains constant, determine the long-run proportions of city and suburban residents.

3 A country has a three-party political system and the results of elections follow a definite pattern: if a party wins an election, the probability of it winning the next election is 0.5 and, if it loses the next election, each of the other two parties has a probability of 0.5 of winning.

(i) Write down the transition matrix to describe this situation.

(ii) What proportion of the elections does each party win over a long period of time?

4 A firm hires out specialist earth-moving equipment to two large construction companies A and B. One particular piece of equipment is hired out for a week at a time, but sometimes has to spend a whole week undergoing maintenance. (The piece of equipment is never idle; it is always either out on hire or undergoing maintenance.) It is found that, after a week on hire to company A, this piece of equipment has probability of $\frac{1}{2}$ of again being hired to A for the next week and probability $\frac{1}{6}$ of needing maintenance for the next week. After a week on hire to company B, it has probability $\frac{1}{4}$ of again being hired to B for the next week and probability $\frac{1}{12}$ of needing maintenance for the next week. After a week undergoing maintenance, it will certainly be back on hire in the next week and is equally likely to be with either A or B.

(i) Write down the transition matrix to describe this situation.

(ii) In a certain week (week 1), this piece of equipment is on hire to company B. Find the probabilities of it being with A, B and under maintenance in the second subsequent week (week 3).

(iii) Find the long-run proportions of weeks spent with A and B and under maintenance.

[MEI]

5 A 2×2 transition matrix, $\mathbf{P}$, is given by $\begin{pmatrix} a & c \\ b & d \end{pmatrix}$, where $0 \leqslant a, b, c, d \leqslant 1$.

Show that equilibrium probabilities p_1 and p_2 are given by $p_1 = \dfrac{c}{b+c}$ and $p_2 = \dfrac{b}{b+c}$, provided $b + c \neq 0$.

6 A maintenance team divides its time between three places, its base A, a nearby plant at B and a more distant plant at C, spending a whole number of days in each. After a day at A they go to B with probability of $\frac{3}{4}$. After a day at B they go to C with probability of $\frac{2}{3}$. After a day at C they go back to B with probability of $\frac{1}{2}$. They never go directly from A to C or vice-versa and they never spend two consecutive days at B.

(i) Write down the transition matrix for this Markov chain.

(ii) If the team spends Monday at A, find the probability of their being at C on Thursday.

(iii) Find the proportions of its time that the team spends in each place, over a long period.

[O & C]

7 A school canteen has been provided with an automatic hot drink dispenser. The beverages available are tea, coffee or chocolate. The tea is so awful that only 20% of those having it on any one day have it again the next day, the remainder changing with equal probability to the other two drinks. The coffee drinkers have coffee again with the same probability that they change to chocolate, and this change is twice as likely as a change to tea. The chocolate is so popular that 60% of those drinking it have it again the next day; the remainder change in equal numbers to one of the other two drinks.

(i) Set up a transition matrix for this system.

(ii) If 800 students buy hot drinks every day, how many drinks of tea type should the school budget for in the long run?

(iii) Show that, after a week, demand will be expected to have settled down to a steady state.

[SMP]

8 A crane spends each working day in one of three states: working, under repair or waiting for work. On each day its state depends only on the state it was in on the previous day. After working for a day, the probability of working next day is 0.8 and of being under repair is 0.125. After days spent under repair or waiting for work, the probabilities of working next day are 0.5 and 0.9 respectively; neither of these states is ever followed by the other.

(i) Write down the transition matrix for this Markov chain.

(ii) If the crane is under repair on Monday, find the probability that it will be under repair the following Wednesday.

(iii) If it is under repair on both a Monday and the following Wednesday, find the probability that it was also under repair on the intervening Tuesday.

(iv) Deduce the proportions of its time that the crane spends over a long period in working, being repaired and waiting for work.

[O & C]

9 Six chairs, labelled 1 to 6, are placed clockwise, in order, around the sides of a hexagonal table. Peter has a biased coin which shows a head with probability p and a tail with probability q $(= 1 - p)$. He tosses it once each second and moves one place clockwise or anticlockwise depending on whether a head or tail appears. Therefore his positions at successive times form a six-state Markov chain.

(i) Write down the transition matrix of the chain.

(ii) Peter starts on chair 1 at time 0. Explain why his positions at times 0, 2, 4, 6, … form a three-state Markov chain, and deduce the transition matrix of this chain.

(iii) Show that, after $2n$ seconds (where n is large), he is equally likely to be on chairs 1, 3 or 5.

[Oxford]

10 Secret tunnels connect the four rooms on the ground floor of a castle. There are four tunnels between rooms A and B, three tunnels between A and C, two tunnels between B and D and three tunnels between C and D. Robert and Daniel are initially in rooms A and B respectively; once every minute, John blows a whistle, whereupon Robert and Daniel each select one tunnel at random in the room they are in, and travel along it to its end in another room. Thus each of their positions at times 0, 1, 2, ... form a 4-state Markov chain.

(i) Write down its transition matrix.

(ii) Find the probability distributions of the rooms Robert and Daniel are in after two movements.

(iii) Explain why they will never be in the same room at the same time.

(iv) Show that, if Peter enters one of the four rooms at random, and moves according to the same rules, the long-term probability of his being in a given room is proportional to the number of tunnels in that room.

[Oxford]

11 A Markov chain has two states A and B. The probability of a transition from A to B is p_1 ($\neq 0$) and the probability of a transition from B to A is p_2 ($\neq 0$).

(i) Write down the transition matrix **P**.

(ii) The system is initially in state A. Show that the probability that the system is in state B after n transitions is

$$\frac{p_1[1-(1-p_1-p_2)^n]}{p_1+p_2}.$$

(iii) Find also the proportions of time that the system spends in states A and B over a long period.

Run lengths in Markov chains

Returning once more to Tony's weather forecasting problem, you know that it is fine on Monday. What is the probability that it is fine for the rest of the week (Tuesday to Friday inclusive), but wet on Saturday? This can easily be found from an extended tree-diagram by the appropriate multiplication of probabilities.

$$\tfrac{2}{3}\times\tfrac{2}{3}\times\tfrac{2}{3}\times\tfrac{2}{3}\times\tfrac{1}{3} = \left(\tfrac{2}{3}\right)^4\times\tfrac{1}{3} = \tfrac{16}{243}$$

This gives you the probability of exactly four further consecutive fine days, given that Monday was fine. Similarly you can find the probability of any number of further consecutive fine days: the probability that, after Monday, the next seven days will be fine and the following Tuesday wet is

$$\tfrac{2}{3}\times\tfrac{2}{3}\times\tfrac{2}{3}\times\tfrac{2}{3}\times\tfrac{2}{3}\times\tfrac{2}{3}\times\tfrac{2}{3}\times\tfrac{1}{3} = \left(\tfrac{2}{3}\right)^7\times\tfrac{1}{3} = \tfrac{128}{6561}.$$

You can formalise this idea as follows.

Let X represent the number of further consecutive days on which it is fine, given that Monday is fine, then

$$P(X=r) = \left(\tfrac{2}{3}\right)^r\times\tfrac{1}{3}, \quad \text{for } r=0,1,2,3,4,\ldots.$$

This is a discrete probability distribution. The terms form a geometric sequence. The expected run length is the expected value of X, denoted by E(X). To find its value, construct a table as follows.

r	0	1	2	3	4	...
P(*X* = *r*)	$\frac{1}{3}$	$\frac{2}{3}\times\frac{1}{3}$	$\left(\frac{2}{3}\right)^2\times\frac{1}{3}$	$\left(\frac{2}{3}\right)^3\times\frac{1}{3}$	$\left(\frac{2}{3}\right)^4\times\frac{1}{3}$	...
$r\times$ **P(*X* = *r*)**	0	$\frac{2}{3}\times\frac{1}{3}$	$2\times\left(\frac{2}{3}\right)^2\times\frac{1}{3}$	$3\times\left(\frac{2}{3}\right)^3\times\frac{1}{3}$	$4\times\left(\frac{2}{3}\right)^4\times\frac{1}{3}$	...

The expected run length is given by

$$\mathrm{E}(X)=\sum[r\times \mathrm{P}(X=r)] = \tfrac{2}{3}\times\tfrac{1}{3}+2\times\left(\tfrac{2}{3}\right)^2\times\tfrac{1}{3}+3\times\left(\tfrac{2}{3}\right)^3\times\tfrac{1}{3}+4\times\left(\tfrac{2}{3}\right)^4\times\tfrac{1}{3}+\ \ldots$$

$$= \tfrac{2}{3}\times\tfrac{1}{3}\left[1+2\times\tfrac{2}{3}+3\times\left(\tfrac{2}{3}\right)^2+4\times\left(\tfrac{2}{3}\right)^3+\ \ldots\right]$$

The series $1+2\times\frac{2}{3}+3\times\left(\frac{2}{3}\right)^2+4\times\left(\frac{2}{3}\right)^3+$ is generated by the binomial expansion of $\dfrac{1}{\left(1-\frac{2}{3}\right)^2}$ and so has the value 9.

$$\mathrm{E}(X)=\tfrac{2}{3}\times\tfrac{1}{3}\times 9$$
$$=2$$

So the expected (mean) number of further consecutive days on which it will be fine is 2. This is the expected run length.

Notice that the run length is the number of 'no change' transitions. This is one less than the number of times the state is repeated.

Having examined a specific case, you can now generalise for a Markov chain with two, three or any number of states. For any state A, let α be the probability that the system remains in that state at the next stage. Hence the probability that it changes from state A to state A′ in one step is $1-\alpha$.

Let X represent the number of further consecutive stages in which the state of the system is A, given that it is initially in state A, then

$$\mathrm{P}(X=r)=\alpha^r\times(1-\alpha),\qquad \text{for } r=0, 1, 2, 3, 4, \ldots .$$

To find the expected run length, again construct a table.

r	0	1	2	3	4	...
P(*X* = *r*)	$1-\alpha$	$\alpha(1-\alpha)$	$\alpha^2(1-\alpha)$	$\alpha^3(1-\alpha)$	$\alpha^4(1-\alpha)$	...
$r\times$ **P(*X* = *r*)**	0	$\alpha(1-\alpha)$	$2\alpha^2(1-\alpha)$	$3\alpha^3(1-\alpha)$	$4\alpha^4(1-\alpha)$	...

The expected run length is given by

$$\mathrm{E}(X) = \sum [r \times \mathrm{P}(X = r)] = \alpha(1-\alpha) + 2\alpha^2(1-\alpha) + 3\alpha^3(1-\alpha) + 4\alpha^4(1-\alpha) + \ldots$$
$$= \alpha(1-\alpha)[1 + 2\alpha + 3\alpha^2 + 4\alpha^3 + \ldots].$$

Since $1 + 2\alpha + 3\alpha^2 + 4\alpha^3 + \ldots$ is the binomial expansion of $\dfrac{1}{(1-\alpha)^2}$:

$$\mathrm{E}(X) = \alpha(1-\alpha) \times \frac{1}{(1-\alpha)^2} = \frac{\alpha}{1-\alpha}$$

So the expected (mean) number of further consecutive stages in which the state of the system is A is $\dfrac{\alpha}{1-\alpha}$.

EXAMPLE 5.2

Look again at the three-state Markov chain concerning Bob's old car. The only event that can take place two days running is that the car starts by itself. Given that the car starts by itself one day, find the expected number of further consecutive days on which it starts by itself.

SOLUTION

The probability that it starts by itself the next day is $\frac{1}{2}$. Hence $\alpha = \frac{1}{2}$.

Let X represent the number of further consecutive days on which the car starts by itself, given that it starts by itself on Monday, then

$$\mathrm{P}(X = r) = \left(\tfrac{1}{2}\right)^r \times \tfrac{1}{2}, \qquad \text{for } r = 0, 1, 2, 3, 4, \ldots.$$

$$\Rightarrow \quad \mathrm{E}(X) = \frac{\alpha}{1-\alpha} = \frac{\frac{1}{2}}{1-\frac{1}{2}} = 1.$$

So the expected (mean) number of further consecutive days on which the car starts by itself is 1.

EXERCISE 5D

1 For each of the following, given the initial state, find the expected number of consecutive further stages that the initial state remains unchanged.

		Initial state
(i)	Exercise 5A, Question 2	It is sunny
(ii)	Exercise 5A, Question 2	It is cloudy
(iii)	Exercise 5A, Question 4	Tina goes to the disco
(iv)	Exercise 5A, Question 4	Tina goes to the cinema
(v)	Exercise 5A, Question 5	Hits to opponent's backhand
(vi)	Exercise 5A, Question 5	Hits to opponent's forehand
(vii)	Exercise 5B, Question 3	Subscribes to the *Tribune*
(viii)	Exercise 5B, Question 3	Subscribes to the *Herald*
(ix)	Exercise 5B, Question 3	Subscribes to the *Gazette*
(x)	Exercise 5B, Question 4	Writes about tennis

2 A trucking company offers its drivers three approved routes between two cities: over the Mystic Bridge, on the Interstate Parkway and on Route 1.

If a trucker goes on the Mystic Bridge the chance of getting into a traffic jam is $\frac{1}{3}$; if he does get in a traffic jam, the next day he takes the Interstate Parkway with probability $\frac{2}{3}$ and Route 1 with probability $\frac{1}{3}$; if he does not get in a traffic jam, the next day he takes the Mystic Bridge again with probability $\frac{1}{2}$, the Interstate Parkway with probability $\frac{1}{6}$ and Route 1 with probability $\frac{1}{3}$.

If he takes the Interstate Parkway, the chance of his getting into a traffic jam is $\frac{1}{2}$; if he does get in a traffic jam, the next day he takes the Mystic Bridge; if he does not get in a traffic jam, the next day he takes the Mystic Bridge, the Interstate Parkway and Route 1 with equal probability.

If he takes Route 1, the trucker is invariably late, so he never takes Route 1 two days in a row and the next day he takes the Mystic Bridge with probability $\frac{1}{3}$ and the Interstate Parkway with probability $\frac{2}{3}$.

(i) Form a 3×3 transition matrix, $\mathbf{P}$, for this problem.

(ii) On Monday, the trucker takes Route 1. Find the probability that he takes

(a) Route 1 on Wednesday

(b) Interstate Parkway on Wednesday

(c) Mystic Bridge on Thursday

(d) Route 1 on Friday.

(iii) In the long run, what proportion of the time does the trucker go on the Mystic Bridge, the Interstate Parkway and Route 1 respectively?

(iv) One day the trucker takes the Interstate Parkway. Find the expected number of consecutive further days that he takes the Interstate Parkway.

3 A TV news camera team may be allocated for a whole day to either of two reporters *A* and *B*, and the team also sometimes spend a day on 'stand-by' to cover any sudden unexpected news items.

After a day on 'stand-by', the team are always allocated to one of the reporters on the next, and are equally likely to be with either reporter. After a day with either reporter, the team have probability 0.6 of being allocated to the same reporter for the next day; after a day with reporter *A*, the probability of being allocated to 'stand-by' on the next day is 0.25, but after a day with reporter *B* this probability is only 0.1.

(i) Model this situation as a Markov chain.

(ii) On a certain Monday, the team are on 'stand-by'. Find, for the immediately following Tuesday and Wednesday, the probabilities that they are on 'stand-by', with reporter *A* and with reporter *B*.

(iii) On a certain day, the team are with one of the reporters. Find the expected number of consecutive further days that they will remain with this reporter.

[MEI]

4 An aircraft is based at airport *A*. It serves two routes, one between airport *A* and airport *B* and the other between airport *A* and airport *C*; on each route, it makes one out-and-back journey in a day. The aircraft also has sometimes to spend a whole day at airport *A* undergoing maintenance.

After a day operating the route to airport *B*, the probability that the aircraft will require maintenance on the next day is $\frac{1}{6}$; but after a day operating the route to airport *C*, the probability of requiring maintenance on the next day is $\frac{1}{3}$. After a day undergoing maintenance, the aircraft will certainly be back in operation on the next, with, respectively, probabilities $\frac{3}{5}$ and $\frac{2}{5}$ of serving the routes to airports *B* and *C*. After a day in operation on either route, the probability of operating the airport *B* route on the next is $\frac{1}{2}$.

(i) Model this situation as a Markov chain.

(ii) On the Wednesday of a certain week, the aircraft is undergoing maintenance. Find, for the Thursday and Friday of that week, the probabilities that it is undergoing maintenance, operating the route to airport *B*, and operating the route to airport *C*. Find also the long-run proportions of days spent under maintenance and operating the routes to airports *B* and *C*.

(iii) On a certain day, the aircraft is operating the route to airport *C*. What is the expected number of consecutive *further* days that it operates this route?

[MEI]

5 In a study of the climate in Tel Aviv, it was found that during a certain part of the year the occurrence of dry and wet days was well modelled by a Markov chain having just two states, 'dry day' and 'wet day', with transition probabilities P(wet day follows dry day) = 0.250 and P(dry day follows wet day) = 0.338.

(i) Write down the transition matrix.

(ii) Obtain the equilibrium probabilities of a day being 'dry' or 'wet'.

(iii) Show that in this model, no matter what the climate on the current day, the equilibrium conditions will be very nearly reached after only about ten days.

(iv) Given that the current day (day 1) is wet, show that the probability that the next dry day occurs on day $n + 1$ is $(0.662)^{n-1}(0.338)$. Hence find the expected length of a 'wet spell' (i.e. a period of successive wet days after which the next day is dry). Find similarly the expected length of a 'dry spell'. Deduce that the expected length of a 'weather cycle' (i.e. a wet spell followed by a dry spell) is very nearly one week.

[MEI]

6 On any day, a factory machine may be in working order, requiring minor service or requiring major service. If it is in working order, the probability that on the following day it requires minor service is 0.1 and the probability that it requires major service is also 0.1. If it is in the state of requiring minor service, the probability that on the following day it is still in this state is 0.2 and the probability that it is in working order is 0.6. If it is requiring major service, the probability that on the following day it is still requiring major service is 0.4 and the probability that it is in working order is 0.3.

(i) Write down the transition matrix for the Markov chain model of this situation.

(ii) Given that on day 1 the machine is in working order, use the Markov chain model to find the probability that the machine is in each possible state on day 3.

(iii) Over a long period, what are the proportions of days that the machine spends in working order, requiring minor service and requiring major service?

(iv) Given that on day 1 the machine is in working order, find the probability distribution of N, the number of *further* days before that on which the first service of any kind is needed. Obtain the expected value of N.

[MEI]

7 A three-state Markov chain has transition matrix

$$\mathbf{P} = \begin{pmatrix} 0.9 & 0.25 & 0.1 \\ 0 & 0.5 & 0 \\ 0.1 & 0.25 & 0.9 \end{pmatrix}$$

where, for example, the entry 0.25 in the (1, 2) position is the transition probability from state 2 to state 1.

(i) Obtain the transition matrices for two steps of the process and for three steps of the process.

(ii) Deduce the probabilities of being in each state after three steps if the process is initially in state 2.

(iii) Find also the equilibrium probabilities of being in each state.

Suppose, instead that the transition matrix is

$$\mathbf{Q} = \begin{pmatrix} 1 & 0.25 & 0 \\ 0 & 0.5 & 0 \\ 0 & 0.25 & 1 \end{pmatrix}.$$

(iv) Describe what happens after the system enters

(a) state 1 **(b)** state 2 **(c)** state 3.

(v) Explain what will happen to the system eventually if it starts in state 2.

[MEI]

Classifying Markov chains

A full classification of Markov chains, and the possible types of state, is beyond the scope of this book. The description that follows is a simplified summary.

Regular chains

The Markov chain situations described so far have all had something in common. They are all examples of *regular* Markov chains. A transition matrix is regular if some power of the matrix contains only positive entries. A Markov chain is regular if its transition matrix is regular. In the example of Bob's old car, the transition matrix **P** contains two zeros, but

$$\mathbf{P}\times\mathbf{P} = \begin{pmatrix} \frac{1}{2} & \frac{1}{3} & \frac{5}{6} \\ \frac{1}{3} & 0 & \frac{1}{6} \\ \frac{1}{6} & \frac{2}{3} & 0 \end{pmatrix}\begin{pmatrix} \frac{1}{2} & \frac{1}{3} & \frac{5}{6} \\ \frac{1}{3} & 0 & \frac{1}{6} \\ \frac{1}{6} & \frac{2}{3} & 0 \end{pmatrix} = \begin{pmatrix} \frac{1}{2} & \frac{13}{18} & \frac{17}{36} \\ \frac{7}{36} & \frac{2}{9} & \frac{5}{18} \\ \frac{11}{36} & \frac{1}{18} & \frac{1}{14} \end{pmatrix} = \mathbf{P}^2.$$

Since $\mathbf{P}^2$ contains no zeros, the Markov chain is regular. In a regular Markov chain, it is possible to pass from any state to any other state and there is a unique limiting probability vector.

Of those Markov chains which are not regular, you will be studying properties of some other types, those which can be classified as *periodic* or those which have one or more *absorbing* states, with or without *reflecting barriers*.

Random walks

In some Markov chains it is possible to assign an order to the various states. An example is a lift going from the ground floor to the third floor. Each floor is a state and there is a natural order to them: G, 1, 2, 3. Such a chain can be described as a *random walk*. The term random walk is a mathematical one describing a process of moving between ordered states; it is not restricted to cases where someone is walking about. Some random walks involve moving exactly one state at each stage; in others the moves can involve any number of states, including zero when there is no change of state. The example of the lift illustrates a one-dimensional random walk.

Periodic chains

Think about the following situation. A bag contains two balls, both of which are either black or white. A ball is drawn at random and replaced by a ball of the *opposite* colour. The number of black balls in the bag at any particular time depends on the number of black balls present previously and the colour of the ball drawn to be replaced by a ball of the opposite colour.

How would you represent the possible sequences of states?

If the bag contains no black balls, then a white ball will be drawn and replaced by a black one. Similarly, if the bag contains two black balls, then a black ball will be drawn and replaced by a white one. If the bag contains one black ball, then a black ball will be drawn with a probability of $\frac{1}{2}$, to be replaced by a white ball, and vice-versa.

The transition matrix **P** relating to the number of black balls in the bag is given by

$$\mathbf{P} = \begin{pmatrix} 0 & \frac{1}{2} & 0 \\ 1 & 0 & 1 \\ 0 & \frac{1}{2} & 0 \end{pmatrix}.$$

Computation of the next three powers of **P** reveals an interesting pattern.

$$\mathbf{P}^2 = \begin{pmatrix} \frac{1}{2} & 0 & \frac{1}{2} \\ 0 & 1 & 0 \\ \frac{1}{2} & 0 & \frac{1}{2} \end{pmatrix}, \quad \mathbf{P}^3 = \begin{pmatrix} 0 & \frac{1}{2} & 0 \\ 1 & 0 & 1 \\ 0 & \frac{1}{2} & 0 \end{pmatrix}, \quad \mathbf{P}^4 = \begin{pmatrix} \frac{1}{2} & 0 & \frac{1}{2} \\ 0 & 1 & 0 \\ \frac{1}{2} & 0 & \frac{1}{2} \end{pmatrix}$$

ACTIVITY 5.4 Check that you get the same matrices using your calculator in fraction mode.

You can see that odd powers of **P** are identical to **P** and even powers of **P** are identical to $\mathbf{P}^2$. This Markov chain is *periodic* with period 2. Starting in any of the three states, it is only possible to return to that state after an even number of transitions. In general, a periodic Markov chain is one where successive powers of **P** form a pattern where there is a value of k such that $\mathbf{P}^k = \mathbf{P}$. The period of the Markov chain is $k - 1$, where k is the smallest value for which this is true.

Did the previous example involve a random walk?

Reflecting barriers

The Markov chain above also has two *reflecting barriers*. Whenever the number of black balls is zero it is inevitable that, at the next stage, the number of black balls is one. So the state 0 black balls is a reflecting barrier. Similarly, the state 2 black balls is another reflecting barrier; the inevitable next state is one black ball and one white ball.

Look at the transition matrix **P**. In the first column there is a 0 in position (1, 1) and a 1 next to it at (2, 1). This pattern indicates a reflecting barrier; the same is true in the third column where there is also a 0 in the leading diagonal, at (3, 3), and a 1 next to it.

$$\mathbf{P} = \begin{pmatrix} 0 & \frac{1}{2} & 0 \\ 1 & 0 & 1 \\ 0 & \frac{1}{2} & 0 \end{pmatrix}$$

The pattern described above applies to a random walk with a move of exactly one state at each stage. Will it apply to a reflecting barrier in a random walk in which the move can be zero or one state?

An extension of this situation provides an interesting example.

EXAMPLE 5.3

A bag contains three balls, all of which are either black or white. Again a ball is drawn at random and replaced by a ball of the opposite colour. At any one time the bag will contain either 0, 1, 2 or 3 black balls. Describe what happens.

SOLUTION

Think about the case where all three balls in the bag are initially black. What is the state after one draw? What about after two draws?

How many states are possible at any stage after the first draw?

Describe the reflecting barriers.

The corresponding transition matrix $\mathbf{P}$ is given by

$$\mathbf{P} = \begin{pmatrix} 0 & \frac{1}{3} & 0 & 0 \\ 1 & 0 & \frac{2}{3} & 0 \\ 0 & \frac{2}{3} & 0 & 1 \\ 0 & 0 & \frac{1}{3} & 0 \end{pmatrix}.$$

The next three powers of $\mathbf{P}$ are as follows.

$$\mathbf{P}^2 = \begin{pmatrix} \frac{1}{3} & 0 & \frac{2}{9} & 0 \\ 0 & \frac{7}{9} & 0 & \frac{2}{3} \\ \frac{2}{3} & 0 & \frac{7}{9} & 0 \\ 0 & \frac{2}{9} & 0 & \frac{1}{3} \end{pmatrix}, \quad \mathbf{P}^3 = \begin{pmatrix} 0 & \frac{7}{27} & 0 & \frac{2}{9} \\ \frac{7}{9} & 0 & \frac{20}{27} & 0 \\ 0 & \frac{20}{27} & 0 & \frac{7}{9} \\ \frac{2}{9} & 0 & \frac{7}{27} & 0 \end{pmatrix}, \quad \mathbf{P}^4 = \begin{pmatrix} \frac{7}{27} & 0 & \frac{20}{81} & 0 \\ 0 & \frac{61}{81} & 0 & \frac{20}{27} \\ \frac{20}{27} & 0 & \frac{61}{81} & 0 \\ 0 & \frac{20}{81} & 0 & \frac{7}{27} \end{pmatrix}.$$

The pattern is similar to that in the previous example but this time the probabilities are changing. This leads to the question, what happens to this pattern for larger powers?

From the output of a calculator, in decimal mode, you can see that, for example

$$\mathbf{P}^7 = \begin{pmatrix} 0 & 0.2501 & 0 & 0.2497 \\ 0.7503 & 0 & 0.7499 & 0 \\ 0 & 0.7499 & 0 & 0.7503 \\ 0.2497 & 0 & 0.2501 & 0 \end{pmatrix}, \quad \mathbf{P}^8 = \begin{pmatrix} 0.2501 & 0 & 0.2500 & 0 \\ 0 & 0.7500 & 0 & 0.7499 \\ 0.7499 & 0 & 0.7500 & 0 \\ 0 & 0.2500 & 0 & 0.2501 \end{pmatrix}.$$

Looking at the pattern so far suggests that the pattern is creating two limiting transition matrices as $n \to \infty$.

$$\mathbf{P}^{2n-1} \to \begin{pmatrix} 0 & 0.25 & 0 & 0.25 \\ 0.75 & 0 & 0.75 & 0 \\ 0 & 0.75 & 0 & 0.75 \\ 0.25 & 0 & 0.25 & 0 \end{pmatrix}, \quad \mathbf{P}^{2n} \to \begin{pmatrix} 0.25 & 0 & 0.25 & 0 \\ 0 & 0.75 & 0 & 0.75 \\ 0.75 & 0 & 0.75 & 0 \\ 0 & 0.25 & 0 & 0.25 \end{pmatrix}.$$

? Explain why this Markov chain is not periodic.

Absorbing states

In the last section you saw that if all the balls in the bag are of the same colour, for example all white, then there is only one possible outcome for the succeeding state, which is to move to the adjacent state. This reflecting barrier ensured a particular change of state. Now look at a situation where the opposite is true; where if a particular state occurs, then it becomes impossible, rather than certain, to leave that state. This gives rise to Markov chains which have one or more *absorbing* states. The Markov chain in the following example has two absorbing states.

EXAMPLE 5.4

A straight line is 3 units long. A fly moves along it in unit increments. There are two spiders, one at each end of the line. If it is not at either end of the line, then the fly moves to the left or to the right with probability 0.3 and stays where it is with probability 0.4. If it reaches either end of the line, then it gets eaten by a spider and so the process terminates. Describe what happens in the long run.

SOLUTION

This situation can be illustrated by the following transition state diagram. There are four states: A, B, C and D. States A and D, the end points of the line, are absorbing, since it is impossible to leave either of them.

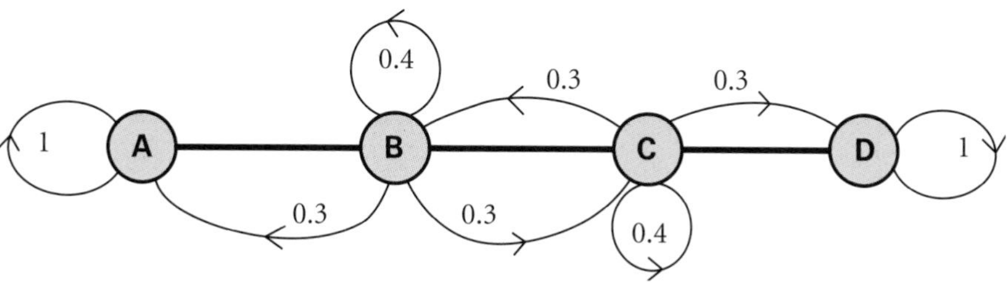

Figure 5.4

The corresponding transition matrix **P** is as follows.

$$\mathbf{P} = \begin{pmatrix} 1 & 0.3 & 0 & 0 \\ 0 & 0.4 & 0.3 & 0 \\ 0 & 0.3 & 0.4 & 0 \\ 0 & 0 & 0.3 & 1 \end{pmatrix}$$

Look at what happens to $\mathbf{P}^n$ for $n = 2$, 3 and 4.

$$\mathbf{P}^2 = \begin{pmatrix} 1 & 0.42 & 0.09 & 0 \\ 0 & 0.25 & 0.24 & 0 \\ 0 & 0.24 & 0.25 & 0 \\ 0 & 0.09 & 0.42 & 1 \end{pmatrix}, \quad \mathbf{P}^3 = \begin{pmatrix} 1 & 0.495 & 0.162 & 0 \\ 0 & 0.172 & 0.171 & 0 \\ 0 & 0.171 & 0.172 & 0 \\ 0 & 0.162 & 0.495 & 1 \end{pmatrix},$$

$$\mathbf{P}^4 = \begin{pmatrix} 1 & 0.5466 & 0.2133 & 0 \\ 0 & 0.1201 & 0.1200 & 0 \\ 0 & 0.1200 & 0.1201 & 0 \\ 0 & 0.2133 & 0.5466 & 1 \end{pmatrix}.$$

It is evident that the first and fourth columns always remain the same, with A and D being the absorbent states. Indeed an absorbing state is indicated by a column containing a 1 in position (i, i) and 0s elsewhere. But what is happening to the probabilities in the middle two columns. Is there any discernable pattern?

Using a calculator you can continue to take higher powers of **P** to investigate what happens to $\mathbf{P}^n$ as $n \to \infty$. In the following matrices, values are given, where appropriate, to 4 decimal places.

$$\mathbf{P}^{10} = \begin{pmatrix} 1 & 0.6525 & 0.3192 & 0 \\ 0 & 0.0141 & 0.0141 & 0 \\ 0 & 0.0141 & 0.0141 & 0 \\ 0 & 0.3192 & 0.6525 & 1 \end{pmatrix}, \quad \mathbf{P}^{20} = \begin{pmatrix} 1 & 0.6663 & 0.3329 & 0 \\ 0 & 0.0004 & 0.0004 & 0 \\ 0 & 0.0004 & 0.0004 & 0 \\ 0 & 0.3329 & 0.6663 & 1 \end{pmatrix},$$

$$\mathbf{P}^{30} = \begin{pmatrix} 1 & 0.6667 & 0.3333 & 0 \\ 0 & 0.0000 & 0.0000 & 0 \\ 0 & 0.0000 & 0.0000 & 0 \\ 0 & 0.3333 & 0.6667 & 1 \end{pmatrix}.$$

This would seem to indicate that the limiting transition matrix is given by

$$\mathbf{P}^n \to \begin{pmatrix} 1 & \frac{2}{3} & \frac{1}{3} & 0 \\ 0 & 0 & 0 & 0 \\ 0 & 0 & 0 & 0 \\ 0 & \frac{1}{3} & \frac{2}{3} & 1 \end{pmatrix}.$$

The interpretation of the limiting form of $\mathbf{P}^n$ is important. If the system is initially in either of the states A or D then it remains in that state – equivalent to the fly being eaten by the spider straight away! If the system is initially in state B, then with a probability of $\frac{2}{3}$ it will end up in state A and with a probability of $\frac{1}{3}$ it will end up in state D – equivalent to the fly being eaten by either spider with probabilities $\frac{2}{3}$ and $\frac{1}{3}$ respectively. A symmetrical state of affairs exists if the system starts in state C.

EXAMPLE 5.5

Four security cameras are mounted on the walls of a building as shown in the diagram. The cameras are connected to a single monitor. The monitor shows pictures from one camera for exactly one minute, and then switches to a different camera for a minute, and so on indefinitely. The camera to which the monitor switches is determined by a computer program.

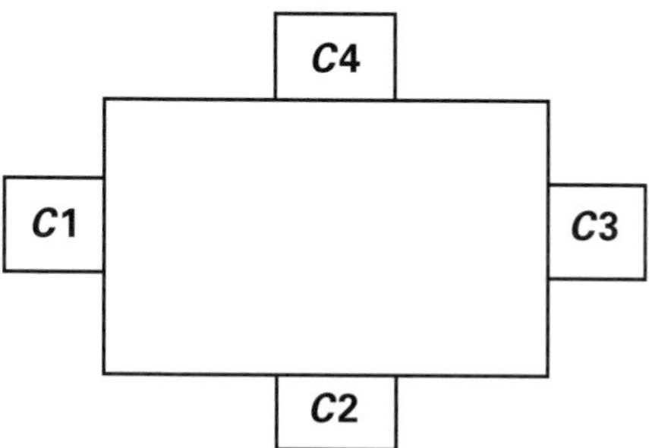

Figure 5.5

(i) The system is programmed so that at the end of each minute the monitor switches from the current camera to one of its two neighbours, each being equally likely.

Write down the transition matrix of the Markov chain that models this process. Show that the four possible states are periodic and state their period.

(ii) A bug develops in the computer program and, as a consequence, once camera *C*4 is monitored it continues to be monitored. That is, no further switches take place.

Modify the transition matrix to represent this new situation. Determine the nature of the four states of the process now.

(iii) Given that camera *C*1 is being monitored during the first minute, determine the probability that *C*4 is being monitored during the sixth minute.

(iv) Given that camera *C*1 is being monitored during the first minute, determine the time by which it is 95% certain that *C*4 is being monitored.

(v) Determine the time by which it is 99% certain that camera *C*4 is being monitored, given that the camera being monitored during the first minute is equally likely to be *C*1, *C*2 or *C*3.

SOLUTION

(i) The transition matrix is given by

$$\mathbf{P} = \begin{array}{c} \\ C1 \\ C2 \\ C3 \\ C4 \end{array} \begin{array}{c} \begin{array}{cccc} C1 & C2 & C3 & C4 \end{array} \\ \begin{pmatrix} 0 & 0.5 & 0 & 0.5 \\ 0.5 & 0 & 0.5 & 0 \\ 0 & 0.5 & 0 & 0.5 \\ 0.5 & 0 & 0.5 & 0 \end{pmatrix} \end{array}.$$

$$\mathbf{P}^2 = \begin{array}{c} \\ C1 \\ C2 \\ C3 \\ C4 \end{array} \begin{array}{c} \begin{array}{cccc} C1 & C2 & C3 & C4 \end{array} \\ \begin{pmatrix} 0.5 & 0 & 0.5 & 0 \\ 0 & 0.5 & 0 & 0.5 \\ 0.5 & 0 & 0.5 & 0 \\ 0 & 0.5 & 0 & 0.5 \end{pmatrix} \end{array} \text{ and } \mathbf{P}^3 = \begin{array}{c} \\ C1 \\ C2 \\ C3 \\ C4 \end{array} \begin{array}{c} \begin{array}{cccc} C1 & C2 & C3 & C4 \end{array} \\ \begin{pmatrix} 0 & 0.5 & 0 & 0.5 \\ 0.5 & 0 & 0.5 & 0 \\ 0 & 0.5 & 0 & 0.5 \\ 0.5 & 0 & 0.5 & 0 \end{pmatrix} \end{array}.$$

Since $\mathbf{P}^3 = \mathbf{P}$, each state (camera) alternates between possible and impossible. The chain is periodic. The period is 2.

(ii) When the bug develops, the corresponding transition matrix is given by

$$\mathbf{P} = \begin{array}{c} \\ C1 \\ C2 \\ C3 \\ C4 \end{array} \begin{array}{c} \begin{array}{cccc} C1 & C2 & C3 & C4 \end{array} \\ \begin{pmatrix} 0 & 0.5 & 0 & 0 \\ 0.5 & 0 & 0.5 & 0 \\ 0 & 0.5 & 0 & 0 \\ 0.5 & 0 & 0.5 & 1 \end{pmatrix} \end{array}.$$

Camera $C4$ is now an absorbing state since, when the system reaches this state, it can never change.

(iii) There are five transitions from the first to the sixth minutes, so you need to examine the bottom left entry of $\mathbf{P}^5$.

$$\mathbf{P}^5 = \begin{array}{c} \\ C1 \\ C2 \\ C3 \\ C4 \end{array} \begin{array}{c} \begin{array}{cccc} C1 & C2 & C3 & C4 \end{array} \\ \begin{pmatrix} 0 & 0.125 & 0 & 0 \\ 0.125 & 0 & 0.125 & 0 \\ 0 & 0.125 & 0 & 0 \\ \boxed{0.875} & 0.75 & 0.875 & 1 \end{pmatrix} \end{array}$$

The entry of 0.875 gives the probability of camera $C4$ being monitored in the sixth minute, given that camera $C1$ is being monitored in the first minute.

(iv) The higher the power of the transition matrix **P**, the larger the entries become in the first three columns of the bottom row. By computing higher powers of **P** you can detect when it is at least 95% certain that camera *C*4 is being monitored.

$$\mathbf{P}^8 = \begin{array}{c} \\ C1 \\ C2 \\ C3 \\ C4 \end{array} \begin{array}{c} \begin{array}{cccc} C1 & C2 & C3 & C4 \end{array} \\ \begin{pmatrix} 0.0313 & 0 & 0.0313 & 0 \\ 0 & 0.0625 & 0 & 0 \\ 0.0313 & 0 & 0.0313 & 0 \\ \boxed{0.9375} & 0.9375 & 0.9375 & 1 \end{pmatrix} \end{array} \text{ and}$$

$$\mathbf{P}^9 = \begin{array}{c} \\ C1 \\ C2 \\ C3 \\ C4 \end{array} \begin{array}{c} \begin{array}{cccc} C1 & C2 & C3 & C4 \end{array} \\ \begin{pmatrix} 0 & 0.0313 & 0 & 0 \\ 0.0313 & 0 & 0.0313 & 0 \\ 0 & 0.0313 & 0 & 0 \\ \boxed{0.9688} & 0.9375 & 0.9688 & 1 \end{pmatrix} \end{array}$$

So the bottom left entry exceeds 0.95 for the first time after nine transitions, i.e. during the tenth minute.

(v) Given that the camera being monitored during the first minute is equally likely to be *C*1, *C*2 or *C*3, you first need to define the initial probability vector as a column matrix.

$$\mathbf{p}_0 = \begin{pmatrix} \frac{1}{3} \\ \frac{1}{3} \\ \frac{1}{3} \\ 0 \end{pmatrix}$$

To determine the time by which it is 99% certain that camera *C*4 is being monitored, you need to compute the matrix product $\mathbf{P}^n\mathbf{p}_0$ for higher values of n until the bottom entry in the probability vector exceeds 0.99 for the first time.

$$\mathbf{P}^{13}\mathbf{p}_0 = \begin{pmatrix} 0.0026 \\ 0.0052 \\ 0.0026 \\ \boxed{0.9896} \end{pmatrix} \quad \text{and} \quad \mathbf{P}^{14}\mathbf{p}_0 = \begin{pmatrix} 0.0026 \\ 0.0026 \\ 0.0026 \\ \boxed{0.9922} \end{pmatrix}$$

So the bottom entry exceeds 0.99 for the first time after 14 transitions, i.e. during the 15th minute.

? How is the solution to this example written if you use the alternative notation, expressing the probabilities as row matrices?

EXERCISE 5E

1 A three-state Markov chain is defined by the following transition matrix.

$$\mathbf{M} = \begin{pmatrix} 1 & 0.6 & 0.2 \\ 0 & 0.3 & 0.3 \\ 0 & 0.1 & 0.5 \end{pmatrix}$$

(i) Calculate $\mathbf{M}^2$ and $\mathbf{M}^5$.

(ii) Describe what happens to $\mathbf{M}^n$ as n gets larger. Hence describe the nature of the Markov chain.

(iii) Initially the system is in state 2. After how many transitions is it at least 99% certain that the system will be in state 1? What about if the system starts in state 3? Account for the difference in your answers.

2 A scientist is studying a colony of a particular organism, and classifies the individuals as being in one of three states: well, ill or dead.

(i) Which of these is an absorbing state?

The scientist observes the organisms at unit time intervals and finds that for an organism that is well in one time interval, the probabilities for the next time interval are 0.7 that it is well, 0.2 that it is ill and 0.1 that it is dead. For an organism that is ill in one time interval, the probabilities for the next time interval are 0.3 that it is well, 0.4 that it is ill and 0.3 that it is dead.

(ii) Write down the transition matrix for this situation.

A particular organism is observed to be well in one time interval.

(iii) What are the probabilities that, after five time intervals, it is

(a) well **(b)** ill **(c)** dead?

(iv) After how many time intervals is the probability of the organism being dead greater than 0.95?

3 A railway company runs a shuttle service between two towns, A and B. At any time, each of its trains is either at A, or travelling from A to B, or at B, or travelling from B to A. These are described as states A, O, B and H respectively.

The journey time is 1 hour and this is taken as the unit time interval in this question. The transition matrix is given by

$$\begin{array}{c} \\ \text{A} \\ \text{O} \\ \text{B} \\ \text{H} \end{array} \begin{array}{c} \begin{array}{cccc} \text{A} & \text{O} & \text{B} & \text{H} \end{array} \\ \begin{pmatrix} 0.75 & 0 & 0 & 1 \\ 0.25 & 0 & 0 & 0 \\ 0 & 1 & 0.5 & 0 \\ 0 & 0 & 0.5 & 0 \end{pmatrix} \end{array}.$$

A train is initially at station A.

(i) Find the probability that six time intervals later it is again at station A.

(ii) Find the long term probabilities that this train is in each of the four states.

Another train is initially at station B.

(iii) Find the probability that six time intervals later it is at station A.

(iv) Use your calculator to demonstrate that the long term probabilities of the train being in each of the different states are the same as those in part **(ii)**.

(v) What do your answers indicate about the number of trains operating the service?

(vi) Is this chain periodic? If so, state its period; if not, say why.

4 A card 'shuffling' machine can be set to produce different chains of the possible suits, spades, hearts, diamonds and clubs.

In one setting, the suits go through a fixed sequence,

Spade $\rightarrow$ Heart $\rightarrow$ Diamond $\rightarrow$ Club $\rightarrow$ Spade ....

(i) Describe this chain.

(ii) Write down the transition matrix for this setting.

In another setting the transition matrix is as follows.

$$\begin{array}{c} \\ \text{S} \\ \text{H} \\ \text{D} \\ \text{C} \end{array} \begin{array}{c} \begin{array}{cccc} \text{S} & \text{H} & \text{D} & \text{C} \end{array} \\ \begin{pmatrix} 0 & 0.25 & 0 & 0.25 \\ 0.4 & 0 & 0.4 & 0 \\ 0 & 0.75 & 0 & 0.75 \\ 0.6 & 0 & 0.6 & 0 \end{pmatrix} \end{array}$$

(iii) Describe this chain.

(iv) Compare this chain with that produced by the first setting.

5 A decorative light glows in one of four colours, purple, blue, red and yellow. The colour changes at the end of a fixed time interval and the transition matrix is as follows.

$$\begin{array}{c} \\ \text{P} \\ \text{B} \\ \text{R} \\ \text{Y} \end{array} \begin{array}{c} \begin{array}{cccc} \text{P} & \text{B} & \text{R} & \text{Y} \end{array} \\ \begin{pmatrix} 0 & 0.2 & 0.4 & 0 \\ 1 & 0 & 0.2 & 0 \\ 0 & 0.4 & 0 & 1 \\ 0 & 0.4 & 0.4 & 0 \end{pmatrix} \end{array}$$

(i) Explain the significance of the zeros in the leading diagonal of the transition matrix.

(ii) Which colour occurs most often in the long run? What proportion of the time does the light show that colour?

The light develops a fault. Once it shows blue it gets stuck there and can no longer change to any other colour.

(iii) Write down the new transition matrix and describe any features that the chain now has.

(iv) When the fault occurs, the light is showing red. What is the probability that seven intervals later it is not showing blue?

6 A three-state Markov chain is defined by the following transition matrix.

$$\mathbf{T} = \begin{pmatrix} 1 & 0.1 & 0 \\ 0 & 0.6 & 0 \\ 0 & 0.3 & 1 \end{pmatrix}$$

(i) Calculate $\mathbf{T}^{10}$ and $\mathbf{T}^{20}$.

(ii) Describe what happens to $\mathbf{T}^n$ as n gets larger. Hence describe the nature of the Markov chain.

(iii) Repeat parts **(i)** and **(ii)** for the following transition matrices.

(a) $\mathbf{U} = \begin{pmatrix} 1 & 0.3 & 0 \\ 0 & 0.2 & 0 \\ 0 & 0.5 & 1 \end{pmatrix}$ **(b)** $\mathbf{V} = \begin{pmatrix} 1 & 0.6 & 0 \\ 0 & 0.1 & 0 \\ 0 & 0.3 & 1 \end{pmatrix}$

How do you account for the quicker convergence?

A three-state Markov chain is defined by the following transition matrix.

$$\mathbf{T} = \begin{pmatrix} 1 & p & 0 \\ 0 & 1-p-q & 0 \\ 0 & q & 1 \end{pmatrix}$$

(iv) Describe the behaviour of $\mathbf{T}^n$ as n gets larger.

7 A four-state Markov chain is defined by the following transition matrix.

$$\mathbf{T} = \begin{pmatrix} 1 & 0.2 & 0.7 & 0 \\ 0 & 0.5 & 0 & 0 \\ 0 & 0 & 0.2 & 0 \\ 0 & 0.3 & 0.1 & 1 \end{pmatrix}$$

(i) Calculate $\mathbf{T}^5$ and $\mathbf{T}^{10}$.

(ii) Describe what happens to $\mathbf{T}^n$ as n gets larger. Hence describe the nature of the Markov chain.

(iii) Initially the system is in state 3. After how many transitions is it at least 99.9% certain that the system will be in states 1 or 4?

After how many transitions is it at least 99.9% certain that the system will be in states 1 or 4 when it is initially in state 2?

Account for the difference in your answers.

A four-state Markov chain is defined by the following transition matrix.

$$\mathbf{T} = \begin{pmatrix} 1 & a & p & 0 \\ 0 & 1-a-b & 0 & 0 \\ 0 & 0 & 1-p-q & 0 \\ 0 & b & q & 1 \end{pmatrix}$$

(iv) Describe the behaviour of $\mathbf{T}^n$ as n gets larger.

8 The diagram illustrates the paths leading west and east from a prison, P. Each division represents one night's walk. One evening a prisoner escapes and walks away from the prison; however, he does not know which side of the prison (west or east) he is on. At W2 there is a high wall which the prisoner cannot climb over, so if he gets there he is forced to turn back. If he gets to E3 he is free. If he walks back to the prison he is re-captured and remains there. The prisoner sleeps by day and walks by night but after the first night he becomes confused and is equally likely to walk west or east on any night.

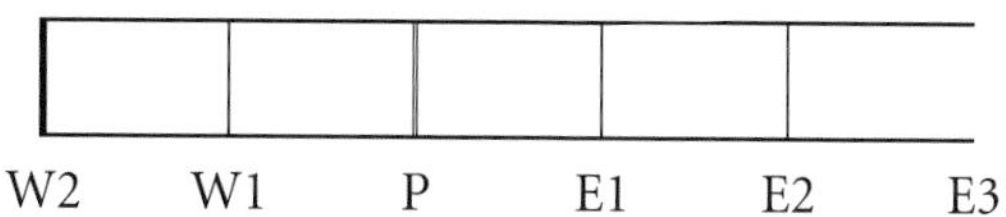

(i) Write down the transition matrix modelling this situation.

(ii) Identify any reflecting barriers or absorbing states.

(iii) Write down a column vector representing the probability distribution for the different states at the end of the first night.

(iv) What is the probability that the prisoner eventually reaches freedom?

(v) When the prisoner escapes he has enough food for six nights. What is the probability that he runs out of food without being recaptured or reaching freedom?

9 Sandy and Tamara are playing a tie-break in a tennis match. They have reached the stage where one player needs to be exactly two points ahead to win. The game can be represented by a Markov chain with five states.

L	The score is level.
S+	Sandy is one point up.
T+	Tamara is one point up.
SW	Sandy wins.
TW	Tamara wins.

The probability of Sandy winning any point is 0.55; the probability of Tamara winning it is 0.45.

(i) Copy and complete this transition matrix.

$$\begin{array}{c} \\ \text{L} \\ \text{S+} \\ \text{T+} \\ \text{SW} \\ \text{TW} \end{array} \begin{array}{c} \begin{array}{ccccc} \text{L} & \text{S+} & \text{T+} & \text{SW} & \text{TW} \end{array} \\ \begin{pmatrix} 0 & 0.45 & 0.55 & \dots & 0 \\ 0.55 & \dots & \dots & \dots & 0 \\ \dots & \dots & \dots & \dots & 0 \\ \dots & \dots & \dots & 1 & 0 \\ \dots & \dots & \dots & \dots & 1 \end{pmatrix} \end{array}$$

(ii) Identify any absorbing states.

(iii) Write down column vectors representing each of the states L, S+ and T+.

(iv) Find the probability that Sandy wins if initially

(a) the score is level

(b) she is one point up

(c) Tamara is one point up.

(v) Initially the score is level. After how many points is the probability that the match is still going on less than 0.05?

10 A small child called Evie is struggling to climb a flight of three steps. When she gets to the top she stays there, but on all other steps (including the bottom of the flight) the probability that, at any attempt, she manages one more step is 0.6 and the probability that she falls to the bottom is 0.4.

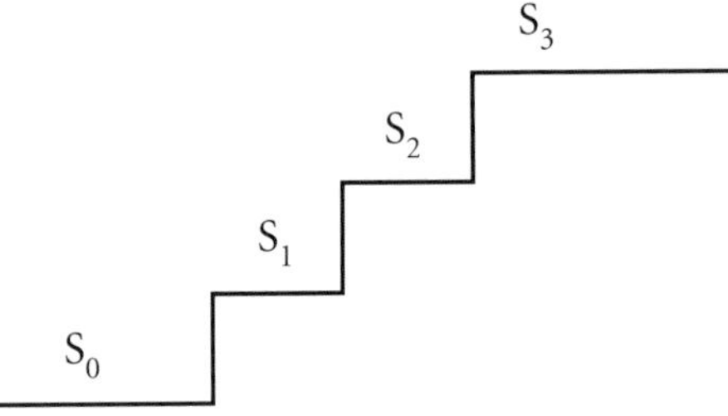

(i) Write down the transition matrix for the Markov chain.

(ii) Identify any absorbing states or reflecting barriers.

Evie starts at the bottom level, S_0. The probability that she is still at the bottom after n attempts is denoted by p_n.

(iii) Show that $p_1 = p_2 = p_3$ but that $p_4 < p_3$.

(iv) Show, using algebra, that the result in part **(iii)** is true for any value, p, of the probability that Evie manages a step, and not just for $p = 0.6$.

11 An automatic lift moves between four floors, denoted by G, 1, 2 and 3. The lift stops at each floor for a fixed time and then moves on.

Jane and Kate try to model the situation by a Markov chain.

Jane says 'There are four states. The transition matrix is given by

$$\mathbf{M} = \begin{array}{c} \\ G \\ 1 \\ 2 \\ 3 \end{array}\begin{array}{c} \begin{array}{cccc} G & 1 & 2 & 3 \end{array} \\ \begin{pmatrix} 0 & 0.5 & 0 & 0 \\ 1 & 0 & 0.5 & 0 \\ 0 & 0.5 & 0 & 1 \\ 0 & 0 & 0.5 & 0 \end{pmatrix} \end{array}$$

and so the transition matrix for two moves is given by

$$\mathbf{M}^2 = \begin{array}{c} \\ G \\ 1 \\ 2 \\ 3 \end{array}\begin{array}{c} \begin{array}{cccc} G & 1 & 2 & 3 \end{array} \\ \begin{pmatrix} 0.5 & 0 & 0.25 & 0 \\ 0 & 0.75 & 0 & 0.5 \\ 0.5 & 0 & 0.75 & 0 \\ 0 & 0.25 & 0 & 0.5 \end{pmatrix} \end{array}\text{'.}$$

Kate says 'You can work it out just by thinking about where the lift will be two moves later. You get

$$\begin{array}{c} \\ G \\ 1 \\ 2 \\ 3 \end{array}\begin{array}{c} \begin{array}{cccc} G & 1 & 2 & 3 \end{array} \\ \begin{pmatrix} 0 & 0 & 0.5 & 0 \\ 0 & 0.5 & 0 & 1 \\ 1 & 0 & 0.5 & 0 \\ 0 & 0.5 & 0 & 0 \end{pmatrix} \end{array}\text{'.}$$

(i) Jane and Kate get different answers. What mistake are they making?
(ii) How should the transition matrix be written?
(iii) Is this chain periodic? If so, state its period; if not, say why.

Historical note

The study of linked chains of events was started in Russia in 1906 by Andrei Markov (1856–1922). Since then many others have developed the theory of Markov chains and their numerous applications, most notably Andrei Kolmogorov (1903–1987) in the 1930s.

KEY POINTS

1 A sequence of events where the probability of an outcome at one stage depends only on the outcome of the event at the previous stage is known as a *Markov chain*.

2 The conditional probabilities of passing from one stage to the next are called *transition probabilities*. They are most usefully arranged in a *transition matrix*, **P**, which is always a square matrix. Each column of **P** is a *probability vector*.

3 Statisticians use a different convention in which each row of a transition matrix is a probability vector. In this case the transition matrix is the transpose of that described in this chapter.

4 If the column vector **p** represents the probabilities at one stage, the vector **Pp** represents the probabilities at the next stage.

5 In the statisticians' convention **p** is a row vector and the next stage probability is given by **pP**.

6 Powers of the transition matrix, **P**, give conditional probabilities of moving from one outcome to another over 2, 3, 4, ... steps.

7 A transition matrix is *regular* if some power of the matrix contains only positive entries.

8 **Regular matrices**

- In the long run, successive powers of **P** converge towards an *equilibrium matrix*, each probability vector of which is the same. The entries in any column are called *equilibrium probabilities*.
- The equilibrium probabilities may be found directly by solving the equation

  $$\mathbf{Pp} = \mathbf{p}$$

  where **P** is the transition matrix and **p** is a column matrix of equilibrium probabilities.

  When the statisticians' convention is used this becomes $\mathbf{pP} = \mathbf{p}$ where **p** is now a row matrix.
- Given an initial state, with probability α, the run length, i.e. the number of further consecutive stages, X, in which the state of the system remains in the initial state is given by

  $$P(X = r) = \alpha^r(1 - \alpha), \qquad \text{for } r = 0, 1, 2, 3, \ldots .$$

  The expected run length is given by

  $$E(X) = \frac{\alpha}{1 - \alpha}.$$

9 A *periodic* Markov chain is one where successive powers of **P** form a pattern where there is a value of k such that $\mathbf{P}^k = \mathbf{P}$. The period of the Markov chain is $k - 1$ where k is the smallest value for which this is true.

10 A Markov chain has a *reflecting barrier* if following some state the next state is inevitable. In the corresponding column of the transition matrix there is a 0 in position (i, i) and a 1 in an adjacent position.

11 A Markov chain has an *absorbing state* if the system is unable to leave that state. In the corresponding column of the transition matrix there is a 1 in position (i, i) and 0s in the rest of that column.

Answers

Chapter 1

? (Page 6)

No

Exercise 1A (Page 8)

1 (i) $\begin{pmatrix}-23\\13\\2\end{pmatrix}$ **(ii)** $\begin{pmatrix}37\\41\\19\end{pmatrix}$ **(iii)** $\begin{pmatrix}-8\\34\\27\end{pmatrix}$ **(iv)** $21\mathbf{i} - 29\mathbf{j} + 9\mathbf{k}$

3 (i) $\begin{pmatrix}5\\19\\-2\end{pmatrix}$ **(ii)** $\begin{pmatrix}14\\-62\\-9\end{pmatrix}$ **(iii)** $\begin{pmatrix}-3\\-2\\3\end{pmatrix}$ **(iv)** $\begin{pmatrix}-18\\57\\47\end{pmatrix}$

4 $\begin{pmatrix}\frac{19}{\sqrt{635}}\\\frac{15}{\sqrt{635}}\\\frac{-7}{\sqrt{635}}\end{pmatrix}$

5 (i) $5x + 4y - 8z = 5$
(ii) $24x + y - 29z = 1$
(iii) $19x + 40y + 3z = 188$
(iv) $30x - 29y - 24z = 86$

6 (i) $\begin{pmatrix}-1\\-12\\-31\end{pmatrix}$; $\sqrt{1106}$, $\sqrt{\frac{1106}{1155}}$
(ii) $\frac{7}{\sqrt{1155}}$
(iv) Using $\sin\theta$ does not indicate whether θ is acute or obtuse.

7 The plane containing **a** and **b** also contains **c**.

8 $\mathbf{a} \times \mathbf{b}$ is perpendicular to **a**.

9 $k = -5$

? (Page 13)

π_3 is parallel to π_1 and π_2 (the common line is at infinity).

Exercise 1B (Page 13)

1 (i) $\frac{x-3}{15} = \frac{y-1}{27} = \frac{z}{7}$
(ii) $x = y + 3 = \frac{z-5}{-4}$
(iii) $\frac{x}{16} = \frac{y+1}{15} = \frac{z+1}{13}$
(iv) $\frac{x-2}{11} = \frac{y}{4} = \frac{z-4}{21}$

2 (i) 56.5° **(ii)** 80.0° **(iii)** 24.9° **(iv)** 63.5°

3 (i) $x + 2 = y - 3 = -(z - 5)$
(ii) $\frac{x-4}{3} = \frac{y+3}{2} = \frac{z-2}{-6}$

4 $41x - 19y + 26z = 33$

5 $x + 3y - z + 8 = 0$

6 $\frac{x-4}{21} = \frac{y+2}{4} = \frac{z+7}{11}$

7 $60x + 11y + 100z = 900$; $60x - 11y - 100z + 300 = 0$;
$\mathbf{r} = \begin{pmatrix}5\\0\\6\end{pmatrix} + t\begin{pmatrix}0\\100\\-11\end{pmatrix}$; 6.3°

8 (i) $x + 3z + 800 = 0$
(ii) Normal is approx. 18.4° to horizontal
(iii) $14x - 15y + 3450z - 15\,950 = 0$
(iv) $x = 15\lambda$, $y = -1136\lambda - 62\,396.7$, $z = -5\lambda - 266.7$
(v) 62 km (assuming seam is sufficiently extensive)

Exercise 1C (Page 17)

1 (i) (3, 2, –13)
(ii) (1, 2, 7)
(iii) Do not meet
(iv) (4, –7, 11)
(v) Do not meet

2 No

3 (–2, –6, –1); 30 units

4 6, 9, $\sqrt{77}$

5 (i) $7\mathbf{i} - 7\mathbf{j} + 14\mathbf{k}$
(ii) (11, 6, –2)
(iii) $x - y + 2z - 1 = 0$
(iv) $11x - 5y - 8z - 107 = 0$

6 (i) $-\mathbf{i} + 6\mathbf{j} - 18\mathbf{k}$
(ii) 6, (–17, 22, 14)
(iii) $-x + 6y - 18z + 103 = 0$
(iv) 5

8 (ii) $(3p - 1, -4p - 4, 7p + 5)$, $(12, 2q, -3q + 2)$
(iii) $\mathbf{r} = \begin{pmatrix}8\\6\\-8\end{pmatrix} + t\begin{pmatrix}2\\1\\-1\end{pmatrix}$
(iv) (–4, 0, –2), (12, 8, –10)

9 (iii) (1, –5, 1), (–1, –1, 5), (–1, 5, –1), (1, 1, –5), (–3, –3, –3), (–5, 1, 1)

10 (ii) $\begin{pmatrix}1\\2\\-2\end{pmatrix}, \begin{pmatrix}22\\-1\\10\end{pmatrix}$

(iii) $22x - y + 10z = 123$

(iv) $(-1, -15, 13)$

(v) $\dfrac{x+1}{1} = \dfrac{y+15}{2} = \dfrac{z-13}{-2}$

(vi) $(8, 3, -5)$; 27 units

11 41.9 m; $(8, 42, -11)$, $(41, 21, 4)$

Activity 1.3 (Page 23)

(i) $(0, -\dfrac{c}{b}, 0)$

(ii) e.g. $p = b$, $q = -a$, $r = 0$

Activity 1.4 (Page 24)

P_1Q_1 is the hypotenuse of a right-angled triangle, of which another side equals PQ. Therefore $PQ < P_1Q_1$.

Activity 1.5 (Page 27)

(x_1, y_1, z_1) and (x_2, y_2, z_2) are on opposite sides of the plane $ax + by + cz + d = 0$.

Exercise 1D (Page 27)

1 (i) $\sqrt{29}$ **(ii)** 7 **(iii)** $\sqrt{104}$

2 (i) 13 **(ii)** $\sqrt{45}$ **(iii)** 1

3 (i) 5 **(ii)** 5 **(iii)** $5\sqrt{2}$

4 (i) no **(ii)** yes **(iii)** no (Q is on π)

5 (i) 4 **(ii)** 0.4 **(iii)** 0 (ℓ intersects ℓ')

6 (i) $(10, 8, 14)$ **(ii)** $(7, 9, -5)$ **(iii)** $(-3, 2, 6)$

7 (i) A(4, 8, 3), B(9, −2, 8)

(ii) Lines meet at A = B = (1, 4, 11)

(iii) A(1, 8, 20), B(7, −14, 10)

8 $\dfrac{|(\mathbf{a}-\mathbf{c}).((\mathbf{a}-\mathbf{b}) \times (\mathbf{c}-\mathbf{d}))|}{|(\mathbf{a}-\mathbf{b}) \times (\mathbf{c}-\mathbf{d})|}; \dfrac{89}{\sqrt{521}}$

10 Any line joining points on ℓ_1 and ℓ_2 which is not perpendicular to both can be shortened by fixing one end (on ℓ_1 say) and moving the other along ℓ_2 until the line is perpendicular to ℓ_2.

11 (ii) $x - 2 = \dfrac{y-5}{-2} = \dfrac{z-4}{-3}$

12 (ii) $7 + \frac{2}{3}k$

(iii) $-10\frac{1}{2}$

(iv) $\mathbf{r} = \begin{pmatrix}4\\12\\5\end{pmatrix} + t\begin{pmatrix}2\\10\\11\end{pmatrix}$

13 (i) PQ = PA cos QPA

14 $-\dfrac{(\mathbf{v}_1-\mathbf{v}_2).(\mathbf{a}_1-\mathbf{a}_2)}{|\mathbf{v}_1-\mathbf{v}_2|^2}$

? (Page 31)

No, since $(\mathbf{a} \,.\, \mathbf{b}) \times \mathbf{c}$ does not exist.

Activity 1.6 (Page 32)

1 No difference, provided that the bracketing changes too.

2 (i) Volume of tetrahedron

$= \frac{1}{3} \times \triangle\text{OBC} \times \text{height of A above OBC}$

$= \frac{1}{3} \times \frac{1}{2}$ parallelogram OBDC × height of A

$= \frac{1}{6} \times$ volume of parallelepiped

$= \frac{1}{6}\,|\mathbf{a}\,.\,(\mathbf{b} \times \mathbf{c})|$.

(ii) Taking P as origin, the position vectors of Q, R, S are $\mathbf{q} - \mathbf{p}$, $\mathbf{r} - \mathbf{p}$, $\mathbf{s} - \mathbf{p}$.
The result follows from part **(i)**.

Activity 1.7 (Page 34)

d and **e** are parallel, so $\mathbf{d} \times \mathbf{e} = \mathbf{0}$. The formula for the shortest distance takes the indeterminate form $\frac{0}{0}$. There are infinitely many common perpendiculars, all of the same length.

Exercise 1E (Page 37)

1 (i) 30 **(ii)** −77 **(iii)** 26

2 (i) yes **(ii)** no **(iii)** no

3 (i) yes **(ii)** yes **(iii)** no

4 (i) left **(ii)** neither (coplanar vectors)

(iii) right

5 (i) 35 **(ii)** 5 **(iii)** 0 **(iv)** (−)36

6 (i) 1 **(ii)** 2 **(iii)** $(-)24\frac{1}{3}$

9 (ii) C lies on both lines; $\mathbf{b} + \dfrac{\mathbf{a}.(\mathbf{b} \times \mathbf{d})}{\mathbf{b}.(\mathbf{d} \times \mathbf{e})}\mathbf{e}$

10 (ii) $\mathbf{b} = \sqrt{3}\mathbf{i} + \mathbf{j}$; $\mathbf{c} = \dfrac{2}{\sqrt{3}}\mathbf{i} + \dfrac{2\sqrt{2}}{\sqrt{3}}\mathbf{k}$

(iii) $4\sqrt{2}$

(iv) The three planes forming the faces of the parallelepiped through O divide the sphere with centre O into eight portions, one of which is inside the parallelepiped. The other portions, when translated, give the parts of the spheres which are centred at the other vertices and which lie inside the parallelepiped.

Exercise 1F (Page 39)

1 (i) $-25\mathbf{i} + 5\mathbf{j} - 35\mathbf{k}$

(ii) $\mathbf{r} = \begin{pmatrix} 2 \\ 4 \\ -4 \end{pmatrix} + \lambda \begin{pmatrix} -5 \\ 1 \\ -7 \end{pmatrix}$

(iii) $\mathbf{r} = \begin{pmatrix} 2 \\ 4 \\ -4 \end{pmatrix} + \lambda \begin{pmatrix} 5 \\ -31 \\ -8 \end{pmatrix}$

2 (ii) e.g. $\begin{pmatrix} 13 \\ -26 \\ 52 \end{pmatrix}$

(iii) $x - 2y + 4z - 37 = 0$

3 (i) $|15a - 60|$

(iii) D is in the plane ABC, and AB, DC are parallel. Least distance = 15.

4 (i) (a) 75 **(b)** $\frac{1}{3}|250 - 50k|$ **(c)** $\frac{1}{3}|10 - 2k|$
(d) 20

(ii) $15\sqrt{2}$

5 (i) $\dfrac{135\lambda}{2}$, right-handed

(ii) 5λ

(iii) $\dfrac{45\lambda}{\sqrt{9\lambda^2 - 4\lambda + 81}}$, approximately $\dfrac{45\lambda}{\sqrt{81}}$ when λ is small and $\dfrac{45\lambda}{\sqrt{9\lambda^2}}$ when λ is large

6 (i) $\begin{pmatrix} 28 \\ -21 \\ 7 \end{pmatrix}$

(ii) $\mathbf{r} = \begin{pmatrix} 8 \\ 9 \\ 0 \end{pmatrix} + \lambda \begin{pmatrix} 4 \\ -3 \\ 1 \end{pmatrix}$

(iii) $x = 16, y = 3, z = 2$

(iv) $k = 10$, no solution, planes form a triangular prism

Chapter 2

Exercise 2A (Page 46)

1 (i)

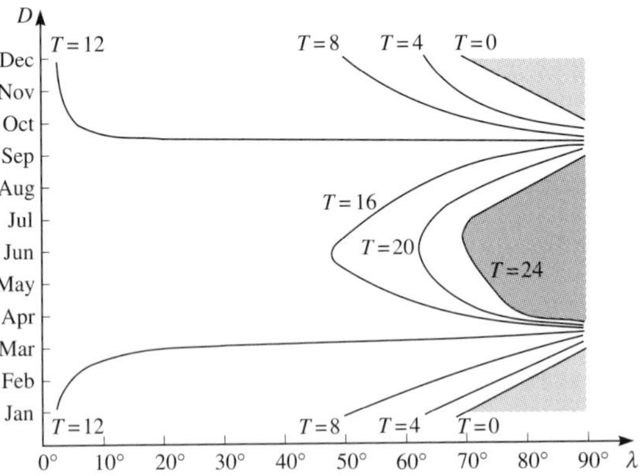

(ii)

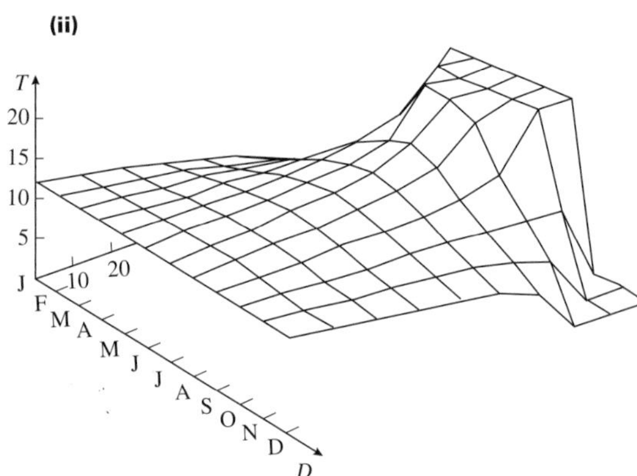

The surface has flat regions since the length of day cannot be negative or more than 24.

2 (i) B **(ii)** A **(iii)** B

3

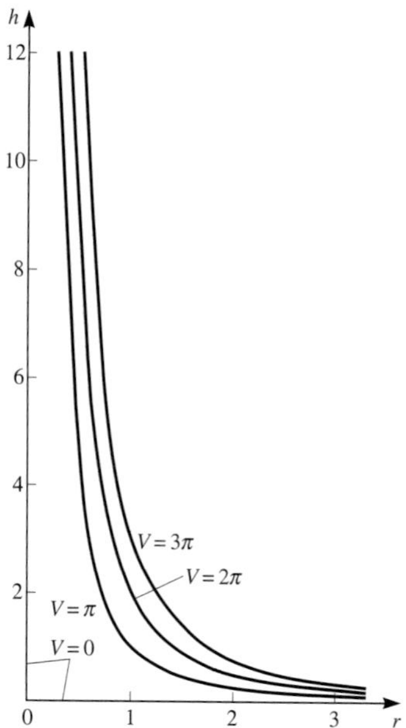

4 If $x^2 + y^2 = a^2$ then $z = \mathrm{f}(a^2)$, which is constant. So circles centre O are contours.

(i)

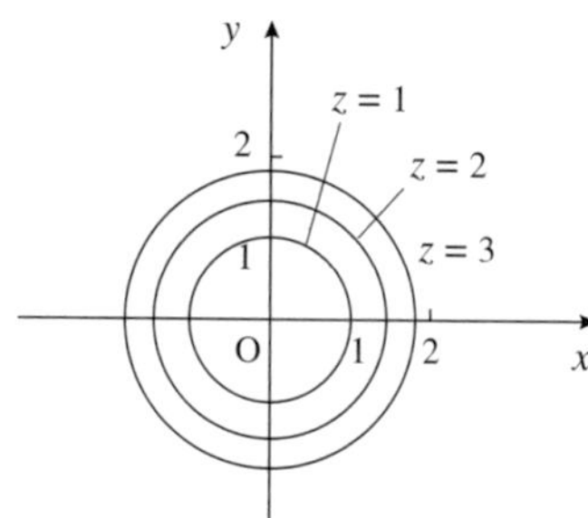

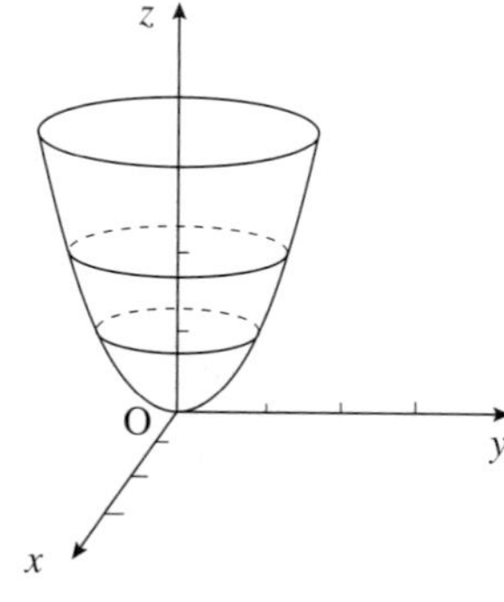

(ii)

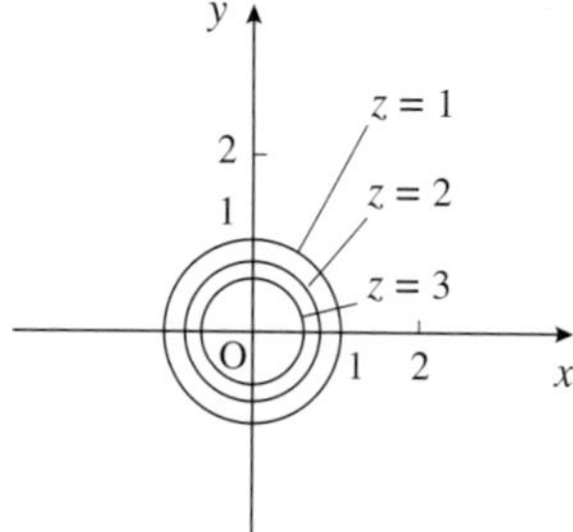

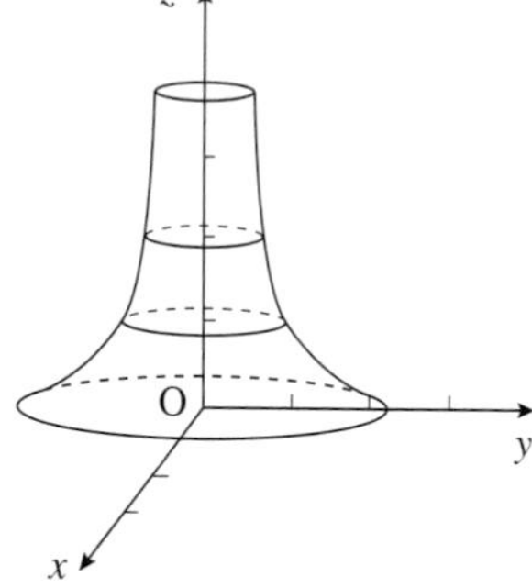

(iii)

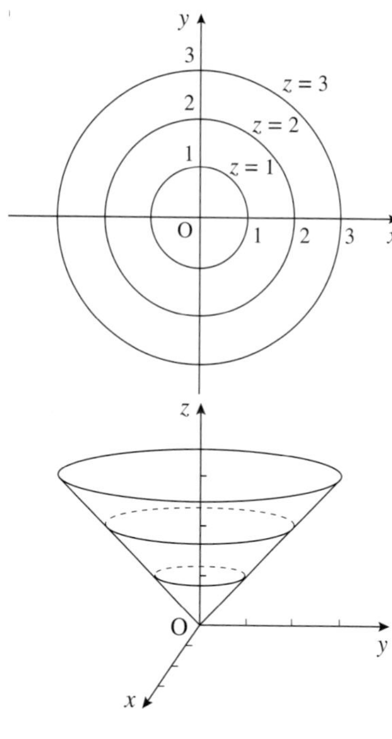

(iv)

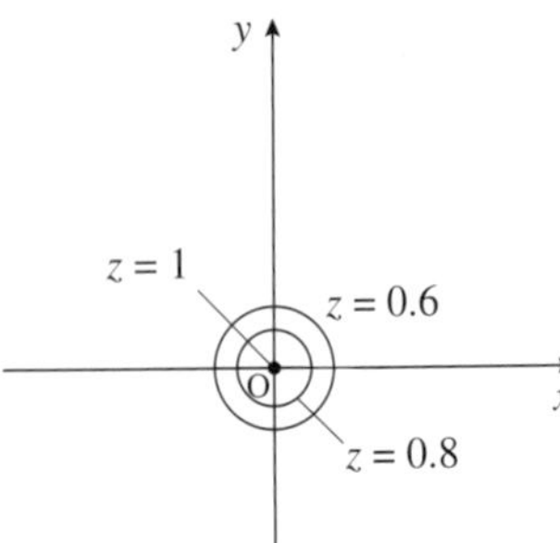

5 Contour $z = k\ (\neq 0)$ is the circle $x^2 + y^2 - \dfrac{x + 2y}{k} = 0$,

through O with centre $\left(\dfrac{1}{2k}, \dfrac{1}{k}\right)$;

contour $z = 0$ is the line $x + 2y = 0$.

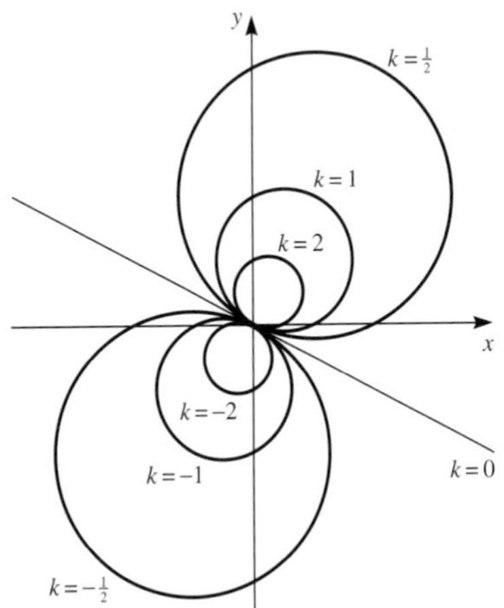

6 (i)

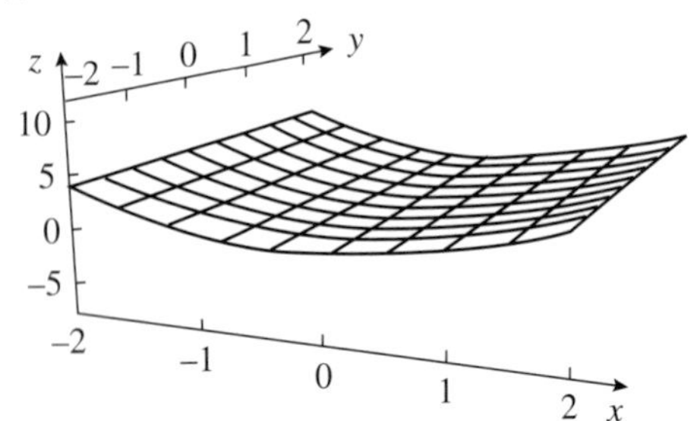

(ii)

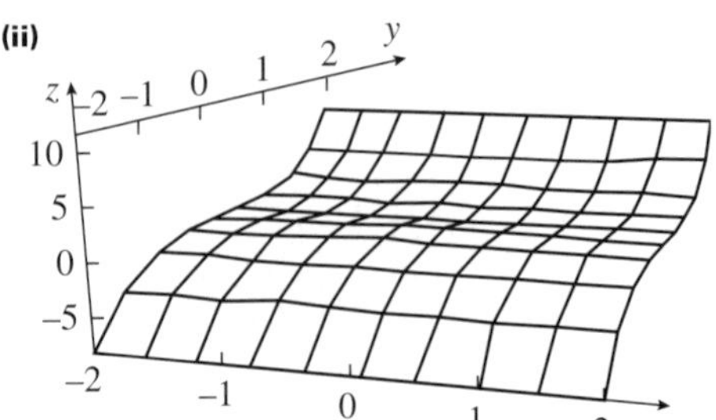

(iii)

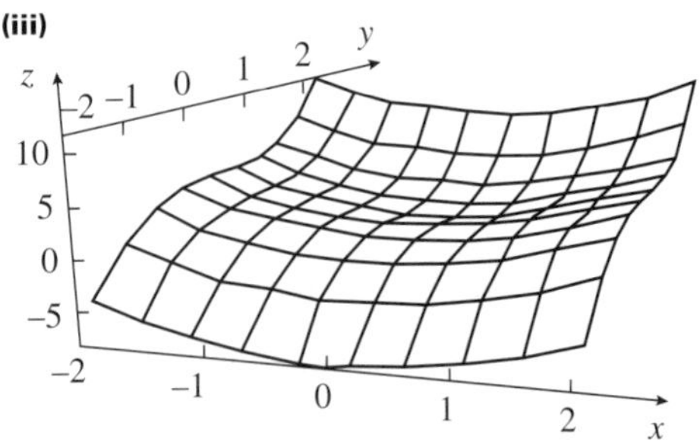

7

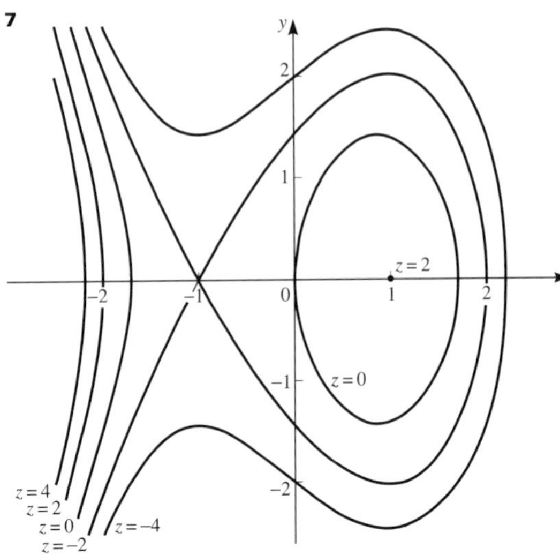

A curved cliff opposite an island.

8 (i)

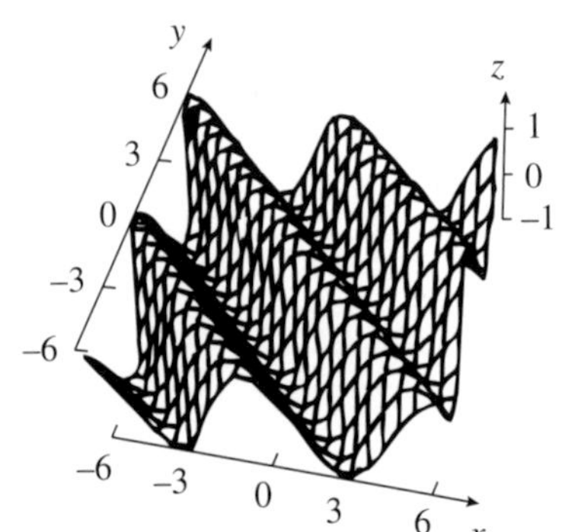

(ii)

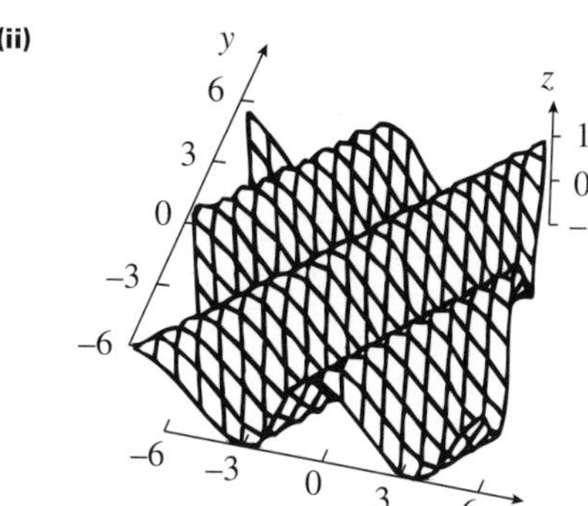

(iii)

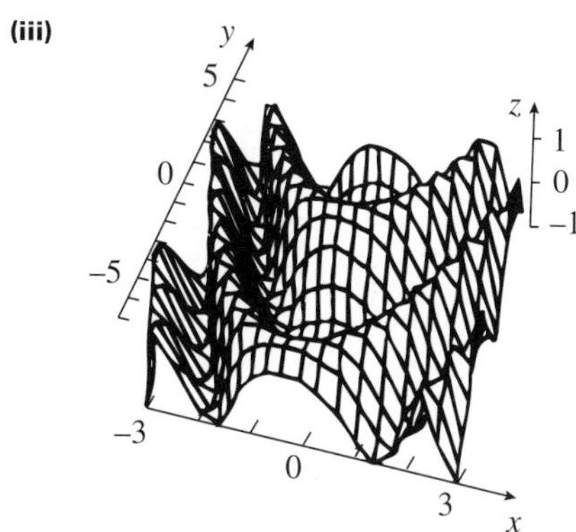

9 **(i)** $(ct, ct, 0)$

(ii) NE (if the x and y axes are E and N, respectively)

(iii) ellipses

(iv) pressure falls exponentially with height

10

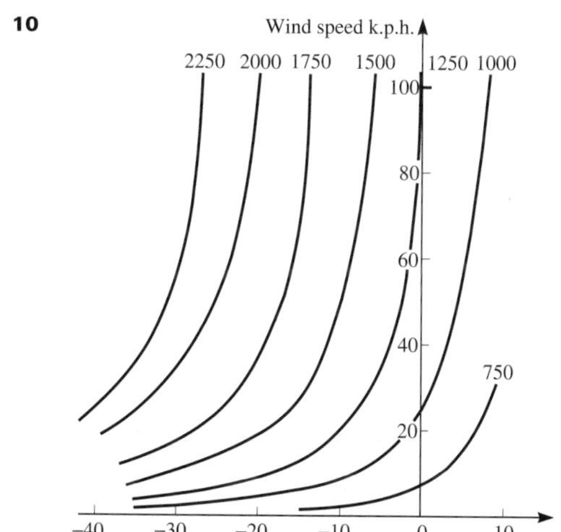

Exercise 2B (Page 50)

1

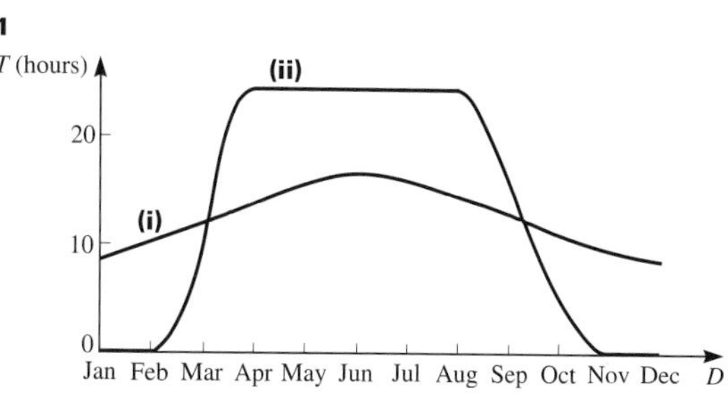

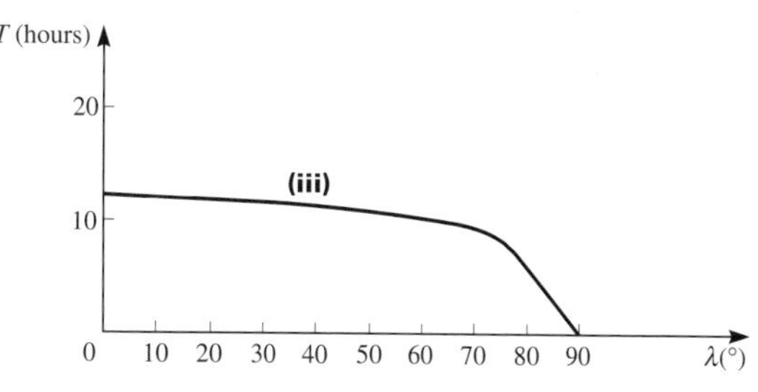

2

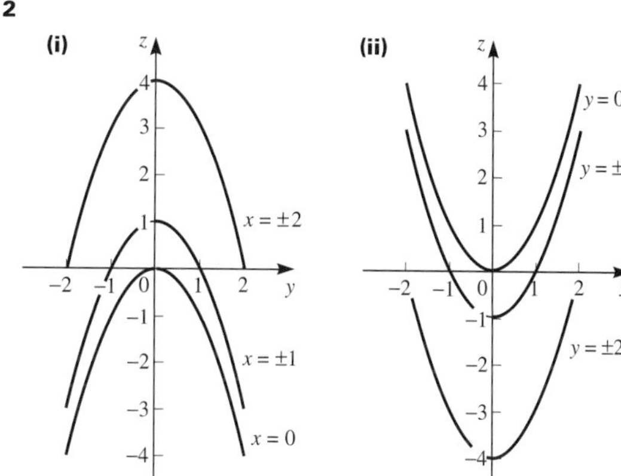

3 **(i)**

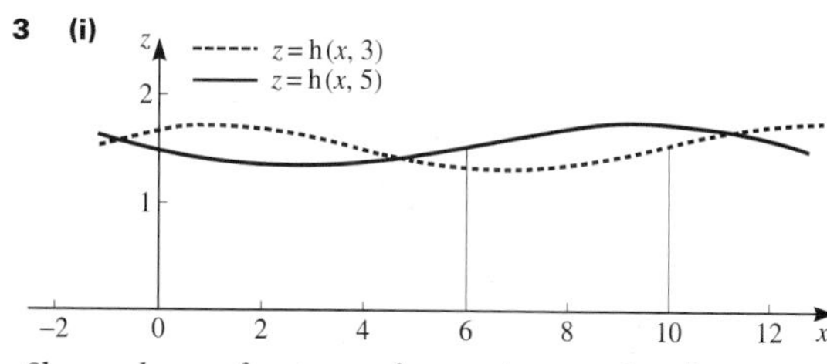

Shows shape of water surface at time, $t = 3$ and $t = 5$.

(ii)

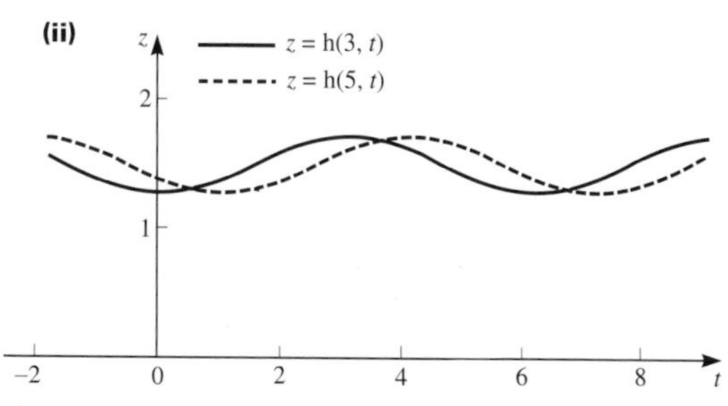

Shows variation of depth at positions $x = 3$ and $x = 5$.

(iii) $2\ \text{ms}^{-1}$

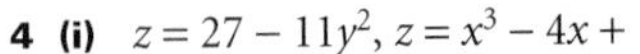

4 (i) $z = 27 - 11y^2$, $z = x^3 - 4x + 1$

(ii)

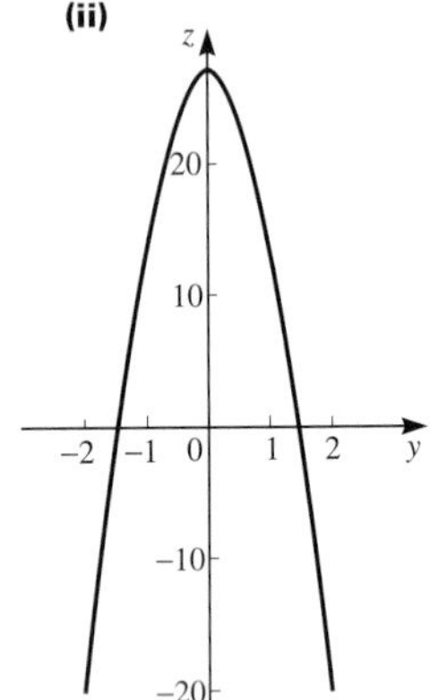

Section $x = 3$

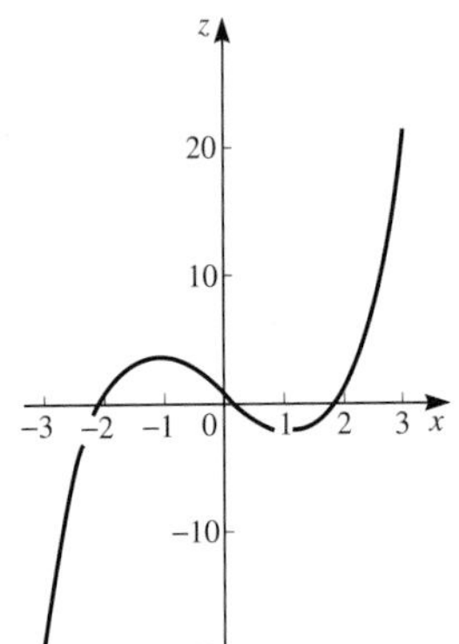

Section $y = 1$

(iii) −22, 23

5 Corrugations parallel to $0.4x - 0.3y = 0$, i.e. $y = \frac{4x}{3}$. To E: 7.7°, to N: −5.8°.

6 (i) 12.5 **(ii)** $z = \frac{125}{y^2+1}$, $z = \frac{x^3}{10}$ **(iii)** −7.5, 7.5

7 $z = (a - 2y)\ln(a^2 + 3y)$,

$z = (x - 2b)\ln(x^2 + 3b)$; $\frac{3(a-2b)}{a^2+3b} - 2\ln(a^2 + 3b)$,

$\frac{2a(a-2b)}{a^2+3b} + \ln(a^2 + 3b)$.

8 (ii) $\left(10,\ \mu,\ \frac{\mu}{5}\right)$, $\left(-10,\ \mu,\ -\frac{\mu}{5}\right)$

(iii) The point P dividing EG in the ratio $\alpha : 1 - \alpha$ is $\left(\lambda,\ 10 - 20\alpha,\ (1-2\alpha)\frac{\lambda}{5}\right)$.

If $10 - 20\alpha = \mu$ then P is $\left(\lambda,\ \mu,\ \frac{\lambda\mu}{50}\right)$.

By a similar argument P also lies on FH.

(v) The contour $z = c$ is the hyperbola $xy = 50c$. If $c = 0$ the 'hyperbola' degenerates to the x and y axes.

(vi) If $y = x$ then $z = \frac{x^2}{50}$, i.e. $z = \frac{u^2}{100}$, where $u\ (= \sqrt{2}x)$ is the distance from O to $(x, x, 0)$.

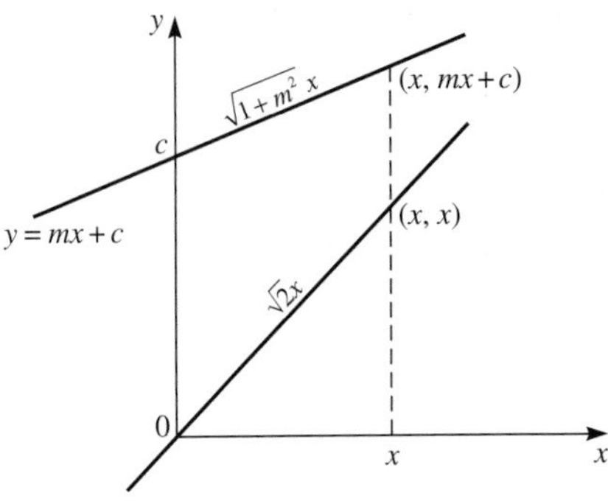

Similarly, on the section cut by the plane $y = mx + c$,

$$z = \frac{mx^2 + cx}{50} = \frac{mu^2 + \sqrt{1+m^2}\,cu}{50\sqrt{1+m^2}},$$

where $u\ (= \sqrt{1+m^2}\,x)$ is the distance from $(0, c, 0)$ to $(x, mx + c, 0)$. So every vertical section not parallel to the x or y axis is a parabola.

Exercise 2C (Page 53)

1 (i) $\frac{2x}{y^3}$, $-\frac{3x^2}{y^4}$

(ii) $-\frac{y}{(x^2+y^2)}$, $\frac{x}{(x^2+y^2)}$

(iii) $\cos y - y\sin x$, $-x\sin y + \cos x$

(iv) $\left(1 + \frac{1}{2}\sqrt{xy}\right)e^{\sqrt{xy}}$, $\frac{x\sqrt{x}}{2\sqrt{y}}e^{\sqrt{xy}}$

2 111, 190

3 At a point 3 m from the heater 10 minutes after switching the heater on

(i) the temperature decreases by 0.3 °C/m as you move away from the heater

(ii) the temperature increases by 0.1 °C/minute.

4 $d_x(0.4, 2) = -0.0029$, the gradient of the string at $x = 0.4$ after 2 seconds;
$d_t(0.4, 2) = 1.1$, the speed in ms^{-1} of the point of the string at $x = 0.4$ after 2 seconds.

6 $\frac{\partial T}{\partial p} = \frac{V-b}{R}$,

$$\frac{\partial p}{\partial V} = \frac{-RT}{(V-b)^2} + \frac{2a}{V^3} = \frac{aV - 2ab - pV^3}{V^3(V-b)},$$

$$\frac{\partial V}{\partial T} = \frac{RV^3}{pV^3 - aV + 2ab}$$

Activity 2.1 (Page 55)

(i) **(a)** 1200 **(b)** −24 **(c)** 0.12

$dy = 12\,dx$

(ii) $dy = 3x^2\,dx$

Activity 2.2 (Page 57)

(i) $(A') \Leftarrow (B')$

(ii) $(B') \Leftrightarrow (C')$

(iii) $(C') \Rightarrow (A')$

Activity 2.3 (Page 58)

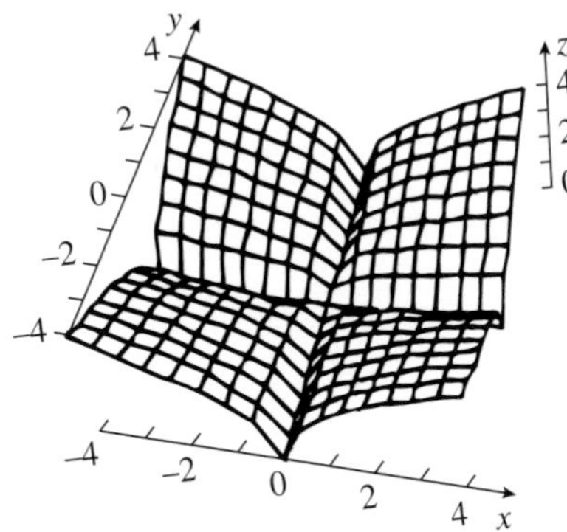

(i) (A′) true, (B′) false, (C′) false

(ii) all false

(iii) all true

Exercise 2D (Page 60)

1 **(i)** $\begin{pmatrix} x \\ y \\ z \end{pmatrix} = \begin{pmatrix} 3 \\ 1 \\ 13 \end{pmatrix} + \lambda \begin{pmatrix} 9 \\ -1 \\ -1 \end{pmatrix}$,

$z = 9x - y - 13$

(ii) $\begin{pmatrix} x \\ y \\ z \end{pmatrix} = \begin{pmatrix} 4 \\ -8 \\ 1 \end{pmatrix} + \lambda \begin{pmatrix} 3 \\ 1 \\ -4 \end{pmatrix}$,

$z = \frac{3}{4}x + \frac{1}{4}y$

(iii) $\begin{pmatrix} x \\ y \\ z \end{pmatrix} = \begin{pmatrix} 2 \\ 4 \\ 1 \end{pmatrix} + \lambda \begin{pmatrix} 1 \\ 2 \\ 5 \end{pmatrix}$,

$z = -\frac{1}{5}x - \frac{2}{5}y + 3$

(iv) $\begin{pmatrix} x \\ y \\ z \end{pmatrix} = \begin{pmatrix} 1 \\ \pi \\ -e \end{pmatrix} + \lambda \begin{pmatrix} e \\ 0 \\ 1 \end{pmatrix}$, $z = -ex$

2 **(i)** Not a linear equation.

(ii) Forgot to evaluate the partial derivatives at (3, 1, 9).

(iii) $z = 6(x - 3) + 36(y - 1) + 9$
$= 6x + 36y - 45$

3 −1878

4 Yes. Such dx, dy give the direction of the horizontal line through the particular point and lying in the tangent plane at that point. If this tangent plane is itself horizontal then any dx, dy will do.

5 (5, −3, −32)

7 $\begin{pmatrix} x \\ y \\ z \end{pmatrix} = \begin{pmatrix} 3 \\ 4 \\ 75 \end{pmatrix} + \lambda \begin{pmatrix} 6 \\ 8 \\ -1 \end{pmatrix}$,

$z = 6x + 8y + 25$

8 **(i)** $2acx + 6bcy - (a^2 + 3b^2)z = \dfrac{c^2}{k}$

? (Page 62)

The direction of the contour is undefined (stationary point, see page 64).

Exercise 2E (Page 63)

1 **(i)** $\begin{pmatrix} y \\ x \end{pmatrix}$

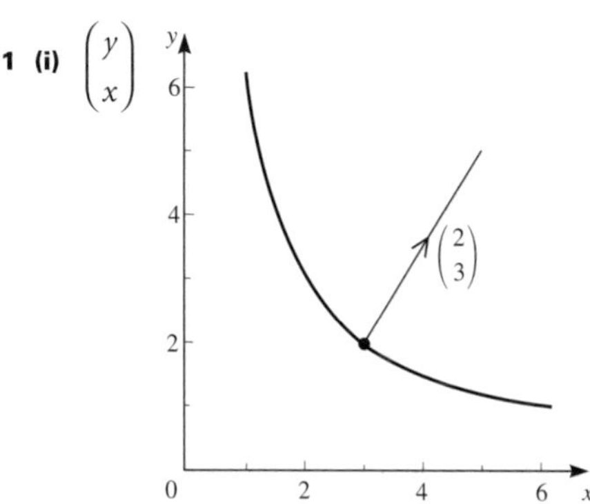

(ii) $\begin{pmatrix} \frac{1}{y} \\ -\frac{x}{y^2} \end{pmatrix}$

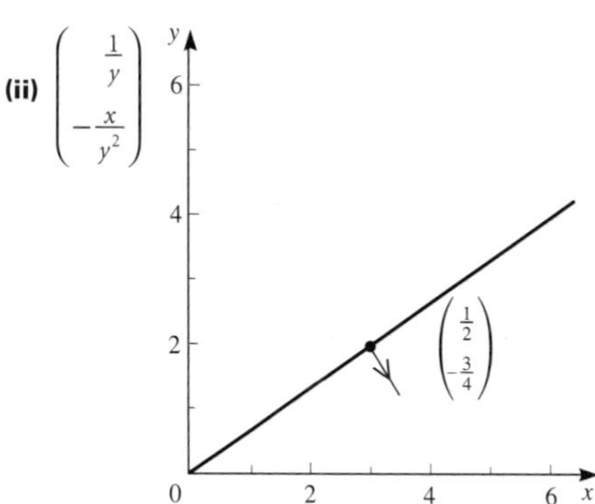

(iii) $\begin{pmatrix} 2x \\ 6y \end{pmatrix}$

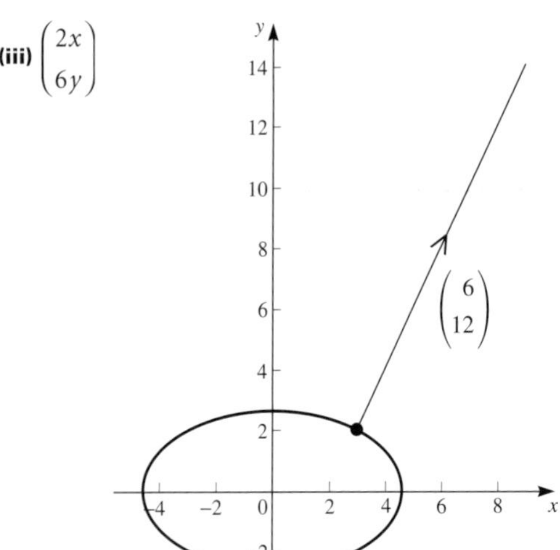

(iv) $\begin{pmatrix} \dfrac{y^2 - x^2}{(x^2 + y^2)^2} \\ \dfrac{-2xy}{(x^2 + y^2)^2} \end{pmatrix}$

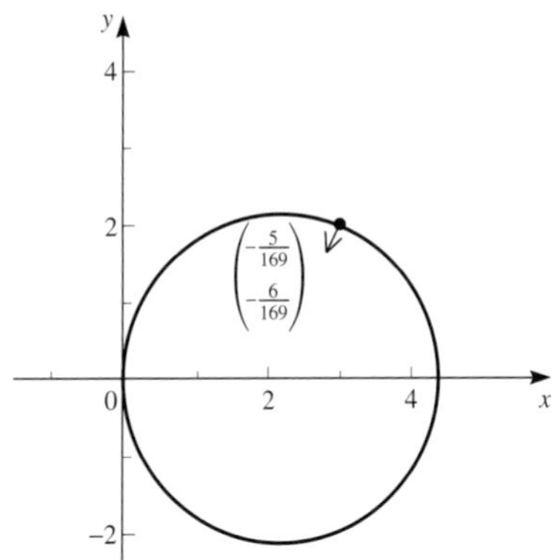

2 N: −6, NE: $\sqrt{2}$, E: 8, SE: $7\sqrt{2}$, S: 6, SW: $-\sqrt{2}$, W: −8, NW: $-7\sqrt{2}$.

3 **(i)** $-\frac{1}{\sqrt{2}}$, −35.3°

(ii) $\frac{9}{5\sqrt{5}} \approx 0.805$, 38.8°

4 **(i)** (0, 0), (20, 10)

(ii) $\begin{pmatrix} \frac{8}{\sqrt{65}} \\ \frac{1}{\sqrt{65}} \end{pmatrix} \approx \begin{pmatrix} 0.992 \\ 0.124 \end{pmatrix}$, 0.089

(iii) $\pm\begin{pmatrix} \frac{7}{\sqrt{449}} \\ -\frac{20}{\sqrt{449}} \end{pmatrix} \approx \pm\begin{pmatrix} 0.330 \\ -0.944 \end{pmatrix}$

5 $p \sin \theta + q \cos \theta$

Activity 2.4 (Page 65)

(i) minimum **(ii)** saddle
(iii) maximum **(iv)** saddle

Exercise 2F (Page 66)

1 minimum

2 (4, 2, 5), saddle

3 (0, 0, 0), saddle; (144, 24, −6912), minimum

4 **(i)** (1, −1, 0), saddle; (−1, 1, 0), saddle
(ii) (1, 2, 7), minimum; (1, −2, −1), saddle
(iii) $(2, -\frac{1}{2}, \ln 2 - \frac{1}{2})$, saddle; $(-2, \frac{1}{2}, \ln 2 - \frac{1}{2})$, saddle

5 (0, ±2), $(\pm\sqrt{2}, 0)$; maximum

6 **(i)** $B^2 < 4AC$ and $A < 0$
(ii) $B^2 < 4AC$ and $A > 0$
(iii) $B^2 > 4AC$

7 **(ii)** Edges in ratio 2:2:3, with a square base.

8 Maxima at $(2m\pi, 0, 2)$, minima at $((2m + 1)\pi, 0, -2)$ for all integer m.

9 Each of the lines $y = 2m\pi$, $z = 0$ (where m is an integer) is a horizontal line of stationary points.

10 $(\pm 2^{1/4}, 2^{-1/4}, 2^{-1/4})$ or $(\pm 2^{1/4}, -2^{-1/4}, -2^{-1/4})$

11 $\theta = \frac{\pi}{3}$, $d = \sqrt{\frac{20}{\sqrt{3}}} \approx 3.40$, $w = 3.92$

12 **(iv)** $m = 0.7$, $c = 2.15$
(v) Q is a quadratic expression in m, c which is large when the point (m, c) is far from (0, 0) in any direction, so the surface is a 'bowl', and its single stationary point is a minimum point.

13 **(i)** A bowl whose vertical sections are parabolas.

Activity 2.5 (Page 70)

The argument uses
(i) these properties of moduli:
$|a + b + c| \leqslant |a| + |b| + |c|$, $|pq| = |p||q|$
(ii) δx, δy, δz all $\to 0$ as $\delta s \to 0$.
(iii) ε_1, ε_2, ε_3, η_1, η_2 all $\to 0$ as δx, δy, $\delta z \to 0$.

Activity 2.6 (Page 72)

(i) 58.7 m² **(ii)** 43.2 m²

Exercise 2G (Page 72)

1 $(p - q - r)\%$

2 100; $\delta T \approx 2.64$ (actually $\delta T = 2.69$)

3 $\delta V \approx S\varepsilon$

4 1%, 2%

5 (i) (A) $V = \frac{1}{3}\pi r^3 \cot\alpha$ (B) $V = \frac{1}{3}\pi r^2\sqrt{\ell^2 - r^2}$

(ii) (A) $\dfrac{\delta V}{V} \approx 3\dfrac{\delta r}{r} - \dfrac{\operatorname{cosec}^2\alpha}{\cot\alpha}\delta\alpha$

$= 3\dfrac{\delta r}{r} - 2\operatorname{cosec} 2\alpha \times \delta\alpha$

(B) $\dfrac{\delta V}{V} \approx \dfrac{2\ell^2 - 3r^2}{r(\ell^2 - r^2)}\delta r + \dfrac{\ell}{\ell^2 - r^2}\delta\ell$

(iii) (A) cosec 2α is least when $\alpha = \dfrac{\pi}{4}$

(B) the coefficient of δr is zero when $2\ell^2 = 3r^2$, i.e. when $\alpha = \arcsin\sqrt{\frac{2}{3}}$

6 (i) $2b - 2c\cos A$, $2c - 2b\cos A$, $2bc\sin A$

(ii) $\delta(a^2) \approx 2(b - c\cos A)\delta b$
$+ 2(c - b\cos A)\delta c + 2bc\sin A\delta A$

(iii) 11.2 cm

(iv) 11.0%

7 $\delta b \approx b\left(\dfrac{h}{a} + \cot B\,\delta B - \cot(B+C)(\delta B + \delta C)\right)$.

If $B + C < \dfrac{\pi}{2}$ the greatest error is

$b\left(\dfrac{h}{a} + \alpha\cot B\right)$, when $\delta B = \alpha$ and $\delta C = -\alpha$.

If $B + C > \dfrac{\pi}{2}$ the greatest error is

$b\left(\dfrac{h}{a} + \alpha(\cot B - 2\cot(B+C))\right)$, when

$\delta B = \delta C = \alpha$, since $\cot(B + C) < 0$.

Exercise 2H (Page 76)

1 (i) $-\frac{14}{\sqrt{3}} \approx -8.08$ (ii) $-\frac{1}{3}$ (iii) $-\frac{9}{5}$

2 (i) $yz + zx + xy + c$ (ii) $\frac{1}{2}\ln(x^2 + y^2 + z^2) + c$

4 Along the generators of a cone with vertex P, axis in the direction of **grad** g, and semi-vertical angle $\dfrac{\pi}{3}$.

5 (i) $\begin{pmatrix} \frac{2}{\sqrt{38}} \\ \frac{5}{\sqrt{38}} \\ \frac{3}{\sqrt{38}} \end{pmatrix}$ (ii) 18.5 unit s^{-1}

6 (i) $\dfrac{1}{\sqrt{2}}(-\sin t\,\mathbf{i} + \cos t\,\mathbf{j} + \mathbf{k})$

(ii) $\dfrac{1000\sqrt{2}(6\sin t - t)}{(12\cos t + t^2 + 37)^2}$

(iv) 29.9

Exercise 2I (Page 79)

1 $3x - 10y + 4z = 39$

2 (i) $\begin{pmatrix} x \\ y \\ z \end{pmatrix} = \begin{pmatrix} 3 \\ -1 \\ 1 \end{pmatrix} + \lambda\begin{pmatrix} 6 \\ -1 \\ -2 \end{pmatrix}$,

$6x - y - 2z = 17$

(ii) $\begin{pmatrix} x \\ y \\ z \end{pmatrix} = \begin{pmatrix} -4 \\ 24 \\ -2 \end{pmatrix} + \lambda\begin{pmatrix} -8 \\ -\frac{1}{4} \\ -6 \end{pmatrix}$,

$32x + y + 24z = -152$

3 (12, 14, 6) or (−12, −14, −6)

5 (i) (a) point $(-a, -b, -c)$

(b) no real points

7 66.8°, parallel to $\begin{pmatrix} 4 \\ -5 \\ 0 \end{pmatrix}$

8 (i) $6x - 2y$, $-2x + 4y$, $2z + 4$

(ii) $\begin{pmatrix} x \\ y \\ z \end{pmatrix} = \begin{pmatrix} 2 \\ 1 \\ 3 \end{pmatrix} + \lambda\begin{pmatrix} 1 \\ 0 \\ 1 \end{pmatrix}$

(iii) (−3, 1, −2)

(iv) 5, −9

9 (iv) $\begin{pmatrix} -2v/bc \\ (v^2 - 1)/ca \\ (v^2 + 1)/ab \end{pmatrix}$

(v) $\begin{pmatrix} 2(1 - u^2v^2)/a^2bc \\ -2(u + v + u^2v + uv^2)/ab^2c \\ 2(uv^2 - u + v - u^2v)/abc^2 \end{pmatrix}$,

which has $\dfrac{-2(1 + uv)}{abc}$ as a common factor.
The tangent plane contains both generators, and $\mathbf{d} \times \mathbf{e}$ is normal to this.

Investigation (Page 81)

(i) (a) $4u^3$, $12u^2$

(b) $1 + u\ln u$, $1 + \ln u$

(c) $\arctan\left(\dfrac{2u}{1 - u^2}\right) = 2\arctan u$, $\dfrac{2}{1 + u^2}$

(iv) $\delta W \approx \frac{dW}{dt}\delta t = \left(\frac{\partial W}{\partial T}\frac{dT}{dt} + \frac{\partial W}{\partial R}\frac{dR}{dt}\right)\delta t$, where t is the time in years
$= (-4.8 \times 0.07 + 1.2 \times (-0.16)) \times 1$
$= -0.528$ unit/year

Exercise 2J (Page 82)

1 (i) $\frac{\partial z}{\partial x} = 2xy - 2y, \frac{\partial z}{\partial y} = x^2 - 2x - 2y - 3$
(ii) $(-1, 0, 8), (3, 0, 8), (1, -2, 12)$
(iii) $2x + 5y + z = 9$
(iv) $\left(2, -\frac{10}{3}, \frac{62}{9}\right)$

2 (i) $\frac{\partial g}{\partial x} = 6x - y + 2z, \frac{\partial g}{\partial y} = 2y - x, \frac{\partial g}{\partial z} = 4z + 2x$
(ii) $\begin{pmatrix} x \\ y \\ z \end{pmatrix} = \begin{pmatrix} 1 \\ -1 \\ -2 \end{pmatrix} + t\begin{pmatrix} 1 \\ -1 \\ -2 \end{pmatrix}$
(iii) $(-1, 1, 2)$
(iv) $(2, 1, -1), (-2, -1, 1)$

3 (i) $\frac{\partial z}{\partial x} = 4x - 4y^2, \frac{\partial z}{\partial y} = -8xy + 1$
(ii) $\left(\frac{1}{4}, \frac{1}{2} - \frac{5}{8}\right)$
(iii) $y - z = 1, 3x - 3y - z = 1$
(iv) A is a point in the tangent plane at B.
(v) $\sin^{-1}\left(\frac{1}{\sqrt{7}}\right) \approx 22.2°$

4 (i) $\frac{\partial z}{\partial x} = 8xy - y^2 - 16x + 4, \frac{\partial z}{\partial y} = 4x^2 - 2xy$
(ii) $(0, 2, 4), (0, -2, 4), (1, 2, 4), \left(\frac{1}{3}, \frac{2}{3}, \frac{124}{27}\right)$
(iii) $z = 11x + 4y - 24$

5 (i) $\frac{\partial \theta}{\partial x} = 10(1 + x)yz^2e^{x-2y}$,
$\frac{\partial \theta}{\partial y} = 10x(1 - 2y)z^2e^{x-2y}, \frac{\partial \theta}{\partial z} = 20xyze^{x-2y}$
(ii) $\delta\theta \approx 100\delta x - 120\delta y + 160\delta z$
(iii) $\mathbf{r} = \begin{pmatrix} 4 \\ 2 \\ 1 \end{pmatrix} + t\begin{pmatrix} \frac{5}{\sqrt{125}} \\ -\frac{6}{\sqrt{125}} \\ \frac{8}{\sqrt{125}} \end{pmatrix}$

Chapter 3

Activity 3.2 (Page 87)

(i) $x \sec\theta + y \operatorname{cosec}\theta - 15 = 0$
(ii) $\frac{x}{L} + \frac{y}{\sqrt{225 - L^2}} - 1 = 0$

? (Page 89)

Since SR = RQ = OR, the circle with SQ as diameter passes through O. Therefore ∠QOS = 90° (angle in semi-circle), and so S is on OY.

Exercise 3A (Page 91)

1

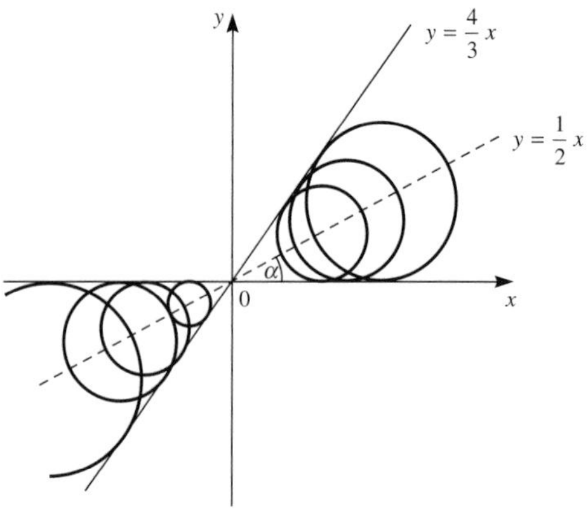

The circles touch $y = 0$ and $y = \frac{4x}{3}$ (the reflection of $y = 0$ in $y = \frac{x}{2}$).

2 $y^2 = 4ax$

4 $4(x - 2a)^3 = 27ay^2$

5 (ii) $y = \frac{kx}{p} + hp$
(iii) Further steps give lines touching the parabola beyond the points where it touches AX and BX.

6 (ii) $A^2 + B^2 = C^2$

7 (ii) $y = \frac{u^2}{2g} - \frac{gx^2}{2u^2}$, vertex $\left(0, \frac{u^2}{2g}\right)$, focus $(0, 0)$

8 Ellipse $\frac{x^2}{2} + y^2 = 1$

9 Hint: Show that the centre of one of the family of circles can be expressed as $(1 + \cos\alpha, \sin\alpha)$. Find the equation of this circle and then use Question 6**(ii)**.

11 (i) The given diameter
(ii) $x^2 + y^2 - 4ax\cos\theta - 4ay\sin\theta + 4a^2\cos^2\theta = 0, x = 2a\cos\theta(2\sin^2\theta + 1)$,
$y = 4a\sin^3\theta$; or $y = 0$.
[**Hint:** Start by eliminating x between $f = 0$ and $\frac{\partial f}{\partial \theta} = 0$.]

Activity 3.3 (Page 94)

(i)

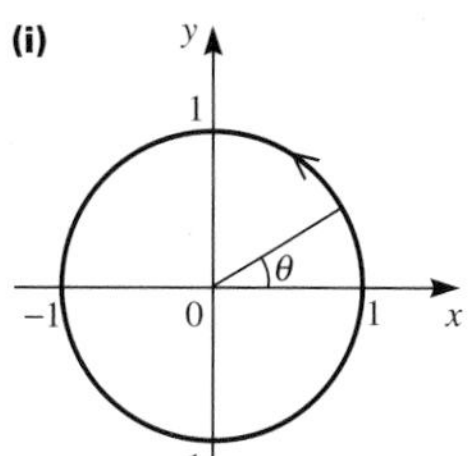

(ii)

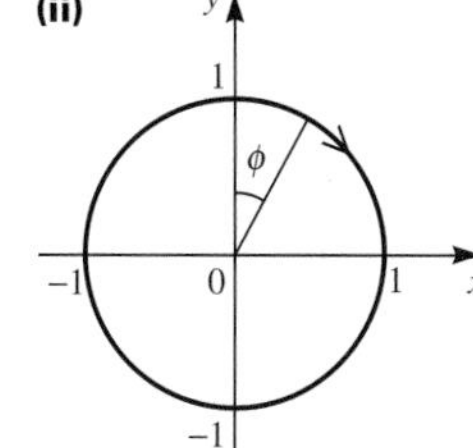

(iii)

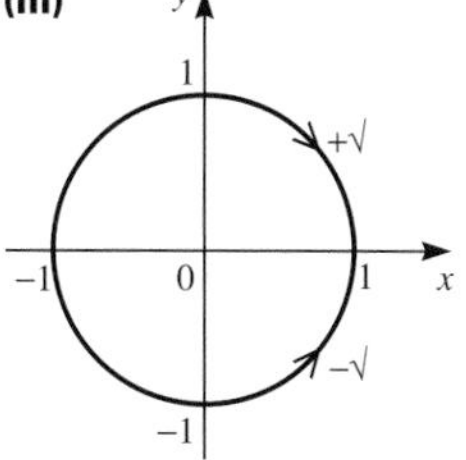

? (Page 97)

PQ = δs, QK = δr, KP = $r\delta\theta$. Use Pythagoras on 'triangle' PQK.

Exercise 3B (Page 97)

1 $\dfrac{8(10^{3/2}-1)}{27} \approx 9.07$

2

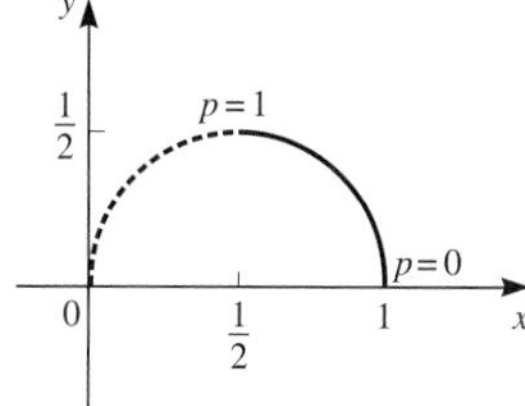

$\dfrac{\pi}{4}$

3 $c \sinh\left(\dfrac{X}{c}\right)$

6 $24a$

7 $\dfrac{\sqrt{1+k^2}}{k}$

8 $8a$

Exercise 3C (Page 102)

1 **(i)** 45π

(ii) $4\pi a^2$

(iii) $2\pi ac + \pi c^2 \sinh\left(\dfrac{2a}{c}\right)$

(iv) $\dfrac{8\pi a^2(5^{3/2}-2^{3/2})}{3} \approx 70a^2$

(v) $\dfrac{64\pi a^2}{3}$

(vi) $\dfrac{12\pi a^2}{5}$

(vii) $\left(2-\sqrt{2}\right)\pi a^2$

(viii) $\dfrac{32\pi a^2}{5}$

2 **(i)** $2\pi a^2(1 - \cos\alpha)$

(ii) $4\pi a^2(\sin\alpha - \alpha\cos\alpha)$

4 **(i)** $4\pi a^2$

(ii) 2.03×10^8 km^2

Investigation (Page 104)

(vi) $2\pi^2 a^2 b$, $4\pi^2 ab$

(vii) On axis of symmetry

(a) $\dfrac{4r}{3\pi}$ **(b)** $\dfrac{2r}{\pi}$ from the diameter

(viii) $2\pi chk$, $4\pi c(h + k)$

Activity 3.4 (Page 105)

(i) Centre at origin

(ii) Centre at $\left(1, \dfrac{\pi}{2}\right)$

(iii) Apply the cosine rule to △COP, then expand $\cos\left(\theta - \dfrac{\pi}{4}\right)$ or change to cartesian co-ordinates.

Activity 3.5 (Page 106)

$s = 0$ at the lowest point of the circle, s increases in the anticlockwise sense, $\psi = 0$ in the direction of the positive x axis.

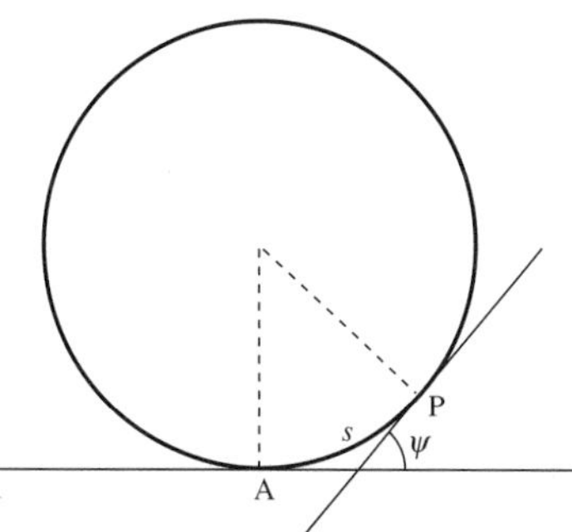

Exercise 3D (Page 108)

1 $s = \ln|\sec\psi + \tan\psi|$ with $s = 0$ when $\psi = 0$

2 $s = 2a(\sec^3\psi - 1)$ with $s = 0$ when $\psi = 0$

4 (vi) $x = a(\phi + \sin\phi)$, $y = a(1 - \cos\phi)$, where $\phi = \theta - \pi$.

6 $x = \ln \sin y$

8 Choose the origin so that $z = \dfrac{ak(k-j)}{k^2+1}$ when $\psi = 0$.

Then $z = \dfrac{ake^{(k+j)\psi}}{k+j} = \dfrac{ake^{k\psi}}{\sqrt{k^2+1}}e^{j(\psi-\alpha)}$, where

$\alpha = \operatorname{arccot} k$.

Therefore $r = |z| = \dfrac{ake^{k\psi}}{\sqrt{k^2+1}}$ and

$\theta = \arg z = \psi - \alpha$, so $r = \dfrac{ak}{\sqrt{k^2+1}}e^{k(\theta+\alpha)}$.

Activity 3.6 (Page 111)

ψ decreases as s increases.

Activity 3.7 (Page 111)

$$\frac{-\dfrac{d^2x}{dy^2}}{\left\{\left(\dfrac{dx}{dy}\right)^2+1\right\}^{3/2}}$$

Exercise 3E (Page 112)

1 $\dfrac{6}{10^{3/2}} \approx 0.190$, $\quad -\dfrac{12}{145^{3/2}} \approx -0.006\,87$

2 $-2^{-3/2} \approx -0.354$

5 $\arctan\sqrt{\dfrac{2}{33}} \approx 13.8°$

6 (i) $\dfrac{2\operatorname{cosec} 2\psi}{3a}$

(ii) $-\dfrac{2\operatorname{cosec} 2p}{3a}$;

$\psi = \pi - p$, with positive sense clockwise in part **(i)** and anticlockwise in part **(ii)**.

9 $ab(a^2\sin^2\theta + b^2\cos^2\theta)^{-3/2}$ $\left(= \dfrac{1}{a} \text{ when } a = b\right)$

11 $\dfrac{2}{3\sqrt{3}}$, at $\left(-\dfrac{1}{2}\ln 2, \dfrac{1}{\sqrt{2}}\right)$

15 (iii) PK $= r\,\delta\theta$, KQ $= \delta r$, and $\angle$PQK $\approx \phi$

(v) Hint: Show that $\tan\phi = -\cot\left(\dfrac{\theta}{2}\right)$, and deduce that $\psi = \dfrac{3\theta}{2} + \dfrac{\pi}{2}$. Then proceed as in part **(iv)**.

Exercise 3F (Page 117)

1 (8, 8)

2 $\begin{pmatrix}\frac{1}{\sqrt{5}}\\ \frac{2}{\sqrt{5}}\end{pmatrix}, \begin{pmatrix}-\frac{2}{\sqrt{5}}\\ \frac{1}{\sqrt{5}}\end{pmatrix}, \begin{pmatrix}\frac{\pi}{4}-\frac{5}{2}\\ \frac{9}{4}\end{pmatrix}$

4 $(-ke^{\theta}\sin\theta, ke^{\theta}\cos\theta)$

6 $a = 3p^2 + 6p^4$, $b = -6p - 8p^3$, $c = -3p^4 - 8p^6$

7 (i) $e < \frac{1}{\sqrt{2}}$

(ii) $e = \frac{1}{\sqrt{2}}$

(iii) $e > \frac{1}{\sqrt{2}}$

? (Page 120)

(i) If the evolute is continuous it passes through the cusp (e.g. $x = p^2$, $y = p^3$), but the evolute may have a discontinuity corresponding to the cusp point (e.g. $x = p^2$, $y = p^5$).

(ii) The evolute is discontinuous; the normal to the curve at the point of inflection is an asymptote of the evolute (e.g. $x = p$, $y = p^3$ at $p = 0$).

(iii) The evolute has a cusp (e.g. $x = p^2$, $y = p$ at $p = 0$).

Exercise 3G (Page 120)

1 $x = \dfrac{c}{2}\left(3t + \dfrac{1}{t^3}\right)$, $y = \dfrac{c}{2}\left(\dfrac{3}{t} + t^3\right)$

2

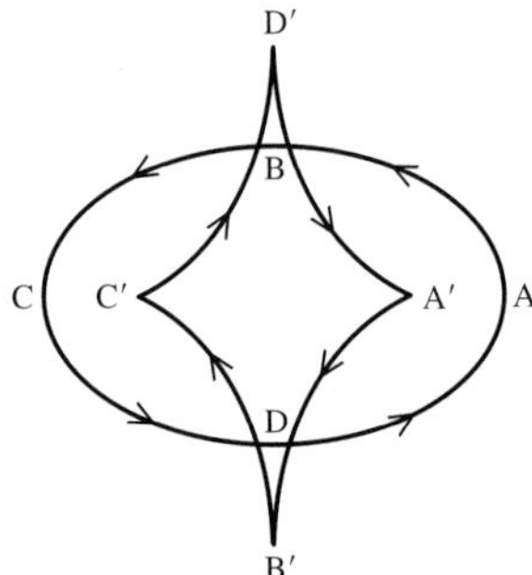

3

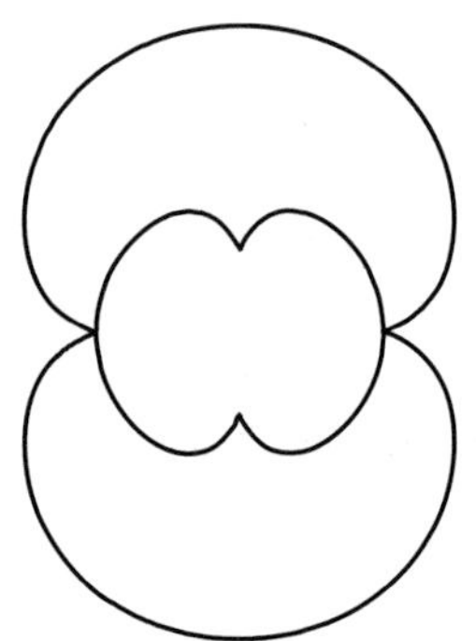

4 $(a(\cos\theta+\sin\theta), a(\cos\theta+\sin\theta))$,
$(a(\cos\theta-\sin\theta), a(\sin\theta-\cos\theta))$

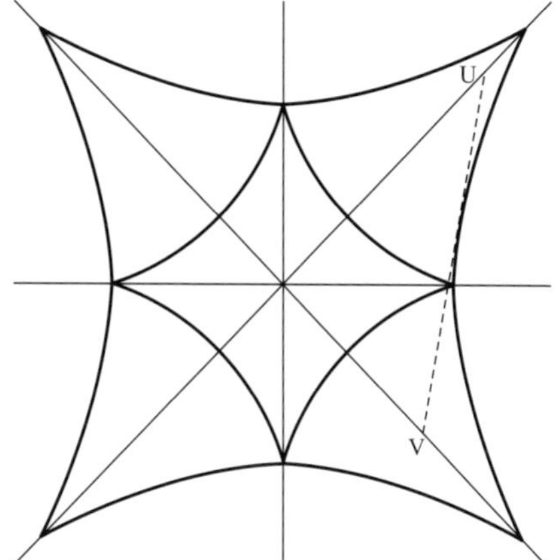

5 **(i)** $\angle ONP = \alpha$, so $ON = OP \cot\alpha$, so the locus of N is the original spiral enlarged by $\cot\alpha$ and turned through $\frac{\pi}{2}$ about O.

(ii) $\angle ONP = \alpha$, which is the angle between ON and the tangent at N, so PN is the tangent at N.

(iv) Yes, e.g. if α is increased until the normal touches the *original* spiral (when $\tan\alpha = k^{3\pi/2}$).

6

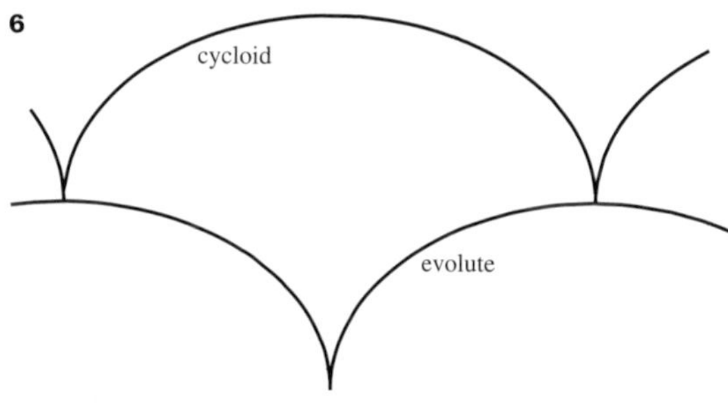

Exercise 3H (Page 123)

1 $\dfrac{4(a^3-b^3)}{ab}$

2 **(i)** $12a$ **(ii)** $6a$

4 Every involute is determined by **(a)** its starting point on the circle and **(b)** the sense of unwinding. Neither of these affects the size or shape of the involute.
$x = a(\cos\theta + \theta\sin\theta)$, $y = a(\theta\cos\theta - \sin\theta)$.

5 **(ii)** Relative to the wheel with centre A, P is a fixed point on the unwinding string XP.

Exercise 3I (Page 127)

1 **(i)** **(a)** $\dfrac{5^{3/2}}{4}$ **(b)** $\left(-\dfrac{5}{2}, \dfrac{9}{4}\right)$

(ii) **(a)** $t^2x + y - t^3 = 0$ **(b)** $y = -\frac{4}{27}x^3$

2 **(ii)** $\left(-36, -6\frac{1}{4}\right)$

(iii) $16\sqrt{3}$

(iv) 192π

3 **(i)** $5(e^{\alpha} - 1)$

(iii) $\frac{5}{2}e^{\alpha}$

4 **(ii)** **(a)** $\dfrac{10^{3/2}}{2\lambda}$

(b) $\left(-\dfrac{15}{\lambda}, -\lambda^2 + \dfrac{5}{\lambda}\right)$

(c) $y = \frac{1}{4}x^4 + 3x$

5 **(i)** $\frac{4}{3}a$

(iii) $x + y\sinh\theta - a\cosh\theta\sinh\theta - a\theta = 0$;
$x = a(\theta - \cosh\theta\sinh\theta)$, $y = 2a\cosh\theta$

Chapter 4

? (Page 130)

Numbers: no division by zero, no square root of negative numbers; vectors: no vector product in 2 or n (> 3) dimensions; matrices: no multiplication or inverse of 2×3 matrices.

Activity 4.1 (Page 131)

(i) Finding the modulus of a vector, differentiating a function.

(ii) E.g. finding the mean of three numbers, finding the centroid of the triangle formed by three points.

Activity 4.2 (Page 132)

(i) Vectors, scalar product; points, finding the distance between two points.

(ii) Functions (polynomial, rational, or with $f(0) = f(1) = 0$), composition of functions.

(iii) Points, finding the mid-point.

(iv) Three-dimensional vectors, vector product.

Activity 4.3 (Page 132)

(i) E.g. 89, 65, −7

(ii) Any three factors of 48 (except 1 and 12).

Exercise 4A (Page 133)

1 (i)

$+_5$	0	1	2	3	4
0	0	1	2	3	4
1	1	2	3	4	0
2	2	3	4	0	1
3	3	4	0	1	2
4	4	0	1	2	3

(ii)

$\times_7$	0	1	2	3	4	5	6
0	0	0	0	0	0	0	0
1	0	1	2	3	4	5	6
2	0	2	4	6	1	3	5
3	0	3	6	2	5	1	4
4	0	4	1	5	2	6	3
5	0	5	3	1	6	4	2
6	0	6	5	4	3	2	1

2 (i) Wednesday; $100 = 2 \pmod 7$

(ii) 03.17 next day; $27.17 = 03.17 \pmod{24}$

(iii) No; no perfect square has 3 as its final digit i.e. no square $= 3 \pmod{10}$.

3 (i) $x + 2 = y + 4 + 12m \Rightarrow x = y + 2 + 12m$.

(ii) False, e.g. $x = 0$, $y = 3$.

4 (iii) Neither converse is true.

5 x is divisible by 3 $\Leftrightarrow$ the digit sum of x is divisible by 3.

Examples (Pages 133–135)

A

$+_6$	0	1	2	3	4	5
0	0	1	2	3	4	5
1	1	2	3	4	5	0
2	2	3	4	5	0	1
3	3	4	5	0	1	2
4	4	5	0	1	2	3
5	5	0	1	2	3	4

B $PU = W$

Other combinations: see text that follows.

C

		First transformation					
	followed by	i	p	q	u	v	w
Second transformation	i	i	p	q	u	v	w
	p	p	q	i	w	u	v
	q	q	i	p	v	w	u
	u	u	v	w	i	p	q
	v	v	w	u	q	i	p
	w	w	u	v	p	q	i

D (i) $1, \omega, \omega^2, -1, -\omega, -\omega^2$

(ii)

$\times$	1	ω	ω^2	-1	$-\omega$	$-\omega^2$
1	1	ω	ω^2	-1	$-\omega$	$-\omega^2$
ω	ω	ω^2	1	$-\omega$	$-\omega^2$	-1
ω^2	ω^2	1	ω	$-\omega^2$	-1	$-\omega$
-1	-1	$-\omega$	$-\omega^2$	1	ω	ω^2
$-\omega$	$-\omega$	$-\omega^2$	-1	ω	ω^2	1
$-\omega^2$	$-\omega^2$	-1	$-\omega$	ω^2	1	ω

Activity 4.7 (Page 135)

See text that follows.

Activity 4.8 (Page 137)

Only +.

Exercise 4B (Page 137)

1 (i)

~	0	1	2	3	4
0	0	1	2	3	4
1	1	0	1	2	3
2	2	1	0	1	2
3	3	2	1	0	1
4	4	3	2	1	0

(ii) yes

(iii) no

(iv) yes, 0

(v) yes, each element is self-inverse

2 (i) yes

(ii) yes; e.g. $S = \{x: x \geqslant 0\}$, identity 0, no element except 0 has an inverse in S.

3 Both operations are associative.

4 (i) Closed, associative, no identity (0 is not an identity, since $-\mathrm{j} \bullet 0 = (-1)^{1/2} = +\mathrm{j}$), no inverses.

(ii) Closed, associative, identity 0, no inverses (except that 0 is self-inverse).

(iii) $m = 2k + 1$ (k is a positive integer), $q^2 = 2pr$.

5 If $y = \pm k$ then every x except $\mp k$ is a solution.

6 (i) $xy + 3x + 3y + 6$

(ii) $\dfrac{3xy - 2x - 2y + 1}{2xy - x - y}$

(iii) $\dfrac{x + y}{1 - xy}$

7 Not associative; $P = (0, 0)$, $Q = (a_1 - a_2, a_2 - a_1)$, $I = (0, 0)$, no J.
The argument is invalid since it uses associativity.

Activity 4.10 (Page 140)

(i) 0 has no inverse under ×

(ii) there is no identity under + (0 is not positive)

Activity 4.11 (Page 143)

(i) $ah = bh \Rightarrow (ah)h^{-1} = (bh)h^{-1}$
$\Rightarrow a(hh^{-1}) = b(hh^{-1}) \Rightarrow ae = be \Rightarrow a = b.$

(ii) e.g., in group B, $PU = UQ$ (= W), but $P \neq Q$.

Activity 4.12 (Page 143)

(i) $x = ba^{-1}$ **(ii)** $x = a^{-1}cb^{-1}$

Exercise 4C (Page 144)

1

Second transformation: followed by	First transformation: I	R	H	S	X	Y	A	B
I	I	R	H	S	X	Y	A	B
R	R	H	S	I	A	B	Y	X
H	H	S	I	R	Y	X	B	A
S	S	I	R	H	B	A	X	Y
X	X	B	Y	A	I	H	S	R
Y	Y	A	X	B	H	I	R	S
A	A	X	B	Y	R	S	I	H
B	B	Y	A	X	S	R	H	I

2 e.g., with no identity,

	a	b	c	d
a	d	c	b	a
b	a	d	c	b
c	b	a	d	c
d	c	b	a	d

4 $x = a^{-1}b$, $y = ab$

5 **(ii)**, **(iii)**, **(iv)** are groups, **(iii)** is Abelian.

6 **(ii)** $X = \{1, 3, 4, 6, 8\}$

7 e.g. the group of Question 6**(i)**.

8 **(ii)**

$\times_8$	1	2	3	4	5	6	7
1	1	2	3	4	5	6	7
2	2	4	6	0	2	4	6
3	3	6	1	4	7	2	5
4	4	0	4	0	4	0	4
5	5	2	7	4	1	6	3
6	6	4	2	0	6	4	2
7	7	6	5	4	3	2	1

Not closed. E.g. {1, 3}, {1, 3, 5, 7}

9 All elements of G are self-inverse.

Activity 4.13 (Page 146)

1 = single stripe, 2 = double stripe, 3 = triple stripe

Activity 4.14 (Page 147)

(i) a self-inverse and $a \leftrightarrow x \Rightarrow x^{-1} \leftrightarrow a^{-1}$
(by theorem **C**)
$\Rightarrow x^{-1} \leftrightarrow a$ (since $a^{-1} = a$) $\Rightarrow x^{-1} = x$.

(ii) No; B has four self-inverse elements, but D has two.

Activity 4.15 (Page 149)

Six isomorphisms

Exercise 4D (Page 149)

1 e.g. $n \leftrightarrow 5n$, $n \leftrightarrow -5n$

2 Yes, e.g. $k \leftrightarrow (-\omega)^k$ for $k = 0, 1, 2, 3, 4, 5$.

5 **(ii)**

e	a	b
a	b	e
b	e	a

e.g. $(\{1, \omega, \omega^2\}, \times)$

9 **(i)**, **(ii)**, **(iii)**, **(vi)** are isomorphic; **(iv)**, **(v)** are isomorphic.

10 **(i)** $ab = a \Rightarrow b = e$, $ab = b \Rightarrow a = e$; both are impossible since a, b, e are distinct.

(iii) **(a)** gives

	e	a	b	c
e	e	a	b	c
a	a	c	e	b
b	b	e	c	a
c	c	b	a	e

(d) gives

	e	a	b	c
e	e	a	b	c
a	a	b	c	e
b	b	c	e	a
c	c	e	a	b

or

	e	a	b	c
e	e	a	b	c
a	a	e	c	b
b	b	c	e	a
c	c	b	a	e

or

	e	a	b	c
e	e	a	b	c
a	a	e	c	b
b	b	c	a	e
c	c	b	e	a

Activity 4.16 (Page 151)

No, not closed.

Chapter 4

Exercise 4E (Page 153)

1 $\{I\}$, $\{I, H\}$, $\{I, X\}$, $\{I, Y\}$, $\{I, A\}$, $\{I, B\}$, $\{I, R, H, S\}$, $\{I, H, X, Y\}$, $\{I, H, A, B\}$

2 (i) (1 2 3 4), (2 1 4 3), (3 4 1 2), (4 3 2 1)

(ii) (1 2 3 4 5 6 7 8), (2 3 4 1 7 8 6 5), (3 4 1 2 6 5 8 7), (4 1 2 3 8 7 5 6), (5 8 6 7 1 3 4 2), (6 7 5 8 3 1 2 4), (7 5 8 6 2 4 1 3), (8 6 7 5 4 2 3 1)

3 e.g. $G =$ (integers, +), $H = \{$multiples of 2$\}$, $K = \{$multiples of 3$\}$; $H \cup K$ is not closed under +, since $2 + 3 \notin H \cup K$.

5 (iii) e.g. {all rotations about any fixed point}, {rotations through multiples of $\frac{2\pi}{n}$ about any fixed point}.

6 Matrices of the form $\begin{pmatrix} 1 & 0 & q \\ 0 & 1 & 0 \\ 0 & 0 & 1 \end{pmatrix}$.

7 e.g. $ba \notin \{e, a, b, c, d\}$.

Activity 4.18 (Page 154)

(i) $IQ = QH = H$, $VH = WH = \{U, V, W\}$.
The union is S.

Exercise 4F (Page 156)

1 $XK = RK = \{X, Y, R, S\}$, $AK = \{I, A, H, B\}$

4 (iv) e.g. the subgroup $\{I, X\}$ of the symmetry group of the square is not normal, since $A^{-1}XA = Y \notin \{I, X\}$.

Investigation (Page 156)

(i)

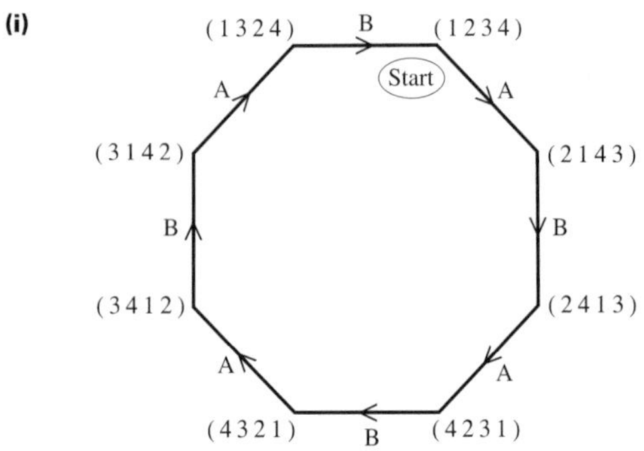

(iv) and **(v)** See below.

(iv)

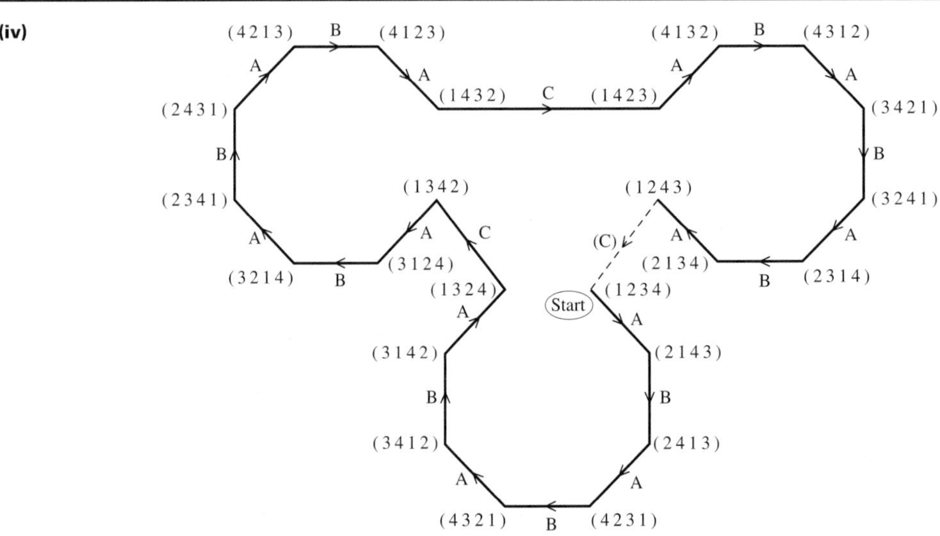

(v)

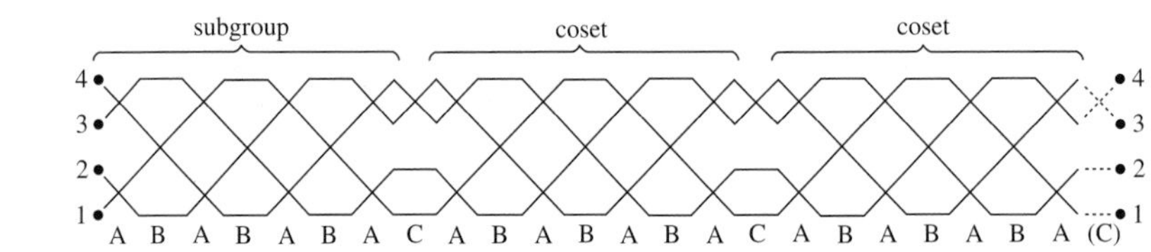

Activity 4.19 (Page 159)

1, 1, …; 2, 4, 8, 1, 2, …; 4, 1, 4, …; 8, 4, 2, 1, 8, …

Activity 4.20 (Page 159)

(i) 6 **(ii)** 2 **(iii)** 3 **(iv)** 6

Activity 4.21 (Page 159)

(i) 1

(ii) −1, 1

(iii) $\omega, \omega^2, 1$

(iv) $-\omega, \omega^2, -1, \omega, -\omega^2, 1$

Activity 4.22 (Page 160)

Yes, A and D are cyclic.

Exercise 4G (Page 160)

1

Element	I	R	H	S	X	Y	A	B
Order	1	4	2	4	2	2	2	2

$\{I\}, \{I, H\}, \{I, X\}, \{I, Y\}, \{I, A\}, \{I, B\}, \{I, R, H, S\}$

4 (ii) True, false

(iii) k, n have no common factor.

5 9 and 20 have no common factor, so rotation through $\frac{9\pi}{10}$ generates the whole set of rotations. Other possible values of n (< 20) are 1, 3, 7, 11, 13, 17, 19.

7 (i) $H = R^2, S = R^3, Y = R^2X, A = RX, B = R^3X$

10 Numbers in G are the products of distinct primes with no repetitions. Show that, if A is the set of prime factors of a, etc., then the correspondence $a \leftrightarrow A$ is an isomorphism between G with operation ● and the set of subsets of prime numbers with operation Δ, the symmetric difference (as in Exercise 4C, Question 6).

Investigation (Page 162)

(i) 6 reflections.

(a) 4 axes, angles $\frac{2\pi}{3}$ or $\frac{4\pi}{3}$ = 8 rotations

(b) 3 axes, angle π = 3 rotations.
8 + 3 + 1 (identity) = 12

(ii) (a) 3 axes joining mid-points of faces,
angles $\frac{\pi}{2}$ or π or $\frac{3\pi}{2}$ = 9 rotations

(b) 6 axes joining mid-points of opposite edges,
angle π = 6 rotations

(c) 4 axes joining opposite vertices,
angles $\frac{2\pi}{3}$ or $\frac{4\pi}{3}$ = 8 rotations.

9 + 6 + 8 + 1 = 24.

(iii) The orientation of the cube is determined by the position of the 4 space diagonals, which are permuted by the rotations.

(v) (a) 6 axes joining mid-points of faces,
angles $\frac{2\pi}{5}, \frac{4\pi}{5}, \frac{6\pi}{5}, \frac{8\pi}{5}$ = 24 rotations

(b) 15 axes joining mid-points of opposite edges,
angle π = 15 rotations

(c) 10 axes joining opposite vertices,
angles $\frac{2\pi}{3}, \frac{4\pi}{3}$ = 20 rotations.

24 + 15 + 20 + 1 = 60.

? (Page 164)

Multiplication over subtraction

Activity 4.23 (Page 164)

Irrationals not closed under + or ×.

Activity 4.24 (Page 165)

If $a \neq 0$ then $ab = 0 \Rightarrow a^{-1}(ab) = a^{-1} \times 0 = 0$ (by Example 4.6) $\Rightarrow (a^{-1}a)b = 0 \Rightarrow 1b = 0 \Rightarrow b = 0$.

Activity 4.26 (Page 165)

Rotation about O through θ, where $\cos\theta : \sin\theta : 1 = x : y : \sqrt{x^2 + y^2}$, followed by enlargement with scale factor $\sqrt{x^2 + y^2}$.

Activity 4.27 (Page 166)

Rotation about O through $\frac{\pi}{2}$.

Exercise 4H (Page 166)

4 If and only if m is prime.

5 Identities: 1 for ⊕, 0 for ⊗; inverses: $2 - m$ for ⊕, $\frac{m}{m-1}$ for ⊗ ($m \neq 1$).

6 $(2 + \mathrm{j})z + (4 - 5\mathrm{j}) = (1 + 3\mathrm{j})z$, $\begin{pmatrix} -2.8 & 0.6 \\ -0.6 & -2.8 \end{pmatrix}$

7 $\begin{pmatrix} 5 & 3 \\ -3 & 5 \end{pmatrix}$ or $\begin{pmatrix} 4 & -1 \\ 1 & 4 \end{pmatrix}$

8 $\begin{pmatrix} -1 & 0 \\ 0 & -1 \end{pmatrix}$

9 **(i)** Taking the conjugate

(iii) $\det(Z_1Z_2) = \det Z_1 \det Z_2$

Exercise 4I (Page 168)

1 **(iv)** {1, 5, 13, 17, 25, 29}; 5 is a generator.

(v) {1, 17, 19, 35}; $17^2 = 19^2 = 35^2 = 1 \pmod{36}$

2 **(ii)** B, I, A^2B

(iii) 1, 4, 2, 4, 2, 2, 2, 2 respectively

(v) {I, A, A^2, A^3}, {I, A^2, AB, A^3B}

(vi) Only {I, A, A^2, A^3} is cyclic.

3 (For brevity the elements of each group are called *e*, *a*, *b*, *c* respectively.)
Permutations and matrices: orders 1, 2, 2, 2; non-cyclic; proper subgroups {*e*}, {*e*, *a*}, {*e*, *b*}, {*e*, *c*}
Complex numbers: orders 1, 2, 4, 4; cyclic; proper subgroups {*e*}, {*e*, *a*}

4 **(i)**

	1	3	7	9	11	13	17	19
1	1	3	7	9	11	13	17	19
3	3	9	1	7	13	19	11	17
7	7	1	9	3	17	11	19	13
9	9	7	3	1	19	17	13	11
11	11	13	17	19	1	3	7	9
13	13	19	11	17	3	9	1	7
17	17	11	19	13	7	1	9	3
19	19	17	13	11	9	7	3	1

(ii)

x	1	3	7	9	11	13	17	19
x^{-1}	1	7	3	9	11	17	13	19

(iii)

x	1	3	7	9	11	13	17	19
order	1	4	4	2	2	4	4	2

(iv) {1}, {1, 9}, {1, 11}, {1, 19}, {1, 3, 7, 9}, {1, 9, 13, 17}, {1, 9, 11, 19}, *G*
{1, 9}, {1, 11}, {1, 19} are isomorphic
{1, 3, 7, 9}, {1, 9, 13, 17} are isomorphic

(v) **(a)** 0 has no inverse so *J* is not a group.

(b) *K* is closed and inverses of 0, 1, 2, 3, 4, 5, 6, 7 are 0, 7, 6, 5, 4, 3, 2, 1 respectively so *K* is a group.
Different pattern (2 self-inverse elements) *K* is not isomorphic to *G*.

5 **(i)** e.g. symmetry group of an equilateral triangle

6 **(ii)** 1, 2, 2, 2 respectively

(iii) RT (a rotation matrix) does not have order 2, 4 or 8.
Or **P**, **Q**, **R**, **S**, **T**, **QT**, **RT**, **ST**, **TS** are all distinct, giving nine elements.

Chapter 5

? (Page 172)

Empirical means determined by experiment or on the basis of existing data.

Exercise 5A (Page 175)

1 **(i)** $\begin{pmatrix} \frac{43}{64} & \frac{21}{32} \\ \frac{21}{64} & \frac{11}{32} \end{pmatrix}, \begin{pmatrix} \frac{341}{512} & \frac{171}{256} \\ \frac{171}{512} & \frac{85}{256} \end{pmatrix}, \begin{pmatrix} \frac{2731}{4096} & \frac{1365}{2048} \\ \frac{1365}{4096} & \frac{683}{2048} \end{pmatrix}$

(ii) $\begin{pmatrix} \frac{11}{18} & \frac{7}{16} \\ \frac{7}{18} & \frac{9}{16} \end{pmatrix}, \begin{pmatrix} \frac{107}{216} & \frac{109}{192} \\ \frac{109}{216} & \frac{83}{192} \end{pmatrix}, \begin{pmatrix} \frac{1409}{2592} & \frac{1183}{2304} \\ \frac{1183}{2592} & \frac{1121}{2304} \end{pmatrix}$

(iii) $\begin{pmatrix} \frac{13}{18} & \frac{5}{18} \\ \frac{5}{18} & \frac{13}{18} \end{pmatrix}, \begin{pmatrix} \frac{19}{54} & \frac{35}{54} \\ \frac{35}{54} & \frac{19}{54} \end{pmatrix}, \begin{pmatrix} \frac{97}{162} & \frac{65}{162} \\ \frac{65}{162} & \frac{97}{162} \end{pmatrix}$

(iv) $\begin{pmatrix} 0.52 & 0.16 \\ 0.48 & 0.84 \end{pmatrix}, \begin{pmatrix} 0.412 & 0.196 \\ 0.588 & 0.804 \end{pmatrix}, \begin{pmatrix} 0.3472 & 0.2176 \\ 0.6528 & 0.7824 \end{pmatrix}$

2 **(i)**

	sunny	*cloudy*
sunny	0.7	0.2
cloudy	0.3	0.8

(ii) **(a)** 0.55 **(b)** 0.525 **(c)** 0.4375

3 **(i)**

	Dem	*Rep*
Dem	$\frac{1}{2}$	$\frac{1}{3}$
Rep	$\frac{1}{2}$	$\frac{2}{3}$

(ii) **(a)** $\frac{11}{18}$ **(b)** $\frac{43}{108}$

4 **(i)**

	disco	*cinema*
disco	0.5	0.75
cinema	0.5	0.25

(ii) **(a)** 0.625 **(b)** 0.40625

(iii) 0.5977 *or* 0.6006

5 **(i)**

	fore	*back*
fore	$\frac{1}{5}$	$\frac{1}{3}$
back	$\frac{4}{5}$	$\frac{2}{3}$

(ii) $\frac{32}{45} \approx 0.711$

(iii) **(a)** $\frac{476}{675} \approx 0.705$ **(b)** $\frac{796}{1125} \approx 0.708$

6 (i)

$$\begin{array}{c} \\ Oxf \\ Cam \end{array}\begin{array}{c} \begin{array}{cc} Oxf & Cam \end{array} \\ \begin{pmatrix} \frac{3}{5} & \frac{1}{3} \\ \frac{2}{5} & \frac{2}{3} \end{pmatrix} \end{array}$$

(ii) Oxford won last year: Oxford $\frac{37}{75}$, Cambridge $\frac{38}{75}$

Cambridge won last year: Oxford $\frac{19}{45}$, Cambridge $\frac{26}{45}$

7 (i)

$$\begin{array}{c} \\ late \\ OT \end{array}\begin{array}{c} \begin{array}{cc} late & OT \end{array} \\ \begin{pmatrix} 0.25 & 0.5 \\ 0.75 & 0.5 \end{pmatrix} \end{array}$$

(ii) (a) 0.625 **(b)** 0.602 (3 s.f.)

8 (i) $a + b = 1, c + d = 1$

(ii) $\mathbf{P}^2 = \begin{pmatrix} a^2 + bc & ac + cd \\ ab + bd & bc + d^2 \end{pmatrix}$;

The sum of the first column $= a^2 + bc + ab + bd$
$= a(a + b) + b(c + d)$
$= a + b = 1.$

Similarly for the second column.

(iii) $\mathbf{P}^3 = \begin{pmatrix} a^3 + abc + abc + bcd & a^2c + acd + bc^2 + a^2c \\ a^2b + b^2c + abd + bd^2 & abc + bcd + bcd + d^3 \end{pmatrix}$;

The sum of the first column
$= a^3 + abc + abc + bcd + a^2b + b^2c + abd + bd^2$
$= a^2(a + b) + bc(a + b) + ab(c + d) + bd(c + d)$
$= a^2 + bc + ab + bd$
$= a(a + b) + b(c + d)$
$= a + b = 1.$

Similarly for the second column.

Activity 5.1 (Page 179)

(i) $\begin{pmatrix} 1 \\ 0 \\ 0 \\ 0 \end{pmatrix}$ **(ii)** $\begin{pmatrix} 0 \\ 0.4 \\ 0.6 \\ 0 \end{pmatrix}$ **(iii)** $\begin{pmatrix} 0.416 \\ 0 \\ 0 \\ 0.583 \end{pmatrix}$ **(iv)** $\begin{pmatrix} 0 \\ 0.166 \\ 0.833 \\ 0 \end{pmatrix}$

Exercise 5B (Page 179)

1 (i) $\begin{pmatrix} \frac{19}{24} & \frac{5}{24} & \frac{5}{36} \\ 0 & \frac{3}{8} & \frac{5}{12} \\ \frac{5}{24} & \frac{5}{12} & \frac{4}{9} \end{pmatrix}$, $\begin{pmatrix} \frac{25}{144} & \frac{181}{288} & \frac{295}{432} \\ \frac{19}{48} & \frac{5}{48} & \frac{5}{72} \\ \frac{31}{72} & \frac{77}{288} & \frac{107}{432} \end{pmatrix}$,

$\begin{pmatrix} \frac{1133}{1728} & \frac{65}{216} & \frac{335}{1296} \\ \frac{25}{288} & \frac{181}{576} & \frac{295}{864} \\ \frac{445}{1728} & \frac{665}{1728} & \frac{1037}{2592} \end{pmatrix}$

(ii) $\begin{pmatrix} 0.3775 & 0.3250 & 0.3450 \\ 0.4650 & 0.4375 & 0.4050 \\ 0.1575 & 0.2375 & 0.2500 \end{pmatrix}$,

$\begin{pmatrix} 0.3523 & 0.3431 & 0.3488 \\ 0.4496 & 0.4363 & 0.4328 \\ 0.1981 & 0.2206 & 0.2185 \end{pmatrix}$,

$\begin{pmatrix} 0.3480 & 0.3468 & 0.3481 \\ 0.4428 & 0.4387 & 0.4389 \\ 0.2093 & 0.2145 & 0.2130 \end{pmatrix}$

(iii) $\begin{pmatrix} \frac{7}{18} & \frac{1}{3} & \frac{5}{18} \\ \frac{1}{3} & \frac{1}{3} & \frac{1}{3} \\ \frac{5}{18} & \frac{1}{3} & \frac{7}{18} \end{pmatrix}$, $\begin{pmatrix} \frac{19}{54} & \frac{1}{3} & \frac{17}{54} \\ \frac{1}{3} & \frac{1}{3} & \frac{1}{3} \\ \frac{17}{54} & \frac{1}{3} & \frac{19}{54} \end{pmatrix}$, $\begin{pmatrix} \frac{55}{162} & \frac{1}{3} & \frac{53}{162} \\ \frac{1}{3} & \frac{1}{3} & \frac{1}{3} \\ \frac{53}{162} & \frac{1}{3} & \frac{55}{162} \end{pmatrix}$

2 (i)

$$\begin{array}{c} \\ camping \\ city \\ winter \end{array}\begin{array}{c} \begin{array}{ccc} camping & city & winter \end{array} \\ \begin{pmatrix} 0 & 0.5 & 0.5 \\ 0.5 & 0 & 0.5 \\ 0.5 & 0.5 & 0 \end{pmatrix} \end{array}$$

(ii) (a) 0.5 **(b)** 0.25 **(c)** 0.375

3 (i)

$$\begin{array}{c} \\ Herald \\ Tribune \\ Gazette \end{array}\begin{array}{c} \begin{array}{ccc} H & T & G \end{array} \\ \begin{pmatrix} \frac{7}{8} & \frac{3}{4} & \frac{1}{2} \\ \frac{1}{8} & \frac{1}{12} & \frac{1}{6} \\ 0 & \frac{1}{6} & \frac{1}{3} \end{pmatrix} \end{array}$$

(ii) (a) $\frac{1}{6}$ **(b)** $\frac{37}{288} \approx 0.128$ **(c)** 0.122

4 (i)

$$\begin{array}{c} \\ A \\ C \\ T \end{array}\begin{array}{c} \begin{array}{ccc} A & C & T \end{array} \\ \begin{pmatrix} 0 & \frac{1}{6} & \frac{1}{2} \\ \frac{3}{5} & \frac{1}{3} & \frac{1}{4} \\ \frac{2}{5} & \frac{1}{2} & \frac{1}{4} \end{pmatrix} \end{array}$$

(ii) (a) 0.3, 0.3, 0.4 **(b)** 0.25, 0.38, 0.37

5 (i) C with probability $\frac{23}{64}$

(ii) A: 2921, B: 2578, C: 2501

6 (i) $a + b + c = 1, d + e + f = 1, g + h + i = 1$

(ii) $\mathbf{P}^2 = \begin{pmatrix} a^2 + bd + cg & ad + de + fg & ag + dh + gi \\ ab + be + ch & bd + e^2 + fh & bg + eh + hi \\ ac + bf + ci & cd + ef + fi & cg + fh + i^2 \end{pmatrix}$

The sum of the first column
$= a^2 + bd + cg + ab + be + ch + ac + bf + ci$
$= a(a + b + c) + b(d + e + f) + c(g + h + i)$
$= a + b + c = 1.$

Similarly for the second and third columns.

? (Page 182)

As time goes by the influence of any particular result from the past diminishes.

Exercise 5C (Page 187)

1 *Equilibrium probabilities*

Exercise 5A

1 (i) $\frac{2}{3}, \frac{1}{3}$

(ii) $\frac{9}{17}, \frac{8}{17}$

(iii) $\frac{1}{2}, \frac{1}{2}$

(iv) 0.25, 0.75

2 0.4, 0.6

3 0.4, 0.6

4 0.6, 0.4

5 $\frac{5}{17}, \frac{12}{17}$

Exercise 5B

1 (i) $\frac{4}{9}, \frac{2}{9}, \frac{1}{3}$

(ii) 0.3475, 0.4402, 0.021 24

(iii) $\frac{1}{3}, \frac{1}{3}, \frac{1}{3}$

2 $\frac{1}{3}, \frac{1}{3}, \frac{1}{3}$

3 $\frac{28}{33}, \frac{4}{33}, \frac{1}{33}$

4 $\frac{45}{179}, \frac{66}{179}, \frac{68}{179}$

2 (i)

$$\begin{array}{c} \\ \textit{city} \\ \textit{suburbs} \end{array} \begin{array}{c} \begin{array}{cc} \textit{city} & \textit{suburbs} \end{array} \\ \begin{pmatrix} 0.95 & 0.02 \\ 0.05 & 0.98 \end{pmatrix} \end{array}$$

(ii) $\frac{2}{7}, \frac{5}{7}$

3 (i)

$$\begin{array}{c|ccc} & A & B & C \\ \hline A & 0.5 & 0.25 & 0.25 \\ B & 0.25 & 0.5 & 0.25 \\ C & 0.25 & 0.25 & 0.5 \end{array}$$

(ii) $\frac{1}{3}, \frac{1}{3}, \frac{1}{3}$

4 (i)

$$\begin{array}{c|ccc} & A & B & \textit{Main} \\ \hline A & \frac{1}{2} & \frac{2}{3} & \frac{1}{2} \\ B & \frac{1}{3} & \frac{1}{4} & \frac{1}{2} \\ \textit{Main} & \frac{1}{6} & \frac{1}{12} & 0 \end{array}$$

(ii) $\frac{13}{24}, \frac{47}{144}, \frac{19}{144}$

(iii) $\frac{51}{92}, \frac{15}{46}, \frac{11}{92}$

6 (i)

$$\begin{array}{c|ccc} & A & B & C \\ \hline A & \frac{1}{4} & \frac{1}{3} & 0 \\ B & \frac{3}{4} & 0 & \frac{1}{2} \\ C & 0 & \frac{2}{3} & \frac{1}{2} \end{array}$$

(ii) $\frac{3}{8}$

(iii) $\frac{4}{25}, \frac{9}{25}, \frac{12}{25}$

7 (i)

$$\begin{array}{c|ccc} & T & Co & Ch \\ \hline T & 0.2 & 0.2 & 0.2 \\ Co & 0.4 & 0.4 & 0.2 \\ Ch & 0.4 & 0.4 & 0.6 \end{array}$$

(ii) 160

(iii)

$$\mathbf{P}^5 = \begin{array}{c|ccc} & T & Co & Ch \\ \hline T & 0.20000 & 0.20000 & 0.20000 \\ Co & 0.30016 & 0.30016 & 0.29984 \\ Ch & 0.49984 & 0.49984 & 0.50016 \end{array};$$

the column vectors are approximately equal.

8 (i)

$$\begin{array}{c|ccc} & \textit{Work} & \textit{Rep} & \textit{Wait} \\ \hline \textit{Work} & 0.8 & 0.5 & 0.9 \\ \textit{Rep} & 0.125 & 0.5 & 0 \\ \textit{Wait} & 0.075 & 0 & 0.1 \end{array}$$

(ii) 0.3125

(iii) 0.8

(iv) 0.75, 0.1875, 0.0625

9 (i)

$$\begin{array}{c|cccccc} & 1 & 2 & 3 & 4 & 5 & 6 \\ \hline 1 & 0 & q & 0 & 0 & 0 & p \\ 2 & p & 0 & q & 0 & 0 & 0 \\ 3 & 0 & p & 0 & q & 0 & 0 \\ 4 & 0 & 0 & p & 0 & q & 0 \\ 5 & 0 & 0 & 0 & p & 0 & q \\ 6 & q & 0 & 0 & 0 & p & 0 \end{array}$$

(ii)

$$\begin{array}{c|ccc} & 1 & 3 & 5 \\ \hline 1 & 2pq & q^2 & p^2 \\ 3 & p^2 & 2pq & q^2 \\ 5 & q^2 & p^2 & 2pq \end{array}$$

(iii) The equilibrium probabilities are $\frac{1}{3}, \frac{1}{3}, \frac{1}{3}$ for values of p and q such that $0 < p, q < 1$.

10 (i)

$$\begin{array}{c} \\ A \\ B \\ C \\ D \end{array}\begin{array}{c} \begin{matrix} A & B & C & D \end{matrix} \\ \begin{pmatrix} 0 & \frac{2}{3} & \frac{1}{2} & 0 \\ \frac{4}{7} & 0 & 0 & \frac{2}{5} \\ \frac{3}{7} & 0 & 0 & \frac{3}{5} \\ 0 & \frac{1}{3} & \frac{1}{2} & 0 \end{pmatrix} \end{array}$$

(ii) Robert: $A\ \frac{25}{42}$, $D\ \frac{17}{42}$; Daniel: $B\ \frac{18}{35}$, $C\ \frac{17}{35}$

(iii) After an odd number of moves, Robert is in B or C and Daniel is in A or D. After an even number of moves, Robert is in A or D and Daniel is in B or C.

(iv) The equilibrium probabilities of being in rooms A, B, C and D are $\frac{7}{24}$, $\frac{6}{24}$, $\frac{6}{24}$ and $\frac{5}{24}$, respectively. These are proportional to the number of tunnels in each room, 7, 6, 6 and 5, respectively.

11 (i)

$$\begin{array}{c} \\ A \\ B \end{array}\begin{array}{c} \begin{matrix} A & B \end{matrix} \\ \begin{pmatrix} 1-p_1 & p_2 \\ p_1 & 1-p_2 \end{pmatrix} \end{array}$$

(iii) $A: \dfrac{p_2}{p_1+p_2}$, $B: \dfrac{p_1}{p_1+p_2}$

Exercise 5D (Page 192)

1 (i) $2\frac{1}{3}$ **(ii)** 4 **(iii)** 1 **(iv)** $\frac{1}{3}$ **(v)** 2

(vi) $\frac{1}{4}$ **(vii)** $\frac{1}{11}$ **(viii)** 7 **(ix)** $\frac{1}{2}$ **(x)** $\frac{1}{3}$

2 (i)

$$\begin{array}{c} \\ MB \\ IP \\ R1 \end{array}\begin{array}{c} \begin{matrix} MB & IP & R1 \end{matrix} \\ \begin{pmatrix} \frac{1}{3} & \frac{2}{3} & \frac{1}{3} \\ \frac{1}{3} & \frac{1}{6} & \frac{2}{3} \\ \frac{1}{3} & \frac{1}{6} & 0 \end{pmatrix} \end{array}$$

(ii) (a) $\frac{2}{9}$ **(b)** $\frac{2}{9}$ **(c)** $\frac{11}{27}$ **(d)** $\frac{16}{81}$

(iii) $\frac{13}{29}$, $\frac{10}{29}$, $\frac{6}{29}$

(iv) $\frac{1}{5}$

3 (i)

$$\begin{array}{c} \\ A \\ B \\ SB \end{array}\begin{array}{c} \begin{matrix} A & B & SB \end{matrix} \\ \begin{pmatrix} 0.6 & 0.3 & 0.5 \\ 0.15 & 0.6 & 0.5 \\ 0.25 & 0.1 & 0 \end{pmatrix} \end{array}$$

(ii) Tuesday: 0, 0.5, 0.5;
Wednesday: 0.175, 0.45, 0.375

(iii) 1.5

4 (i)

$$\begin{array}{c} \\ B \\ C \\ Main \end{array}\begin{array}{c} \begin{matrix} B & C & Main \end{matrix} \\ \begin{pmatrix} \frac{1}{2} & \frac{1}{2} & \frac{3}{5} \\ \frac{1}{3} & \frac{1}{6} & \frac{2}{5} \\ \frac{1}{6} & \frac{1}{3} & 0 \end{pmatrix} \end{array}$$

(ii) Thursday: 0, $\frac{3}{5}$, $\frac{2}{5}$; Friday: $\frac{7}{30}$, $\frac{1}{2}$, $\frac{4}{15}$;
Long run: $\frac{5}{27}$, $\frac{14}{27}$, $\frac{8}{27}$

(iii) $\frac{1}{5}$

5 (i)

$$\begin{array}{c} \\ dry \\ wet \end{array}\begin{array}{c} \begin{matrix} dry & wet \end{matrix} \\ \begin{pmatrix} 0.75 & 0.338 \\ 0.25 & 0.662 \end{pmatrix} \end{array}$$

(ii) 0.57483, 0.42517

(iii)

$$\mathbf{P}^{10} = \begin{array}{c} \\ dry \\ wet \end{array}\begin{array}{c} \begin{matrix} dry & wet \end{matrix} \\ \begin{pmatrix} 0.57489 & 0.57475 \\ 0.42511 & 0.42525 \end{pmatrix} \end{array}$$

The column vectors are approximately equal to the equilibrium probability vector.

(iv) 2.96, 4; $2.96 + 4 \approx 7$

6 (i)

$$\begin{array}{c} \\ Work \\ Minor \\ Major \end{array}\begin{array}{c} \begin{matrix} Work & Minor & Major \end{matrix} \\ \begin{pmatrix} 0.8 & 0.6 & 0.3 \\ 0.1 & 0.2 & 0.3 \\ 0.1 & 0.2 & 0.4 \end{pmatrix} \end{array}$$

(ii) 0.73, 0.13, 0.14

(iii) $\frac{42}{61}$, $\frac{9}{61}$, $\frac{10}{61}$

(iv) $P(N = n) = 0.2 \times 0.8^n$; 4

7 (i) $\begin{pmatrix} 0.82 & 0.375 & 0.18 \\ 0 & 0.25 & 0 \\ 0.18 & 0.375 & 0.82 \end{pmatrix}$, $\begin{pmatrix} 0.756 & 0.4375 & 0.244 \\ 0 & 0.125 & 0 \\ 0.244 & 0.4375 & 0.756 \end{pmatrix}$

(ii) 0.4375, 0.125, 0.4375

(iii) 0.5, 0, 0.5

(iv) (a) Stays in state 1.

(b) Moves to states 1, 2 or 3 with probabilities 0.25, 0.5, 0.25.

(c) Stays in state 3.

(v) The system eventually moves to state 1 with probability 0.5 or to state 3 with probability 0.5.

? (Page 196)

You could call the states 0, 1 and 2, according to the number of black balls in the bag. Then the possible tree diagrams are as follows.

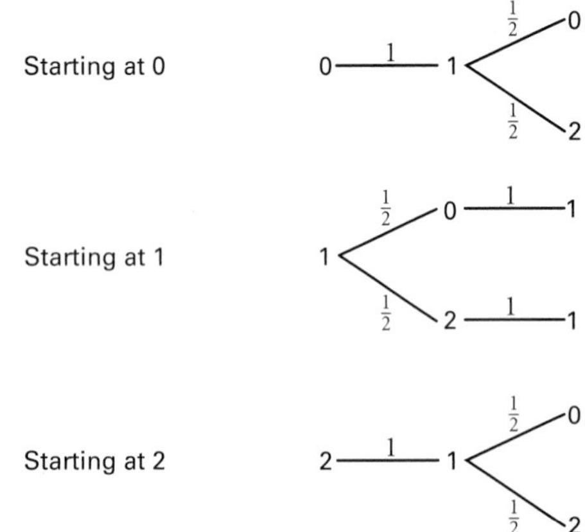

? (Page 197)

Yes, there is a clear order in the states 0, 1 and 2 black balls. At each stage the next state is adjacent to the previous one so in this case there is always a move of one stage, in one direction or the other.

? (Page 198)

No. In that case there is a non-zero probability, p, of staying in the state which is the reflecting barrier, and the adjacent probability will be $1 - p$ rather than 1.

? (Page 198)

After one draw there will be two black balls and one white ball.

After two draws there will either be three black balls or one black ball and two white balls.

After the first draw there are always exactly two states.

The reflecting barriers are 'there are 0 black balls' or 'there are 3 black balls'.

? (Page 199)

The Markov chain is not periodic because $\mathbf{P}^k \neq \mathbf{P}$ for any value of k.

? (Page 203)

Because of its symmetry the original **P**, in part **(i)**, looks just the same but in part **(ii)**, when the bug has developed, it becomes

$$\begin{pmatrix} 0 & 0.5 & 0 & 0.5 \\ 0.5 & 0 & 0.5 & 0 \\ 0 & 0.5 & 0 & 0.5 \\ 0 & 0 & 0 & 1 \end{pmatrix},$$

and all the subsequent matrices are transposed.

In part **(v)** the matrix $\mathbf{p}_0$ becomes $\begin{pmatrix} \frac{1}{3} & \frac{1}{3} & \frac{1}{3} & 0 \end{pmatrix}$ and the multiplications are written $\mathbf{p}_0\mathbf{P}^{13}$ and $\mathbf{p}_0\mathbf{P}^{14}$.

Exercise 5E (Page 204)

1 (i) $\begin{pmatrix} 1 & 0.80 & 0.48 \\ 0 & 0.12 & 0.24 \\ 0 & 0.08 & 0.28 \end{pmatrix}, \begin{pmatrix} 1 & 0.96096 & 0.88352 \\ 0 & 0.01968 & 0.05808 \\ 0 & 0.01936 & 0.05840 \end{pmatrix}$

(ii) As n gets larger, $\mathbf{M}^n$ tends towards $\begin{pmatrix} 1 & 1 & 1 \\ 0 & 0 & 0 \\ 0 & 0 & 0 \end{pmatrix}$.

State 1 of this Markov chain is an absorbing state.

(iii) From state 2, 8 transitions.
From state 3, 10 transitions.
Starting in state 3 takes slightly longer due to the lower transition probability, 0.2 compared with 0.6.

2 (i) Dead

(ii) $\begin{pmatrix} 0.7 & 0.3 & 0 \\ 0.2 & 0.4 & 0 \\ 0.1 & 0.3 & 1 \end{pmatrix}$

(iii) (a) 0.313 **(b)** 0.143 **(c)** 0.544 (to 3 decimal places)

(iv) 18

3 (i) 0.514 (to 3 decimal places)

(ii) 0.5, 0.125, 0.25, 0.125, respectively

(iii) 0.4746

(iv) The probabilities are indeed the same.

(v) The number of trains is 8 or a multiple of 8.

(vi) No. The transition matrix cannot be obtained by raising it to any integer power greater than 1.

4 (i) Periodic with period 4

(ii)

	S	H	D	C
S	0	0	0	1
H	1	0	0	0
D	0	1	0	0
C	0	0	1	0

(iii) Periodic with period 2

(iv) In the first setting the sequence of suits is fixed and periodic. Both the sequence and the transition matrix have period 4.

In the second setting the sequence of suits is not fixed but the transition matrix is periodic with period 2, so the chain is periodic with period 2.

5 (i) The zeros show that the light does not show the same colour for two consecutive time intervals.

(ii) Red; it occurs $\frac{1}{3}$ of the time.

(iii)

$$\begin{array}{c} \\ P \\ B \\ R \\ Y \end{array}\begin{array}{c} \begin{array}{cccc} P & B & R & Y \end{array} \\ \begin{pmatrix} 0 & 0 & 0.4 & 0 \\ 1 & 1 & 0.2 & 0 \\ 0 & 0 & 0 & 1 \\ 0 & 0 & 0.4 & 0 \end{pmatrix} \end{array}$$

Blue is an absorbing state.

(iv) 0.0512

6 (i) $\begin{pmatrix} 1 & 0.24849 & 0 \\ 0 & 0.00605 & 0 \\ 0 & 0.74547 & 1 \end{pmatrix}, \begin{pmatrix} 1 & 0.24999 & 0 \\ 0 & 0.00004 & 0 \\ 0 & 0.74997 & 1 \end{pmatrix}$

(ii) As n gets larger, $\mathbf{T}^n$ tends towards $\begin{pmatrix} 1 & 0.25 & 1 \\ 0 & 0 & 0 \\ 0 & 0.75 & 0 \end{pmatrix}$.

States 1 and 3 of this Markov chain are absorbing states.

(iii) (a) $\mathbf{U}^{10} = \begin{pmatrix} 1 & 0.37500 & 0 \\ 0 & 0.00000 & 0 \\ 0 & 0.62500 & 1 \end{pmatrix}$,

$\mathbf{U}^{20} = \begin{pmatrix} 1 & 0.37500 & 0 \\ 0 & 0.00000 & 0 \\ 0 & 0.62500 & 1 \end{pmatrix}$,

$\mathbf{U}^{n} \to \begin{pmatrix} 1 & 0.375 & 1 \\ 0 & 0 & 0 \\ 0 & 0.625 & 0 \end{pmatrix}$

(b) $\mathbf{V}^{10} = \begin{pmatrix} 1 & 0.66667 & 0 \\ 0 & 0.00000 & 0 \\ 0 & 0.33333 & 1 \end{pmatrix}$,

$\mathbf{V}^{20} = \begin{pmatrix} 1 & 0.66667 & 0 \\ 0 & 0.00000 & 0 \\ 0 & 0.33333 & 1 \end{pmatrix}$, $\mathbf{V}^{n} \to \begin{pmatrix} 1 & \frac{2}{3} & 1 \\ 0 & 0 & 0 \\ 0 & \frac{1}{3} & 0 \end{pmatrix}$

The quicker convergence is due to the relatively small central values in the transition matrices, 0.2 and 0.1 compared with 0.6.

(iv) $\mathbf{T}^n$ tends towards $\begin{pmatrix} 1 & \frac{p}{p+q} & 1 \\ 0 & 0 & 0 \\ 0 & \frac{q}{p+q} & 0 \end{pmatrix}$.

The long term transition probabilities of going from state 2 to state 1, and from state 2 to state 3, are in the ratio of the corresponding single transition probabilities.

7 (i) $\mathbf{T}^5 = \begin{pmatrix} 1 & 0.38750 & 0.87472 & 0 \\ 0 & 0.03125 & 0 & 0 \\ 0 & 0 & 0.00032 & 0 \\ 0 & 0.58125 & 0.12496 & 1 \end{pmatrix}$,

$\mathbf{T}^{10} = \begin{pmatrix} 1 & 0.39961 & 0.87500 & 0 \\ 0 & 0.00098 & 0 & 0 \\ 0 & 0 & 0.00000 & 0 \\ 0 & 0.59941 & 0.1 & 1 \end{pmatrix}$

(ii) As n gets larger, $\mathbf{T}^n \to \begin{pmatrix} 1 & 0.4 & 0.875 & 0 \\ 0 & 0 & 0 & 0 \\ 0 & 0 & 0 & 0 \\ 0 & 0.6 & 0.125 & 1 \end{pmatrix}$.

States 1 and 4 of this Markov chain are absorbing states.

(iii) Starting in state 3, 5 transitions.
Starting in state 2, 10 transitions.
Starting in state 2 takes longer due to the lower transition probability, 0.2 compared with 0.7.

(iv) $\mathbf{T}^n \to \begin{pmatrix} 1 & \frac{a}{a+b} & \frac{p}{p+q} & 0 \\ 0 & 0 & 0 & 0 \\ 0 & 0 & 0 & 0 \\ 0 & \frac{b}{a+b} & \frac{q}{p+q} & 1 \end{pmatrix}$.

The long term transition probabilities of going from state 2 to state 1, and from state 2 to state 4, are in the ratio of the corresponding single transition probabilities. Similarly for going from state 3 to state 1 and from state 3 to state 4 in the long run.

8 (i)

	W2	W1	P	E1	E2	E3
W2	0	0.5	0	0	0	0
W1	1	0	0	0	0	0
P	0	0.5	1	0.5	0	0
E1	0	0	0	0	0.5	0
E2	0	0	0	0.5	0	0
E3	0	0	0	0	0.5	1

(ii) W2 is a reflecting barrier.
P and E3 are absorbing states.

(iii) $\begin{pmatrix} 0 \\ 0.5 \\ 0 \\ 0.5 \\ 0 \\ 0 \end{pmatrix}$

(iv) 0.166…

(v) 0.070 312 5

9 (i)

	L	S+	T+	SW	TW
L	0	0.45	0.55	0	0
S+	0.55	0	0	0	0
T+	0.45	0	0	0	0
SW	0	0.55	0	1	0
TW	0	0	0.45	0	1

(ii) SW and TW are absorbing states.

(iii) $\begin{pmatrix} 1 \\ 0 \\ 0 \\ 0 \\ 0 \end{pmatrix}, \begin{pmatrix} 0 \\ 1 \\ 0 \\ 0 \\ 0 \end{pmatrix}, \begin{pmatrix} 0 \\ 0 \\ 1 \\ 0 \\ 0 \end{pmatrix}$

(iv) (a) 0.599… (b) 0.819… (c) 0.329…

(v) 10

10 (i)

	S_0	S_1	S_2	S_3
S_0	0.4	0.4	0.4	0
S_1	0.6	0	0	0
S_2	0	0.6	0	0
S_3	0	0	0.6	1

(ii) S_3 is an absorbing state.
S_0 is a reflecting barrier. (Note that it is not necessary that you inevitably move away from a reflecting barrier at the next stage.)

(iii) $p_1 = p_2 = p_3 = 0.4, \quad p_4 = 0.3136$

(iv) $p_1 = p_2 = p_3 = 1 - p, \quad p_4 = (1 - p)(1 - p^3)$

11 (i) The use of probabilities of 0.5 in the transition matrix is incorrect. The next move of the lift is always inevitable. So the situation has six states and not four. They are, in order: G, 1↑, 2↑, 3, 2↓ and 1↓. The probability of moving from one state to the next in the sequence is 1; the probability of moving to any other state is 0.

(ii) M =

	G	1↑	2↑	3	2↓	1↓
G	0	0	0	0	0	1
1↑	1	0	0	0	0	0
2↑	0	1	0	0	0	0
3	0	0	1	0	0	0
2↓	0	0	0	1	0	0
1↓	0	0	0	0	1	0

(iii) Yes, 6

Index